MBLEX
TEST PREP

Comprehensive Study Guide and Workbook, 2022-2023

David Merlino, LMT

Published by

PUBLISHER'S DISCLAIMER

The material presented in this study guide is for informational
purposes only. Any information regarding Medications, CPR,
First Aid, and Contraindications should be researched by the
reader to obtain the most up-to-date requirements, as these
subjects are ever-changing.

INTERNET RESOURCES

Information on how to access internet resources may be found
on page 3. If these resources are not functioning properly, please
email the author directly at **david@mblextestprep.com** to notify
us of the situation.

"MBLEx" is a registered trademark of the FSMTB. This study
guide bares no association with, nor is it endorsed by the FSMTB.

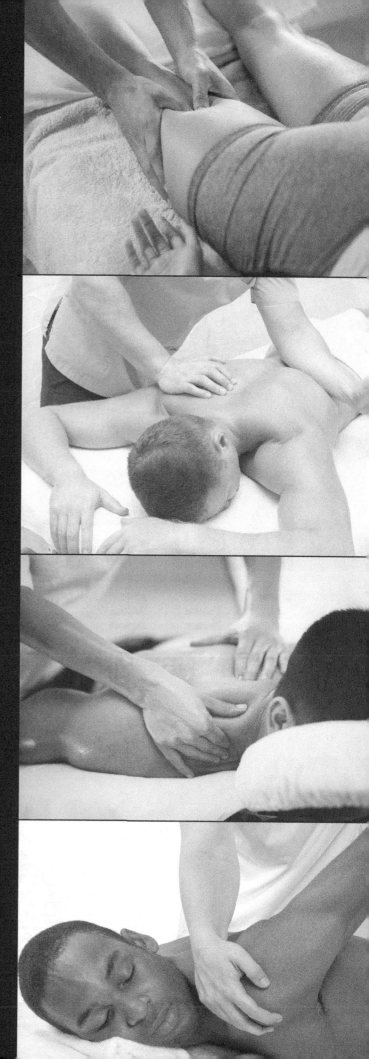

Introduction

Hello! My name is David Merlino, and I am the author of this study guide.

A lot of time and energy has gone in to the creation of this guide. I am extremely proud to share this guide with you, and I am honored that you have chosen my study guide to help you prepare for the MBLEx. You have a tall task ahead of you, but it isn't something you can't overcome. Trust me, I've taken and passed the MBLEx!

I've been a Licensed Massage Therapist for over 15 years, and I've learned and experienced plenty in my career. However, it all began with passing my licensing exam. I understood how to take tests, how to study, and how to give myself the best chance possible to pass the exam and advance into my career. I hope to share this knowledge with you.

In 2011, I began my new career preparing students to take their massage licensing exams at a career college in beautiful Reno, Nevada. It was here I honed my craft, helping students achieve a near-90% pass rate on the licensing exam. How did I do this? Simply put, it's called the minimum effective dose for the MBLEx. I review the information most likely to be seen on the exam, and don't review information I feel is unnecessary, or is unlikely to be seen on the exam. As Olympic pole vaulter Henk Kraaijenhof once said, "Do as little as needed, not as much as possible." This approach makes preparing for the MBLEx much easier to manage.

With this approach, my students achieved amazing success. You can too! Before you begin, however, I need to remind you of something: you will be tested on information that isn't present in this study guide. You will be tested on information you have never seen before. This happened to all of my students, and even happened to me, someone who has been teaching this information for years! Despite not seeing this information before, you can still do extremely well on these questions. Make sure you check out the Study Skills, Test-Taking Techniques, and Reducing Test Anxiety sections for information on optimizing your chances of doing well on the exam!

I've poured months of my life into the production and creation of this study guide. You are now my student. I believe in you, and I know you will do great!

If you have any questions, I am here to help. Please don't hesitate to send me an email with any questions you may have in regards to the study guide, practice tests, or the MBLEx in general.

My personal email address is **david@mblextestprep.com**. Just note, I am very much willing to help, but if your email is rude or disrespectful in any way, there will be no response from me. Just be cool!

Thank you again. I am honored that you have entrusted me with helping you pass the MBLEx. Let's get started!

Your Instructor,

David Merlino, LMT

How To Use This Study Guide

This study guide is designed to not just TELL information, but to help you LEARN information. This is achieved in many different ways, including standard study guides, assignments, and practice exams.

To get the complete, most effective and efficient experience from this study guide, I recommend the following:

Before starting, figure out the area you need to study the most: Massage Therapy(incorporates massage, assessment, business, and ethics), Kinesiology, Pathology, or Anatomy and Physiology. Most people tend to choose Kinesiology first. A common study routine I've helped many students implement is the following(you can change the subjects as you see fit, depending on how comfortable you are with each), with an average of six weeks of study time before the exam. For this example, we'll say the study order is Medical Terminology, Kinesiology, Pathology, Anatomy and Physiology, and Massage Therapy, with ten hours of study per week:

Week 1: Study nothing but Medical Terminology for ten hours.
Week 2: Study Medical Terminology for two hours, and Kinesiology for eight hours.
Week 3: Study Medical Terminology and Kinesiology for two hours, and Pathology for eight hours.
Week 4: Study Medical Terminology, Kinesiology, and Pathology for two hours, and Anatomy and Physiology for eight hours.
Week 5: Study Medical Terminology, Kinesiology, Pathology, and Anatomy and Physiology for two hours, and Massage Therapy for eight hours.
Week 6: Study every subject an equal amount of time, two hours per subject.

> What subjects do you need to study most? Write them down below and include the amount of time to study each!
> Week 1: _____
> Week 2: _____
> Week 3: _____
> Week 4: _____
> Week 5: _____

I've found that this way of studying is great for long-term memory growth in these subjects, as there is a consistent review of information every week.

While studying, be sure to finish the assignments and practice tests in the book. These are great for assessing your knowledge on the subjects you will have just covered, and help you figure out what you still need to study, and what you've learned.

I have created an enormous amount of online content for you to supplement your studying! While studying, especially in the final week before the exam, I highly recommend taking as many practice tests as possible. Watch video lectures I have created, which puts you in a class-like study session with me as your instructor. Go to the following website to access all the online study material: **http://www.mblextestprep.com/online.html**

I do have other products available that are by no means required, but they may be extremely beneficial in your studying efforts! Please check them out below and see if they can help you be even more prepared!

MBLEx Test Prep Podcast

Make sure you subscribe to the MBLEx Test Prep Podcast! Just open any podcast app on your smart phone, search for "MBLEx Test Prep Podcast", and hit "Subscribe"! New episodes are automatically downloaded to your device, so you can listen on-the-go!

MBLEx Test Prep App

I have created a brand new smart phone app that is a fantastic compliment to this study guide! To check it out, just scan the QR code for your selected device with your phone's camera, and it'll take you right to the app listing where you can download it! The free version of the app contains 100 free practice test questions, while upgrading to premium grants access to a complete content review, 2200 practice test questions, and over 1600 flash cards!

Apple iPhone

Android

Tutoring Packages

Finally, if you are looking for tutoring, I recommend checking out my pre-made tutoring packages, available at my personal online store! 25 hours of tutoring video and audio ready for you to learn with, a 100 question practice test with video answer key, and more! Just scan the QR code to the right with your phone's camera to check it out, or visit the website here: **http://www.mblextestprepshop.com**

Study Skills

1. Do not do all of your studying the night before or day of the test. Study consistently, up to several times per week. Cramming is good for short-term learning, but does not help with long-term learning. The more you study, the more likely you are to retain the information.

2. Use all of your class and home work as study material. The information in these assignments is information that may be seen on the exam.

3. Take many short breaks as you study. Memory retention is higher at the beginning and end of study sessions than it is in the middle. This is called the Serial Position Effect. Study for no longer than ten minutes, then take a short break, and resume studying for another ten minutes.

4. Focus on one subject at a time while studying. You don't want to confuse yourself by mixing information.

5. Study the subject you have the most difficulty with more than the subjects you are comfortable with. Studying what you aren't weak in doesn't help. If you need work on a specific subject, focus the majority of your time learning that information, even if it means taking away study time from other areas. You're better off being 80% proficient in every subject than 100% in four subjects and only 50% in the last. Not studying this information could prevent you from passing the exam.

6. While studying, take notes on important information, especially if it's information you don't recognize or remember. Use this information to study with.

7. Assign yourself tests, reports, assignments, and projects to complete. You are more likely to remember information if you write a report on it than if you just read the information.

8. Teach information you are studying to another person. If you are responsible for someone learning something, you have to know and understand the material, and be able to put that information into the simplest terms possible, so someone else can understand it. This will only help you. Trust me, from personal experience, this works extremely well.

9. Understand the material you are studying. Do not just try to memorize certain answers you think may be on the test. Certain "key words" might not be on the test. Learn everything about a subject, and you'll never get any question on that subject wrong.

Test-Taking Tips

1. Go to the restroom before taking the exam. Using the restroom beforehand ensures that you are 100% focused on the exam, and not on your bladder.

2. Read the entire question slowly and carefully. Never make assumptions about what a question is asking. Assuming you know what a question is asking may lead you to missing key words in the question that tell you exactly what the question is asking. Read every single word in every single question, multiple times if necessary.

3. Understand what the question is asking before you try answering it.

4. Identify key words in each question. Key words are words that tell you exactly what the question is asking. Identify these words easily by reading question aloud to yourself. The words you find yourself emphasizing while reading aloud are likely the key words.

Here is an example. Read this question aloud:
Q. Which of the following statements is true regarding Swedish massage?

In this question, there are two key words, which are telling you exactly what the question is asking. Which words did you find yourself putting emphasis on? Most likely, you read the question like this: "Which of the following statements is TRUE regarding SWEDISH massage?" These are the key words.

5. Do not change your answers, unless you misread the question. Changing your answers puts doubt into your mind, and leads to more changing of answers. The answer you put first is usually correct. Do not change your answers!

6. Match key words in the answers with key words in the questions. Sometimes it's as simple as matching terms, if you've exhausted all other avenues.

7. Eliminate answers you know aren't correct and justify the reason they aren't correct. If you can eliminate one answer from each question, that brings your odds of getting that question right up to 33%. If you can eliminate two answers that can't be right, that brings it up to 50%. Then it's just a coin flip!

Here's an example. Read the question, and the answers:
Q. Of the following, which is not contagious?
A. Athlete's foot
B. Herpes simplex
C. Influenza
D. Osgood-Schlatter Disease

Have you ever heard of Osgood-Schlatter Disease? Even if you haven't, you can still get this question right by eliminating the other answers. Athlete's foot is caused by a fungus, and is contagious. That leaves us with three possible answers(33% chance). Herpes simplex is caused by a virus, and is contagious. That leaves us with two possible answers(50% chance). So even if you're guessing at this point, it's only a 50/50 chance you get it right! Influenza is caused by a virus, and is contagious. This process of elimination just gave us the answer, D. Osgood-Schlatter Disease.

8. Read the entire question before looking at the answers. Again, never make assumptions about what the question is asking.

9. Come up with the answer in your head before looking at the answers. If the same answer you come up with is in the list of answers, that's most likely the right answer.

10. Read every answer given to make sure you are picking the most correct answer. Some questions have multiple right answers, and you need to make sure you're picking the most correct answer.

11. Make sure you are properly hydrated before the test. Studies have been done on the effects of proper hydration on those taking tests. People who are properly hydrated tend to score higher than those who are not.

12. Exercise for twenty minutes before the exam. Exercise has also been shown to increase test scores.

Reducing Test Anxiety

1. Study consistently. If you understand the material, you won't be as stressed out about the test. There are ways you can study without this book or your class notes as well. An example, whenever you take a bite of food, think about every structure the food passes through in the digestive tract and what each of the organs do. Another example, whenever you are massaging someone, tell yourself everything about every muscle you work on, like origin, insertion, and action.

2. Keep a positive attitude while preparing for the test and during the test. If you think you're going to fail, you will not be as motivated to study, you won't adhere to your test-taking techniques, you'll become stressed out during the exam much more easily, and you'll be more likely to fail.

3. Try to stay relaxed. Utilize deep breathing techniques to calm down if you start feeling nervous or stressed. You will have two hours to finish the exam. You can afford one or two minutes to calm yourself down if you need to.

4. Exercise consistently up until the day of the test to reduce anxiety. Exercise has been shown to significantly reduce stress, and also helps with memory retention. Try utilizing flash cards while riding an exercise bike.

5. Take your time on the test. If you find yourself rushing, slow down. Again, you have two hours to finish the exam. Do not rush through it. You may miss important information in the exam and answer questions incorrectly because of this.

I hated every minute of training, but I said "Don't quit. Suffer now and live the rest of your life as a champion."

- Muhammad Ali

Massage Therapy

Massage Technique

In western massage, there are six main massage strokes, which have been in a constant state of evolution since being developed.

Effleurage is the most common stroke in western massage, consisting of long, **gliding** strokes that are directed **towards the heart**. Effleurage is used to increase circulation of blood and lymph, remove waste from tissues, introduce the therapist's touch to the client, transition between strokes, and apply massage lubricant. Effleurage may be used throughout the massage, but is the main stroke used at the beginning of the treatment. The majority of the time, effleurage is performed by the therapist in the **archer(bow) stance**.

Petrissage utilizes **kneading** movements, lifting and squeezing tissue, to increase circulation, loosen adhesions that may be present in the tissue, and release metabolic waste from tissues. Petrissage is an important stroke to use in post-event sports massage, as it helps flush waste from the muscles and bring fresh oxygen-rich blood into them.

Friction consists of strokes that move **across tissue**. Friction is especially useful in breaking up adhesions and scar tissue, increasing circulation, and stretching muscles. There are many different forms of friction, such as superficial friction(rubbing the surface of the skin), parallel friction, circular friction, and cross-fiber friction.

Tapotement consists of **percussion** strokes, rhythmically affecting the tissues of the body in many different ways. Tapotement increases spindle cell activity in the muscles, which helps activate them and get them ready for use, which makes tapotement a very important stroke to use in pre-event sports massage. Tapotement may also help loosen any phlegm, or mucous, in the respiratory tract, and is very helpful in conditions such as asthma or chronic bronchitis. There are many different forms of tapotement, including hacking, cupping, tapping, and beating.

Vibration is performed by **shaking** a part of the body, using **trembling** actions. Vibration can have different effects on the body, depending on how fine the vibration is. Slow vibration is used to sedate an area(think of massage chairs that vibrate, numbing the area). Fast vibration is used to stimulate an area.

A **nerve stroke** is an **extremely light** form of **effleurage**. Like effleurage, nerve strokes, also called feather strokes, are directed towards the heart. These strokes are primarily used at the end of a massage, or at the end of work on a specific body part, to separate the therapist from the client(ending the massage session), or to transition from one part of the body to another.

Effects of Massage Therapy

Mechanical Effects

Mechanical effects of massage therapy are any **physical changes** in the body that are the **direct result** of massage being performed on a specific part of the body. For example, massage strokes such as petrissage and effleurage will forcibly move blood and lymph further through the body as the strokes are performed. This increases circulation.

Mechanical effects of the main western massage strokes include:

Effleurage: Increased blood circulation, increased lymph circulation.

Petrissage: Increased blood circulation, increased lymph circulation, removal of waste such as lactic acid from muscle, loosening of adhesions between tissues, loosening of fascia.

Friction: Break up of adhesions between tissues, temporary localized ischemia, removal of waste such as lactic acid from muscle.

Tapotement: Loosening phlegm in the respiratory tract.

Vibration: Sedation of the area, stimulation of the area.

Reflexive Effects

Reflexive effects are changes in the body that occur by **stimulation of the Nervous System** as a result of massage therapy. An example includes effleurage stimulating the blood vessels to dilate, which is known as vasodilation. This makes the blood vessels more permeable, allowing blood to escape the blood vessels, increasing blood concentration in an area, also known as hyperemia. Hyperemia in the area makes the area appear red, and the temperature in the location increases.

Another example is the activation of muscle spindles when tapotement is used, which causes a brief reflexive contraction of the muscle belly to prevent the muscle from stretching too far, preventing injury.

Massage therapy has the ability to stimulate the production and release of certain hormones in the body, which can influence the sympathetic or parasympathetic nervous response. A relaxing massage would likely stimulate the release of hormones such as melatonin and reduce cortisol levels in the body. Massaging the abdomen in a clockwise manner may stimulate peristalsis, which occurs when the parasympathetic response is activated. Massage may also help reduce blood pressure and heart rate due to stimulation of the parasympathetic response.

Joint Movements

Joint movements describe how a joint is moved by a specific person. There are four main types of joint movements, performed by the therapist on the client, the therapist and the client working together, the therapist and the client working against one another, or the client performing the action by themselves.

An **active joint movement** involves the client actively performing a movement **without assistance** from the massage therapist. An example would be a massage therapist asking a client to perform a range-of-motion as part of assessment. The therapist does not help with the action, as they would want to see how much movement the client can perform by themselves, and to see where any restrictions may be.

Active assistive joint movements involve the client performing a movement **with assistance** from the massage therapist. Active assistive joint movements are very helpful in rehabilitative settings, allowing the client to move the joint, but making sure someone is there to help move and support the joint to prevent further injury.

Passive joint movements involve the massage therapist moving the joint, with the **client completely relaxed**, not helping at all. Passive joint movements are helpful for performing stretches, feeling for restrictions in movements, and for assisting the client to further relax.

Resistive joint movements are when the client and massage therapist are moving a joint in **opposite directions** at the same time. This creates an isometric contraction(muscle tension increases, length doesn't change, see page 86), which is extremely helpful in a specific type of stretch known as Proprioceptive Neuromuscular Facilitation.

Stretching

Stretching is an exercise that is performed by **elongating** or lengthening a muscle. Stretching is extremely beneficial to a person's health.

An **unassisted stretch** is performed by the client stretching into resistance **without any help** from the massage therapist. It is similar to an active joint mobilization, but instead of just moving the joint through its normal range-of-motion, it moves past that point and into a stretch.

An **assisted stretch** is performed by the client **with assistance** from the massage therapist. Again, this is similar to an active assistive joint movement, where the massage therapist's role is to help the client move the joint into a stretch while stabilizing the joint to ensure there is no damage to the joint.

Proprioceptive Neuromuscular Facilitation(PNF) is a stretch that is very useful in loosening adhesions and scar tissue in muscles, and is very beneficial in athletes. To perform PNF, a massage therapist moves a client's joint into a stretch. Once resistance is met, the client will actively resist the movement being performed by the massage therapist. This puts the muscle into an **isometric contraction**. After holding this resisted movement for 5-10 seconds, the client **relaxes**, and the massage therapist is able to move the stretch further, until resistance is met again. The process is then repeated. PNF allows a highly noticeable increase in the amount of range-of-motion in a joint.

Step 1. Stretch the Client	Step 2. Isometric Contraction	Step 3. Relax and Stretch Further
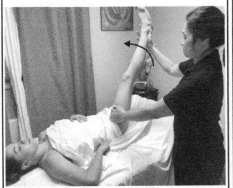	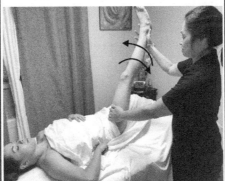	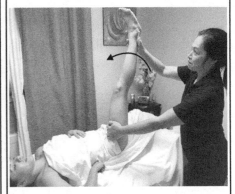
The hamstrings are stretched into resistance by moving the hip into flexion and knee into extension.	The therapist and client then resist each other, performing an isometric contraction for roughly seven to ten seconds.	The client relaxes, and the therapist is able to move the stretch further, and the process is repeated.

End Feels

During stretching and joint mobilizations, we experience **end feels**. An end feel is what causes a joint movement or stretch to not move any further.

Soft End Feel

A **soft end feel** is the result of **soft tissues**, such as muscles and tendons, pulling back on the joint, preventing any further movement. An example is when stretching the quadriceps. The hip joint is moved into extension until resistance is met. The resistance is due to the quadriceps pulling back on the joint. If the quadriceps are loosened, the joint will move further. This is a soft end feel.

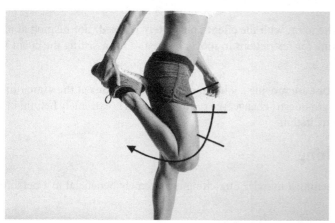

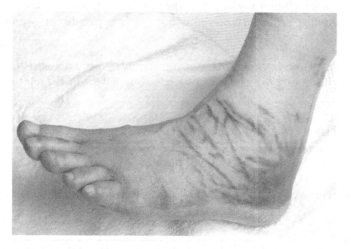

Hard End Feel

A **hard end feel** is the result of structures, primarily **bone**, preventing a joint from moving further. An example is extension of the knee or elbow. Straightening these joints can only go to a certain point. Bones will prevent these joints from extending any further. That's why hyperextension of these joints may result in broken bones. This is a hard end feel.

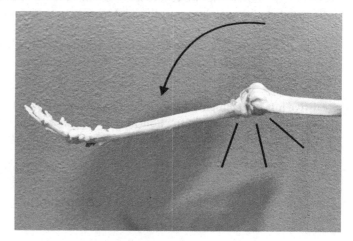

Empty End Feel

An **empty end feel** is caused by neither muscles nor bones interfering with movement. Empty end feels are the result of **trauma** to an area, which prevents movement. An example could be a sprained ankle. With a sprained ankle, bruising and inflammation may be present, which immobilizes a joint to prevent further injury. This is an empty end feel.

 Easy to Remember: A soft end feel is caused by soft tissues; a hard end feel is caused by hard tissues!

Massage Equipment

Massage equipment can enhance the massage by providing the client, and the therapist, with comfortable tables, or add other factors to the treatment that may improve the overall quality of the session.

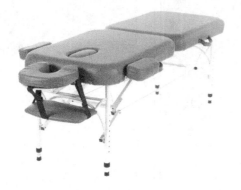

Massage Tables

Massage tables, the primary equipment used by massage therapists, are usually the most expensive pieces of equipment a massage therapist will own. Tables may be lighter and **portable**, foldable at the center and able to be placed into a carrying case that utilizes a shoulder strap for easy transport. Other tables may be heavier and unable to be transported. These tables typically contain a motor that allows the table height to be adjusted with the use of a **foot pedal**. These types of tables are called **hydraulic tables**.

Massage tables will often include a head rest for comfortably placing a client in a prone position. Arm extenders may be added to the table to apply needed width to the table to accommodate larger clients. Bolsters are used to take pressure off certain parts of the body, depending on how a client is positioned on the table. Some massage tables may have a portion that can be removed for the face as a substitute for a head rest. Other tables may have a section that can be removed to accommodate clients with larger breasts who are lying prone. More common with hydraulic massage tables than portable tables, the table may have an incline/decline feature that allows the client to be propped up in a seated position, which may be especially helpful for pregnant clients.

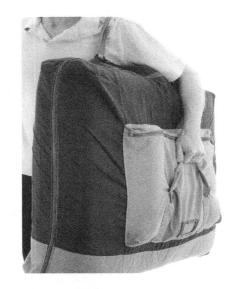

Additionally, a stool may be utilized at certain points during the massage to increase the comfort of the massage therapist while performing massage on regions such as the head, neck, and face.

Massage Chairs

Massage chairs are commonly utilized when performing massage **outside the normal office setting**, and can accommodate clients who are completely clothed. A massage chair features a seat, a head rest the client places their face into, an arm rest, and leg rests. The chair position may be adjusted with the client on the chair, unlike portable massage tables, which are adjusted with the client off the table.

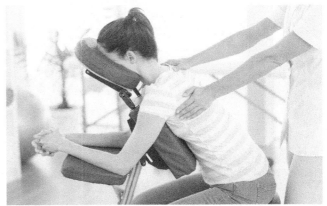

Lubricant

Massage lubricant may be a number of different substances. It is important that whatever substance is used is **hypoallergenic**. Allergies should always be determined before the massage begins to ensure no lubricant being used contains a substance the client may be allergic to. Common forms of massage lubricant include **oil** and **lotion**.

Lubricants may be stored for use in pourable containers, pump containers, cups, jars, and bowls. The container may be placed in specific spots around the table and moved during the course of the massage, or may be held by a holster wrapped around the therapist's waist. A holster allows the container to always be with the therapist no matter where they are in the room, and will almost always require the use of a pump container. After each massage, the container should be cleaned with soap and water to prevent cross-contamination.

If utilizing gloves during a massage session, it is important to **avoid using latex gloves**. Massage lubricant can eat through and dissolve latex easily, and the client may have a latex allergy. An appropriate glove to wear is nitrile, because nitrile gloves do not dissolve as rapidly as latex gloves, and there is not an inherent risk of allergen exposure.

Other Equipment

There are several other pieces of equipment that can help improve the overall quality of the massage. Several types of equipment utilize hydrotherapy in some way. **Hot towel cabinets** (also known as hot towel cabi's) are small boxes that increase internal temperature up to **170 degrees Fahrenheit** in most models. Heating wet towels in a hot towel cabinet can give the massage therapist an effective way to remove oil from a client's feet, while also providing a relaxing experience for the client as the heated towel is wrapped around the feet. In addition, hot packs may be placed in the hot towel cabinet and sufficiently heated this way.

A **hydrocollator** is similar to a hot towel cabinet, but is specifically designed to utilize heating packs that are filled with substances such as silica, gel, or even rice. A hydrocollator will use moist heat to heat the packs, which are then placed on the client's body.

Hot stones may be heated in a **hot stone warmer**. Hot stone warmers are electric, and similar in shape and function to slow-cookers. The stones are placed in the warmer, and the warmer is filled with water. The warmer is then powered on, and the stones are heated. Temperature should be maintained at a comfortable level that will heat the stones, but not burn the client. Stones should always be checked for temperature by the massage therapist before placing the stones on the client. This can be performed by the therapist placing the stone on the anterior forearm. If the stone feels too warm in this area on the massage therapist, then the stone needs to cool before it can be used on a client.

Bolsters

Bolsters are used to place the client into a comfortable position during a massage session. There are many different positions a client may be placed in during a massage, which requires the bolster to be placed in different locations to optimize comfort.

Prone

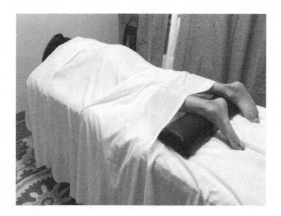

When a client is positioned **prone**(face down) on the massage table, the client may experience low back pain. A bolster should be placed **under the ankles** in this case. Low back pain is likely caused by tight hamstrings. A bolster under the ankles produces slight flexion of the knee, which shortens and takes pressure off the hamstrings.

Supine

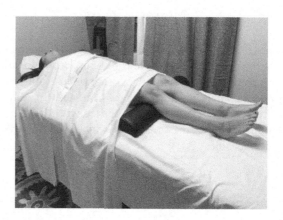

When a client is positioned **supine**(face up) on the massage table, the client may experience low back pain. A bolster should be placed **under the knees** in this case. Low back pain is likely caused by a tight psoas major, iliacus, or rectus femoris. A bolster under the knees produces slight flexion of the hip, which shortens and takes pressure off all these muscles.

Side-Lying

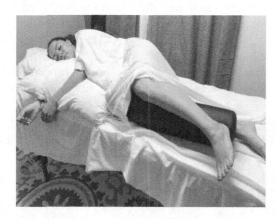

Side-lying position should be used for pregnant clients, or clients who have difficulty lying prone, such as people with kyphosis. Bolstering for side-lying clients includes placing a bolster **between the knees** to relieve pressure on the hips, **under the arms**, and **under the head**.

Semi-Reclined

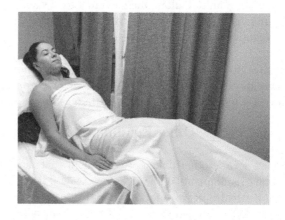

Certain clients may need to be placed in a **semi-reclined position**, such as pregnant clients who experience dizziness from lying supine(caused by the fetus placing pressure on the abdominal aorta). When a client is semi-reclined, a bolster should be placed **under the knees**, and **behind the head**.

Draping

Draping is the use of **linens** to keep a client covered during a massage session. There are many different types of linens that may be used to cover a client. Most commonly, sheets are used. Blankets and towels are other common forms of linens. Draping is a very important step in establishing **boundaries** between the massage therapist and the client. Draping the client tells the client what part of the body the therapist is, and isn't, going to work on, increasing the professionalism required of a massage therapist. Draping also helps the clients establish boundaries, telling the therapist where the client may not want massage to be performed.

Communication is key in establishing boundaries. If there is any question about a client's boundaries with regards to draping, just ask!

Top cover draping refers to the linen placed **atop the client**, which acts as the drape. As previously stated, the most common form is a sheet.

Body Mechanics

Body mechanics are extremely important for massage therapists. Proper body mechanics prevent the therapist from **injuring** themselves during a massage, which increases the longevity of their career. It makes performing a massage less physically strenuous, and allows the therapist to perform a **better massage** by utilizing pressure and leverage more efficiently.

While performing a massage, the massage therapist's **back** should **remain straight**. **Knees** should be in a **slightly flexed** position. While performing compression, **joints** should be **stacked** to relieve pressure on one specific joint. An important factor in body mechanics that often is overlooked, however, is the **height of a massage table**. The table should be at the proper height for the therapist, based on the type of massage being performed. Deep tissue massages require the table to be slightly lower than Swedish massages, for example.

Body stances are very important while performing massage strokes, making them easier to perform, and makes the strokes flow and transition more smoothly.

Bow/Archer Stance

The **bow stance**, also called the **archer stance**, is performed with the therapist's **feet placed parallel** to the massage table. This allows the therapist to perform long, gliding strokes, such as those seen in effleurage.

Horse/Warrior Stance

The **horse stance**, also called the **warrior stance**, is when the therapist's **feet are placed perpendicular** to the massage table. The feet will face the table, the knees will be slightly flexed. This allows short, powerful strokes to be performed, such as compression and friction.

Personal Hygiene

Personal hygiene is an important aspect in massage therapy, as the massage therapist comes in to close contact with the client who may be sensitive to certain aspects of the therapist's cleanliness. A massage therapist should exhibit exceptional personal hygiene.

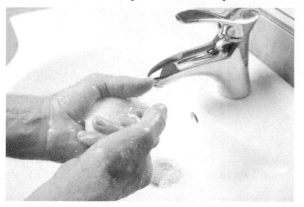

Hand Care

Hands should be washed constantly using **soap and water**, and the area being washed should extend proximally **past the elbow**. The fingernails should be free from dirt beneath them. The fingernails should be trimmed to avoid scratching or pinching the client. Acrylic nails and nail polish should not be applied, as dirt, debris, oil, and skin from the client can become stuck under the nail. Rings and other hand jewelry should not be worn. Calluses on the hands from activities such as weight lifting should be softened with the use of lotion.

Oral Care

Teeth should be **brushed and flossed**. Food that causes lingering odor after being consumed should be avoided, such as onions and garlic. Gum should not be chewed during the massage session. Breathing directly on the client, even through the nose, should be avoided. **Smoking** while at work, even on break, **should be avoided** to prevent cigarette odor from remaining on the therapist.

Bathing

The massage therapist should **bathe daily**. Showering helps remove any residual oil from the body. The therapist's body should be cleaned using a soap that does not contain a perfume base and is not over-bearing in scent. The therapist should **avoid** using **perfumes or essential oils** on their body to avoid complications the client or other coworkers may have with allergies. The therapist should **always wear deodorant** to prevent body odor.

Uniform

The massage therapist's uniform should be **cleaned and washed** after every shift. Any oil stains should be properly treated. Uniforms should be free of stains and holes. The uniform should be free of stray hair from the therapist, client, or pets. A lint roller may be used to remove hair on the uniform.

General Appearance

The massage therapist should have an **overall professional appearance**. This includes a clean uniform, longer hair tied back to prevent it from falling on the client during the massage, no obstructive jewelry, and good posture. The overall appearance of a massage therapist can influence the client's perception of the massage session.

Massage Modalities

There are many different forms of massage, and many different modalities(specialties) that may be performed by massage therapists. Some require training and certification to perform, and others require nothing aside from basic schooling. Check with your local licensing board to determine requirements to perform specific modalities.

Aromatherapy

Aromatherapy is any treatment utilizing **essential oils**, which may affect the brain's **limbic system**. Essential oils have many different effects on the body, depending on the type of oil used, and how it is administered. Examples include oils having a stimulating effect, such as lemon and grapefruit, having a sedative effect, such as eucalyptus on the respiratory tract, having antiseptic properties, such as tea tree on insect bites, or having calming effects on the brain, such as lavender. Always check with a client for any allergies before using essential oils in a treatment.

Deep Tissue

Deep Tissue massage is performed by working the **deeper layers** of tissue in the body, including muscles and fascia. Deep tissue may require deeper pressure to be used by the massage therapist to reach deeper structures(an example could be working deeper through the rectus femoris to reach the vastus intermedius).

Hot Stone

Hot Stone massage is a treatment that utilizes **heated stones**. The stones may be **placed** on certain parts of the body(hands, feet, lumbar, abdomen), may be used to **physically massage** a client, or both. Temperature of the stones should be checked by the massage therapist on their own skin(anterior forearm) before attempting to place on the client, to ensure the client does not suffer any burns. The temperature of the water should be between **120-130 degrees Fahrenheit**, which heats the stones to an appropriate temperature. Hot stone is used to increase circulation into muscles and tissues, and aids in relaxation.

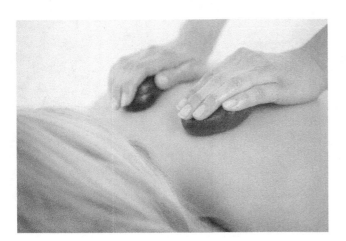

Craniosacral Therapy

Craniosacral Therapy is a very light massage technique that helps to release **blockages** in the flow of **cerebrospinal fluid**, which runs from the **cranium to the sacrum**. Blockages in these fluids may cause numerous side effects, including headaches, dizziness, and difficulty processing and understanding information.

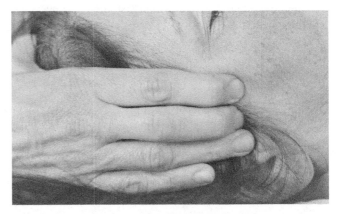

Hydrotherapy

Hydrotherapy is the use of **water** in any treatment. There are several different types of hydrotherapy, utilizing water in solid(ice), liquid(water), or vapor(steam). **Contrast baths** utilize both a **heated bath and a cold bath**. Contrast baths are used to decrease systemic inflammation and increase circulation. A typical contrast bath treatment sees the client use cold water, then hot, then cold, then hot, and **end with cold** for inflammation relief. A **Vichy shower** is a piece of equipment that hangs over a water-proof table. This equipment has **seven shower heads** attached to it, which can pin-point specific areas of the body to be sprayed.

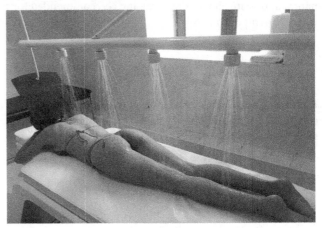

Vichy Shower

Lomi Lomi

Lomi Lomi(Hawaiian "lomi": massage) is a **Hawaiian** massage, similar to a Swedish massage, which utilizes **rhythmic gliding strokes**. These strokes are used on the entire body, and can move from the feet up to the head in one fluid motion. This requires minimal draping, usually nothing more than a hand towel covering the gluteal cleft, exposing the glutes.

Lymphatic Drainage

Lymphatic Drainage is a technique designed to **increase the circulation of lymph** utilizing very light strokes directed towards the heart. Increasing lymph circulation may help reduce swelling in areas such as the limbs or face. During lymphatic drainage on limbs, massage strokes should work from proximal to distal. For example, if lymphatic drainage is performed on the lower limb, the thigh should be cleared of lymph first, then the knee, then the leg, then the foot.

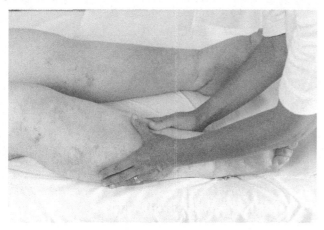

Myofascial Release

Myofascial Release is a type of treatment aimed at releasing **restrictions in muscles and fascia**. Myofascial Release utilizes light strokes that move in the direction of the restriction, helping the muscle "unwind" on its own. **Skin rolling** is a form of myofascial release, and is useful when performed on areas of scar tissue to help loosen adhesions. Muscles such as trapezius can greatly benefit from skin rolling.

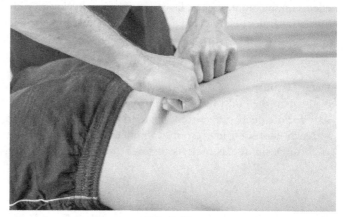

Skin Rolling

Pregnancy Massage

Pregnancy massage is massage for pregnant clients. Pregnant clients may need to be placed into side-lying or semi-reclined position. Endangerment sites for pregnant clients include the **abdomen** and **around the ankles**. Precautions should also be taken into account based on certain factors such as the age of the pregnant client, the trimester the client is in, whether the client has developed associated symptoms such as gestational diabetes or pitting edema, if the client experiences nausea during pregnancy, and more. Specialized training is recommended for work with pregnant clients.

Reflexology

Reflexology is used to treat **reflex points** on the hands, feet, and ears that correspond to other tissues inside the body, such as **organs**. A map of these locations can be found on page 18.

Reiki

Reiki is a form of **energy work**, in which the therapist channels universal energy into and throughout the client. In reiki, the therapist primarily(but not always) holds their hands an inch or two **above the client**, and manipulate the client's energy to promote relaxation or other benefits.

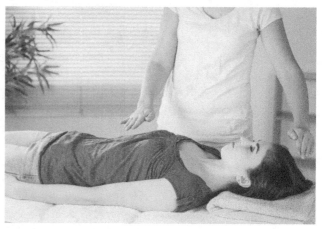

Aura Stroke

Rolfing

Rolfing, developed by **Ida Rolf**, is known as a **structural realignment** technique. The basic principles of Rolfing involve the body being placed back into proper vertical alignment. The Rolfer works on the **fascia** of the body. Loosening the fascia helps the body return to its natural position. Rolfing typically takes place over ten sessions, with a different part of the body worked on during each session.

Sports Massage

Sports massage is a massage designed for **athletes**. Sports massage may be performed in many different ways, depending on the needs of the athlete. **Pre-event** sports massage, which may be performed up to 15 minutes before an event, will typically be **stimulating**, increasing circulation into the muscles, and using tapotement to activate muscle spindles. Inter-event massage will look to achieve the same results as pre-event massage, but does not utilize tapotement. Using tapotement may result in cramping. **Post-event** massage will be much slower, rhythmic, and relaxing. The primary goal of a post-event massage is to **calm the body down**, remove metabolic waste from tissues, and increase the flow of oxygen-rich blood into the muscles to aid in recovery.

Swedish Massage

Swedish massage, the most common massage technique in western massage therapy, is mainly focused on **relaxation**. Effleurage is a stroke commonly utilized in Swedish massage, with strokes aimed towards the heart to increase circulation. Effleurage is also beneficial in increasing lymph circulation. Swedish massage can help reduce mental stress, relax the body's muscles, and improve mobility in joints. Swedish massage is primarily focued on western principles of anatomy and physiology.

Thai Massage

Thai massage, originating in Thailand, isn't necessarily what we consider a normal massage. Thai massage is performed with the client wearing loose-fitting clothes, on a mat, on the floor. The therapist's main goal during a Thai massage is to **stretch** the client. Massage may be incorporated into these stretching techniques.

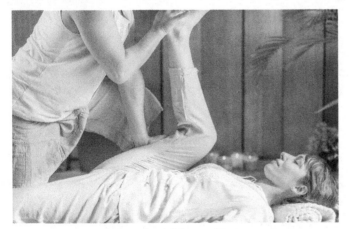

Stretching performed during Thai massage

Tuina

Tuina is the name of **modern Chinese massage**. It is used to balance the eight principles of Chinese medicine. Tuina incorporates rhythmic strokes and techniques focused on specific areas of the body. The eight basic techniques utilized in Tuina are palpating, rejoining, opposing, kneading, pressing, lifting, holding, and pushing.

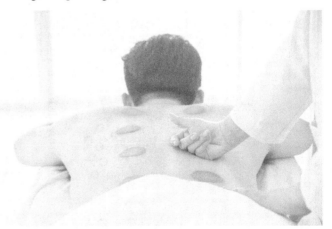

Tuina technique known as rolling

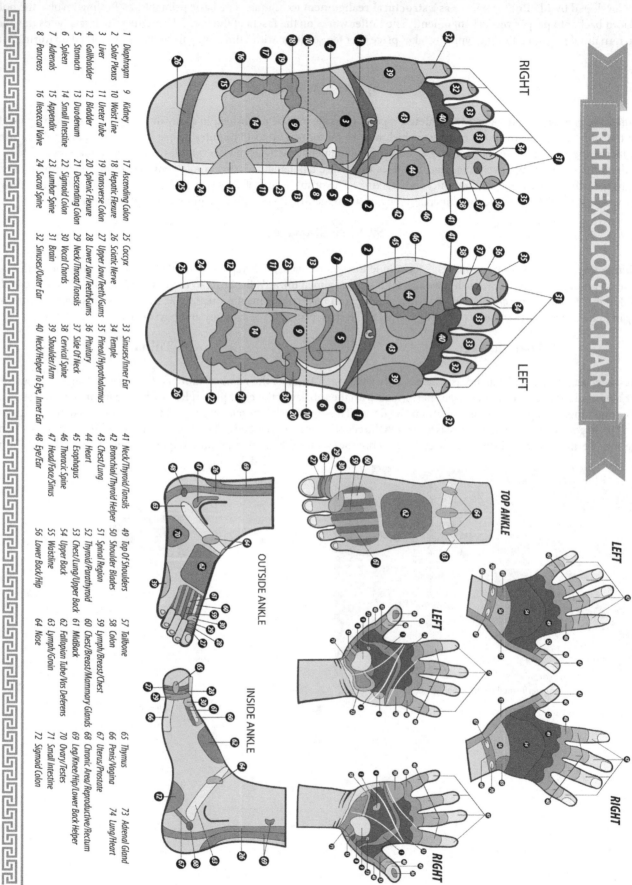

REFLEXOLOGY CHART

RIGHT

LEFT

TOP ANKLE

OUTSIDE ANKLE

INSIDE ANKLE

LEFT

RIGHT

1 Diaphragm
2 Solar Plexus
3 Liver
4 Gallbladder
5 Stomach
6 Spleen
7 Adrenals
8 Pancreas
9 Kidney
10 Waist Line
11 Ureter Tube
12 Bladder
13 Duodenum
14 Small Intestine
15 Appendix
16 Ileocecal Valve
17 Ascending Colon
18 Hepatic Flexure
19 Transverse Colon
20 Splenic Flexure
21 Descending Colon
22 Sigmoid Colon
23 Lumbar Spine
24 Sacral Spine
25 Coccyx
26 Sciatic Nerve
27 Upper Jaw/Teeth/Gums
28 Lower Jaw/Teeth/Gums
29 Neck/Throat/Tonsils
30 Vocal Chords
31 Brain
32 Sinuses/Outer Ear
33 Sinuses/Inner Ear
34 Temple
35 Pineal/Hypothalamus
36 Pituitary
37 Side Of Neck
38 Cervical Spine
39 Thoracic Spine
40 Neck/Helper To Eye, Inner Ear
41 Neck/Thyroid/Tonsils
42 Bronchial/Thyroid Helper
43 Chest/Lung
44 Heart
45 Esophagus
46 Thoracic Spine
47 Head/Face/Sinus
48 Eye/Ear
49 Top Of Shoulders
50 Shoulder Blades
51 Spinal Region
52 Thyroid/Parathyroid
53 Chest/Lung/Upper Back
54 Upper Back
55 Waistline
56 Lower Back/Hip
57 Tailbone
58 Colon
59 Lymph/Breast/Chest
60 Chest/Breast/Mammary Glands
61 MidBack
62 Fallopian Tube/Vas Deferens
63 Lymph/Groin
64 Nose
65 Thymus
66 Penis/Vagina
67 Uterus/Prostate
68 Chronic Area/Reproductive/Rectum
69 Leg/Knee/Hip/Lower Back Helper
70 Ovary/Testes
71 Small Intestine
72 Sigmoid Colon
73 Adrenal Gland
74 Lung/Heart

The Body Meridians

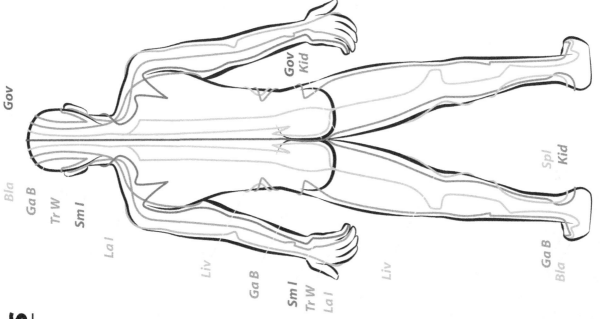

posterior view

anterior view

Two Centerline Meridians:

Conception Vessel
Governing Vessel

Twelve Principal Meridians:

Stomach Meridian
Spleen Meridian

Small Intestine Meridian
Heart Meridian

Bladder Meridian
Kidney Meridian

Pericardium Meridian
Triple Warmer Meridian

Gall Bladder Meridian
Liver Meridian

Lung Meridian
Large Intestine Meridian

Massage Therapy Matching

_____: Stance with feet placed perpendicular to the massage table

_____: Gliding strokes directed towards the heart

_____: Modern Chinese massage

_____: Massage therapist moving a joint without assistance from the client

_____: Percussion strokes

_____: Kneading strokes

_____: Stance with feet placed parallel to the massage table

_____: Client moving a joint without assistance from the massage therapist

_____: Massage designed to increase the flow of fluid between the sacrum and cranium

_____: Treatment utilizing a shower with seven heads performed on a waterproof table

_____: Location a bolster should be placed when a client is positioned supine

_____: Stoppage of range-of-motion due to bone

_____: Keeping a client covered during a massage

_____: Changes in the body that occur by stimulating the Nervous System resulting from massage

_____: Treatment using stones heated to 120-130 degrees Fahrenheit

_____: Massage equipment allowing a massage to be performed from a seated position

_____: Linen placed atop the client

_____: Location a bolster should be placed when a client is positioned prone

_____: Structural realignment therapy

_____: Physical changes that occur in the body as a direct result of massage therapy

_____: Stoppage of range-of-motion due to muscle

_____: Client stretching into resistance without assistance from the massage therapist

A: Tapotement
B: Draping
C: Bow Stance
D: Hard End Feel
E: Massage Chair
F: Rolfing
G: Horse Stance
H: Mechanical Effects
I: Active Joint Mobilization
J: Reflexive Effects
K: Unassisted Stretch

L: Ankles
M: Petrissage
N: Tuina
O: Vichy Shower
P: Passive Joint Mobilization
Q: Hot Stone
R: Top Cover
S: Effleurage
T: Knees
U: Soft End Feel
V: Craniosacral Therapy

Answer Key on Page 308

Massage Therapy Crossword

Across

4. Stance in which the feet are placed parallel to the massage table
5. Type of glove that should be avoided when performing massage due to possible allergies
7. The client and massage therapist moving a part of the client's body in opposite directions
9. Position requiring bolsters to be placed between the legs, under the arms, and under the head/neck
10. Stoppage of range-of-motion due to trauma
11. Stance in which the feet are placed perpendicular to the massage table
13. Structures activated in muscles when tapotement is performed
16. Effects in the body that are caused as a direct result of massage therapy being performed
17. Position requiring bolsters to be placed under the knees and behind the head/neck
19. Pre-event sports massage strokes

Down

1. Type of massage incorporating techniques such as palpating, rejoining, opposing, and kneading
2. Equipment used to heat linens to 170 degrees Fahrenheit
3. Effects in the body that are caused by stimulation of the Nervous System resulting from massage therapy
5. Massage using rhythmic gliding strokes over the entire body with minimal draping
6. Type of essential oil useful in treating nausea
8. Massage table that utilizes a foot pedal to adjust the height
12. Treating reflex points on the hands, feet, and ears that correspond to internal tissues and organs
14. Form of stretch in which a muscle is stretched to resistance, then an isometric contraction is performed, then the muscle is stretched further, abbv.
15. Massage stroke performed by moving across tissue
18. Stroke performed by shaking a part of the body to sedate or stimulate the area

Answer Key on Page 309

Massage Therapy Practice Test

1. In a pre-massage assessment, the client states they have tightness in the hamstrings due to a recent housing move, and it's been causing some pain and discomfort. The therapist palpates the area and notices there seems to be some hypertonicity to the muscle group. The therapist asks the client to perform a range-of-motion, which the client performs. The therapist then asks the client to stretch the muscles. The client moves their hips into flexion and knees into extension, bending forward in front of them trying to touch the floor. Which of the following is occurring
A. The client is performing an unassisted stretch
B. The client is performing Muscle Energy Technique
C. The client is performing an assisted stretch
D. The client is performing proprioceptive neuromuscular facilitation

2. Which of the following is a prime reason to avoid using latex gloves in a massage session
A. The client may not enjoy the feeling of the latex glove on the client's hand
B. The client or therapist may be allergic to latex
C. The therapist may not be able to perform massage strokes as easily with latex gloves
D. The client likely does not have any contagious pathogens present on the skin

3. Certain forms of hydrotherapy require water to be heated. Which of the following is the appropriate temperature to heat water for use in hydrotherapy
A. 80-90 degrees Fahrenheit
B. 60-70 degrees Fahrenheit
C. 120-130 degrees Fahrenheit
D. 160-170 degrees Fahrenheit

4. All of the following are appropriate forms of linens to use to drape a client except
A. Towels
B. Foil
C. Blankets
D. Sheets

5. A massage therapist is performing a pre-massage assessment and doing a verbal intake with a client, determining the best way to help treat the client. The client states they are just looking for general relaxation, but do not want their feet to be massaged. In this statement, what has the client established
A. The client has established a dual relationship
B. The client has established an absolute contraindication
C. The client has established transference
D. The client has established a boundary

6. Which of the following is not a reflexive effect of massage therapy
A. Loosening of adhesions between tissues
B. Reduction of heart rate and blood pressure
C. Dilation of blood vessels
D. Stimulation of peristalsis

7. During a massage session, a client asks the massage therapist to turn the massage music off because they do not enjoy it. Which of the following is the best response from the massage therapist
A. The massage therapist should refuse to turn the music off due to the power differential in the therapeutic relationship
B. The massage therapist should supply the client with noise canceling headphones to mute the audio
C. The massage therapist should turn the music off per the client's request
D. The massage therapist should explain to the client that the music helps the therapist with the timing of their massage sequence and they need the music to stay on

8. A specific type of reflexive effect of massage therapy increases blood flow into a localized region of the skin due to which of the following occurring in blood vessels
A. Blood vessel walls dilating and becoming more permeable
B. Blood vessel lumen constricting and becoming less permeable
C. Blood vessel walls forcing blood to flow backwards
D. Blood vessel lumen performing peristalsis to increase circulation

9. Good body mechanics are important to
A. Perform a shorter massage
B. Prevent injuries to the therapist
C. Massage the head and neck
D. Follow the set massage sequence

10. A client comes in to an office for a massage. The client is greeted by the massage therapist, who notices the client limping slightly. After taking the client into the massage room and closing the door, the therapist asks the client if they have some sort of injury. The client says yes, they sprained their ankle earlier that day. How should the massage therapist proceed with the treatment
A. The therapist should treat the area by performing range-of-motion exercises and applying a hot pack to increase blood flow to the injured area to promote healing
B. The therapist should reschedule the appointment and treat the injury as an absolute contraindication
C. The therapist should treat the area as a local contraindication and ask the client if they'd like a cold pack applied to the area to reduce inflammation
D. The therapist should perform traction on the affected joint to ease pressure built up from inflammation, and cross-fiber friction to break up scar tissue that has formed resulting from the injury

11. Equipment utilizing seven adjustable shower heads which hangs over a waterproof table
A. Swiss shower
B. Russian shower
C. Swedish shower
D. Vichy shower

12. Of the following, which is not an important aspect of a massage therapist's personal hygiene regimen
A. Wearing a clean uniform daily that is free from stains, holes, and animal hair
B. Covering visible tattoos to avoid deeply offending any clients
C. Wearing deodorant to prevent body odor from being detected by the client
D. Washing hands before and after each appointment

13. Stance in which the feet run perpendicular to the massage table
A. Swimmer
B. Bow
C. Archer
D. Horse

14. A client notifies a massage therapist that they feel tightness in the quadriceps. The massage therapist responds by asking the client if they may stretch the muscle group. The client agrees, and the massage therapist positions the client prone, moving the hip into extension and the knee into flexion. The massage therapist then instructs the client to push against the therapist's hand. The client performs the action, but the massage therapist holds the lower limb in place, so no movement takes place. What is occurring
A. The massage therapist and client are performing a resistive joint movement
B. The client is performing an active joint movement
C. The massage therapist is performing a passive joint movement
D. The massage therapist and client are performing an active assistive joint movement

15. Pain resulting from a trigger point being felt in a different region of the body is known as
A. Referred pain
B. Contagious pain
C. Latent pain
D. Contracted pain

16. Swedish massage is based on the Western principals of
A. Life force
B. Energy
C. Anatomy and physiology
D. Chi

17. A client receives a massage in a spa, and after the massage the client asks to speak to management. The client explains to the manager that the massage therapist smelled like cigarette smoke and it was an unpleasant experience. The manager apologizes to the client. Which of the following would the manager speak to the massage therapist about specifically in regards to this complaint
A. The massage therapist's technique
B. The massage therapist's topics of conversation
C. The massage therapist's lack of empathy
D. The massage therapist's personal hygiene

18. All of the following are essential reasons to properly drape the client except
A. To establish consistent professional standards with the client
B. To allow the therapist to establish physical boundaries with the client
C. To prevent the client from accidentally falling off the table after the massage session
D. To instill trust within the client that the therapist is properly trained and knowledgeable

19. A client seeks massage after participating in a marathon. Their muscles are sore, and they feel as if massage therapy will help. During the massage, the massage therapist performs effleurage to increase circulation of blood, petrissage to squeeze waste from the muscles in the lower limb, and friction to reduce the production of adhesions between muscles to keep them as loose as possible. All of these techniques are which of the following
A. Dynamic effects
B. Reflexive effects
C. MET effects
D. Mechanical effects

20. Skin rolling is useful when performed on areas that may have increased amounts of scar tissue to help loosen adhesions, and is a technique used in which modality
A. Lomi Lomi
B. Myofascial release
C. Tuina
D. Feldenkrais

21. A client calls a spa and requests a massage, stating they have never received a professional massage before and are unsure what kind of treatment to book. Which is the best response from the person scheduling the appointment for the client
A. Try to determine the client's needs and expectations and recommend a treatment or therapist that would be most likely to give the client what they are looking for
B. Try to determine if the client is an undercover police officer looking to issue citations for performing massage on underage clients
C. Try to determine how the client may be up-sold on treatments to help the spa bring in more money
D. Try to determine if the client has any scientific or medical background so they can better understand the differences between each modality offered and potential benefits of each

22. Massage involving deep structural realignment, usually taking place over ten sessions
A. Rolfing
B. Lomi Lomi
C. Feldenkrais
D. Myofascial release

23. A client seeks a massage appointment after visiting their primary physician, who has indicated the client has pre-hypertension and a blood pressure reading of 133/87. If during the course of massage and after the massage the client's blood pressure lowers, what occurs
A. A mechanical effect occurs
B. A psychological effect occurs
C. A reflexive effect occurs
D. A sympathetic effect occurs

24. Chris has recently recovered from a severe pneumonia infection and received clearance for massage. A massage technique that may aid in lung decongestion would be
A. Friction
B. Vibration
C. Effleurage
D. Tapotement

25. Stoppage of a range-of-motion due to muscle and other soft tissues
A. Empty end feel
B. Soft end feel
C. Hard end feel
D. Nervous end feel

Answer Key on Page 322

Nobody cares what you did yesterday. What have you done today to better yourself?

- David Goggins

Assessment

Assessment

Assessments are a vital component of any massage treatment. Assessments are **evaluations** of the client primarily done before a massage, but the therapist is constantly assessing, even during and after a treatment.

Assessments have many different uses, from determining any contraindications the client may have, to tailoring a massage session specifically for that client and what they need. An example could be, if a client complains of low back pain, the therapist could then do visual assessment, range-of-motion exercises, and palpation to determine what the possible cause of the low back pain could be. Then, after the assessment is complete, the therapist may tailor the session to work specifically on the areas of concern(possibly the hamstrings, quadratus lumborum, iliopsoas, or rectus femoris).

Assessments may be performed in many different ways:

Subjective Information

Listening to the client and their complaints is the most effective way to determine issues a client may be experiencing. Anything the client details about themselves and their current state is considered **subjective information**. The way a client details areas of concern may be extremely helpful in determining the cause of their issues. An example, if a client begins stating that they have pain in the lower back, and also pain in the hamstrings, then the therapist might inquire as to activities the client is performing that may put strain on the hamstrings. Knowing that tightness in the hamstrings can lead to pain in the low back can help the therapist work with the client to alleviate the pain by working on the root cause.

Pain levels may be utilized by the therapist to determine exactly how painful an area is. A **pain scale** is usually based on numerical value, ranging from 1-5 or 1-10. The higher the number a client states, the more pain they are experiencing. In the scenario above, if the client were to state that their back pain was at a 6 out of 10, then the pain they are feeling is present and noticeable, but probably does not affect their ability to perform every day actions.

Some questions to consider when dealing with pain: Is this pain acute and localized in one specific area, such as sprained ankles? Is the pain widespread and more chronic, such as with Multiple Sclerosis? Does the pain come and go, or is it persistent? What does the pain feel like? How long has the pain been present?

Objective Information

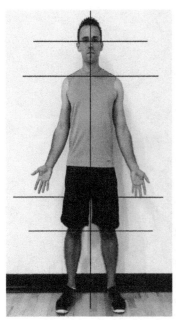
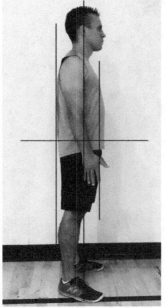

Objective information is anything that the therapist can physically see or observe. This information is measurable, and is not up to a client or therapist's interpretation of the information.

Visual assessment may be performed, focusing on alignment of specific bony landmarks to determine areas of concern. Some of these areas to compare bilaterally include the ears(possible neck tension), acromion processes(shoulder/back/chest tension), iliac crests(back/hip/thigh tension), anterior superior iliac spines (back/hip/thigh tension), and head of fibulae(back/hip/thigh tension). Visual assessment also includes how a client presents themselves while doing things as simple as talking to the therapist or walking. A therapist may be able to tell if a client is limping, or is in some sort of pain just by interacting with them.

Pictured are common areas of visual assessment. These areas can be observed while the client is standing, in addition to the client performing range-of-motion or gait analysis. This allows the therapist to observe any abnormalities between standing and performing an action.

The therapist may be able to see certain things in a person's skin, such as inflammation or pallor. Edema and skin infections are physically observable. Scars may be a sign of past trauma that could be causing pain or discomfort. Physical disabilities can often be observed in people with conditions such as cerebral palsy or paralysis.

Range-of-motion may be performed by the client for the therapist to determine any restrictions of movement. Performing any action can help determine if there is pain present during the movement, if range-of-motion is compromised in any way due to injuries or imbalances, or to determine any muscular restrictions a person may have that can be alleviated through the use of massage therapy and stretching techniques.

Gait analysis may help determine hypertonic muscles unilaterally, and injuries. When observing a client walking, the therapist should pay attention to any imbalances the client has. This may indicate structural issues, pain, muscle weakness, or neurological issues. Observing the feet and their position while walking can give the therapist an idea of muscle tightness or previous injuries if the foot is over-pronated or over-supinated. Pain may be expressed on the face while walking. Gait analysis is a form of range-of-motion assessment.

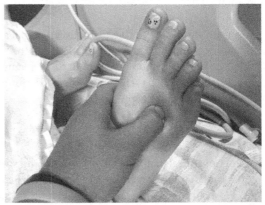

Palpation is useful in feeling for adhesions or restrictions in muscles, localized ischemia, and inflammation. Ischemia, which is the lack of blood flow into an area, will feel cool to the touch. Inflammation, due to an increased amount of blood in the area, should feel warm to the touch. Assessing edema and pitting edema requires the therapist to palpate the area.

Breathing may be observed visually and by listening to the client's breathing rate and pattern. Shortness of breath may be cause for concern if there is no known cause, such as exercise. Increased respiration may be the result of the sympathetic response being activated and indicates stress. Watching a person breathe and how their body moves during respiration can help determine if there are any structural issues affecting breathing. Wheezing and coughing may indicate some sort of infection, or that the client is in the acute stage of a condition such as asthma.

Precautions

During a massage, certain precautions need to be adhered to in order to prevent injury or complications to the client.

Endangerment sites are areas of the body that, while massage may be performed on, need to be treated with **extra caution**. These are commonly due to insufficient tissues in the area to support, cushion, and protect important structures like blood vessels and nerves. Endangerment sites include the anterior triangle of the neck, the axilla, the anterior elbow, and the popliteal region.

Local contraindications are areas of the body that must be **avoided** when performing a massage. While endangerment sites allow for massage to be performed, local contraindications do not permit massage on localized areas. Reasons for a part of the body to be considered a local contraindication vary, from inflammation and trauma to infections(such as athlete's foot). The rest of the body may receive massage, but these specific areas must be avoided.

Absolute contraindications prohibit the use of massage. Massage on a person with an absolute contraindication, such as when a person is infected by a virus like influenza, can worsen the condition for the client, cause damage to the body, or even spread an infection or condition to the massage therapists. Do not perform a massage on a client with an absolute contraindication!

Common Endangerment Sites

Endangerment sites(anterior):
1. Anterior Triangle of Neck
2. Axilla
3. Abdomen
4. Antecubital Region

Endangerment sites(posterior):
1. Posterior Neck
2. Lower Back/Floating Ribs
3. Olecranon Process
4. Popliteal Region

Intake Forms

One of the primary ways a massage therapist can assess a client is by utilizing an intake form. These forms give the massage therapist the ability to ask numerous questions relating to the client and their well-being, which can give the therapist important insights into the client's physical and emotional states.

Intake forms should be constructed neatly, keeping similar information and questions together. This is mainly done to minimize client confusion and to speed up the time it takes for the client to fill out the form.

Medical History

Medical history is one of the primary sections detailed on an intake form. Medical history is important because it can help determine any contraindications before the massage even begins. It may also assist the therapist in developing an effective treatment plan, even if the treatment only lasts one session. The therapist needs to be aware of any past surgeries, current injuries, illnesses, and medications the client may be taking. All of these factors can determine the appropriate type of massage to perform, the appropriate session length, etc.

An intake form should always have a section to detail any allergies a client may have. Clients may be allergic to many different types of chemicals or plants which may be used during the massage treatment. Nut-based massage oils should be avoided. A hypo-allergenic massage lubricant should be sought to avoid any complications. Essential oils should not be automatically added to massage lubricant, as clients may be sensitive to them. Perfume scents should be avoided. Any allergies a client has should be documented by the client on the intake form.

Informed Consent

Informed consent refers to the client **authorizing services** provided by the massage therapist based on all information provided by the massage therapist regarding the services. The client agreeing to these services allows the massage therapist to perform the services. An example, if the client is booked for a hot stone massage, they need to be notified of what the treatment entails, potential benefits, and potential risks. Once the client has all of the information regarding the hot stone massage, they can either approve of the service, or deny the service and book a different type of massage.

The client also needs to be made aware of the massage therapist's training, experience, and credentials in regards to the treatment being offered. This is provided so that the client is aware of the level of training provided by the massage therapist. A client may feel uneasy with a recently licensed massage therapist performing the treatment, and may instead opt for a more experienced massage therapist. Providing training information regarding specific modalities, such as hot stone massage, helps to assure the client that the therapist is knowledgeable in that modality and able to perform the treatment.

HIPAA

The **Health Insurance Portability and Accountability Act**, also known as **HIPAA**, was enacted August 21st, 1996. It was created by the US Department of Health and Human Services. Inside HIPAA lies the **Privacy Rule**, which is used to **protect all individually identifiable health information**. The Privacy Rule ensures client/patient information is kept private. It does, however, allow this information to be transferred between healthcare providers when necessary, which allows high-quality health care. Assessments and diagnoses do not need to be re-done, as the information is already present. HIPAA should be outlined with the client intake form.

Signature and Date

Signatures and dates should always been signed by the client at the time of the intake form being filled out. This allows for a massage therapist to have added protection in case of malpractice or negligence lawsuits.

An example of a client intake form can be found on the following page.

Merlino's Massage Client Intake Form

Name: _____ Date of Birth: _____

Telephone: _____ Email: _____

Emergency Contact: _____ Relationship: _____

Emergency Contact Phone: _____

Occupation: _____ Hobbies: _____

Reason for Visit: _____
_____
_____

Health History

Check all that apply:

_____ Allergies	_____ Cancer	_____ Pregnant
_____ Arthritis	_____ Diabetes	_____ Psoriasis
_____ Asthma	_____ Headaches	_____ Scoliosis
_____ Back Pain	_____ High Blood Pressure	_____ Seizures
_____ Blood Clots	_____ Numbness/Tingling	_____ Skin Conditions
_____ Bruise Easily	_____ Osteoporosis	_____ Varicose Veins

Are you currently taking prescribed medications? If so, please list: _____
_____

Any past surgeries? If so, please list: _____
_____

Do you exercise? If so, how frequently: _____

Have you received massage therapy before? If so, how frequently: _____

Are there any areas you would like the massage therapist to avoid? If so, please list: _____
_____
_____

What are your goals for this and any future treatments? Please detail: _____
_____
_____

Please highlight any areas on the body you would like the massage therapist to focus on during the session

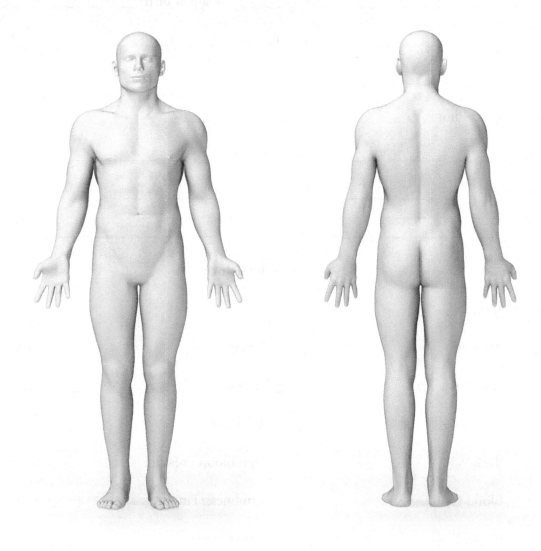

Please explain the areas highlighted: _____
_____
_____
_____

Print Name: _____

Signature: _____

Date: _____

SOAP Notes

SOAP notes are the most common form of post-massage documentation. SOAP notes help a massage therapist **document** everything that happened or was said during a massage session. Documenting this information can be helpful in many different ways, from tailoring future massage treatments to protecting the therapist from any malpractice or negligence lawsuits that may arise.

The "**S**" of SOAP stands for "**Subjective**". Under this section of SOAP notes, a massage therapist documents anything the client details about themselves. This can include where they experience pain, their job or hobbies, etc.

The "**O**" of SOAP stands for "**Objective**" or "**Observation**". Under this section of SOAP notes, a massage therapist documents the type of massage or techniques being performed(objective), and anything about the client the therapist can physically see(observe). This can include bruising, inflammation, visual assessments, and gait analysis.

The "**A**" of SOAP stands for "**Assessment**". Under this section of SOAP notes, a massage therapist documents any changes in the client as a result of the massage treatment. An example could be "Pre-massage, right shoulder elevated. Post-massage, right shoulder less elevated".

The "**P**" of SOAP stands for "**Plan**". Under this section of SOAP notes, a massage therapist documents any recommendations for future treatments, or exercises suggested for the client between sessions(such as increase stretching in a specific muscle or area, or increase water intake).

Client files, including intake forms, SOAP notes, and receipts, should be kept by the massage therapist for a minimum of **six years**, per the IRS. This allows for audits to take place by the IRS. Having all documentation stored can help prevent any possible penalties issued by the IRS.

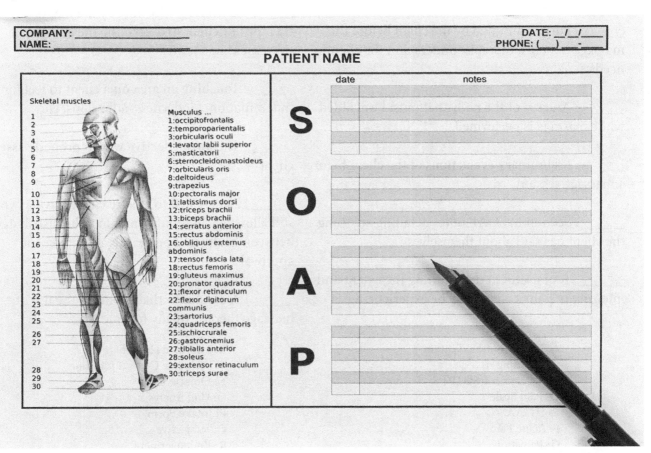

Assessment Matching

_____: Section in SOAP notes detailing measurable information

_____: Section in an intake form detailing medications, past surgeries, or current conditions a client may be experiencing

_____: Analyzing a person's body based on their walking pattern

_____: Pain experienced over a short period of time usually associated with trauma

_____: The client authorizing services based on all information being provided

_____: An area of the body that requires extra caution while being massaged

_____: Form submitted by the client before the massage to help a therapist understand the client's needs

_____: An area of the body that must be avoided while massage is performed

_____: Preliminary evaluations of the client before a massage session

_____: Section in SOAP notes detailing anything the client has said about themselves

_____: Tool useful in determining the extent and intensity of pain a client may be experiencing

_____: Pain experienced over a long period of time

_____: Section in SOAP notes detailing changes in the client resulting from the massage session

_____: Type of lubricant that should be used in massage treatments to avoid potential allergic reactions

_____: Analyzing a person's body based on how they stand

_____: Documentation utilized post-massage to record activites and treatments performed

_____: Section in SOAP notes detailing recommendations for future treatments

_____: Exercise performed by the massage therapist or client to determine the amount of movement in a joint

_____: Touching an area on a client to feel for inflammation, tenderness, adhesions, etc

_____: The most effective way to properly assess a client

_____: Act created to ensure client privacy while still allowing client information to be distributed between healthcare professionals with client approval

_____: A condition that prohibits the use of massage therapy in any form

A: Local Contraindication
B: Listening
C: Assessment(SOAP)
D: Pain Scale
E: HIPAA
F: Acute Pain
G: Palpation
H: Plan
I: SOAP Notes
J: Posture Analysis
K: Health History

L: Informed Consent
M: Absolute Contraindication
N: Objective
O: Gait Analysis
P: Intake Form
Q: Subjective
R: Endangerment Site
S: Hypoallergenic
T: Range-of-Motion
U: Chronic Pain
V: Assessments

Answer Key on Page 308

Assessment Crossword

Across

2. Changes in the client resulting from a massage is documented under
5. Information the client details about themselves is documented under
8. Measurable data regarding the client is documented under
10. Contraindication prohibiting the use of massage on one specific location in the body
11. Recommendations for future treatments is documented under
12. Useful in determining the intensity or severity of a client's pain
13. Contraindication prohibiting the use of any massage treatment
14. Pain that is present for a short period, and is generally more severe
15. Symptom indicative of some sort of infection in the lungs, may be associated with coughing
17. The amount of natural movement seen in a joint
18. Form of range-of-motion interpreting a person's walking pattern

Down

1. Touching a client to physically feel for inflammation or restrictions in tissue
3. Length of time a person is required to keep client documents, per the IRS
4. Pain that is present for a longer period
6. A part of the body that warrants caution while being massaged due to underlying structures
7. Analyzing a person's body based on how they stand is which type of analysis
9. Document submitted by the client sharing their name, health history, HIPAA form, and signature and date
16. The "I" in "HIPAA" stands for this

Answer Key on Page 309

Assessment Practice Test

1. A massage therapist performs a visual assessment of a client's posture. As the client stands, the therapist notices the client's right hip appears to be turned in, and the client acknowledges that they experience slight discomfort in the right hip while walking. What information can the massage therapist assume based on the position of the hip while the client stands
A. The client is likely experiencing a form of sciatica that causes a weakness in the adductor muscle group in the thigh
B. The client is likely experiencing tightness in muscles that medially rotate the hip and weakness in muscles that laterally rotate the hip
C. The client is likely experiencing tightness in muscles that extend the hip and weakness in muscles that flex the hip
D. The client is likely experiencing tightness in muscles that invert the foot and weakness in muscles that evert the foot

2. During a pre-massage assessment, the massage therapist asks the client to slowly walk across the room. While the client walks, the therapist observes a slight limp, with the feet in a semi-pronated position. What type of assessment has been performed
A. Range-of-motion
B. Widespread pain index
C. Gait analysis
D. Palpation

3. Which of the following is not a reason a client may be experiencing shortness of breath
A. Increased sympathetic response
B. Exercise
C. Bacterial infection
D. Excessive hemoglobin

4. On an intake form, a client remarks that they are currently experiencing a fever and slight body chills. The client says they have felt unwell for a couple days, but overall feel better today than the previous couple days. How should the massage therapist proceed
A. The massage therapist should reschedule the appointment as fever is an absolute contraindication
B. The massage therapist should take the client's temperature, and if it is below 101 degrees, they may proceed with the massage as scheduled
C. The massage therapist should ask if the client is experiencing any pain associated with the fever and body chills, and treat any areas of pain as local contraindications
D. The massage therapist should give the client an antipyretic and postpone the massage by 30 minutes to allow the fever to reduce

5. A massage therapist performs a visual assessment of a client, noting the left scapula appears to be more elevated than the right scapula. All of the following may be reasons for the left scapula to appear elevated except
A. The client is experiencing hypertonicity in the levator scapulae on the left side
B. The client is experiencing hypertonicity in the serratus anterior on the right side
C. The client is experiencing hypertonicity in the upper fibers of trapezius on the right side
D. The client is experiencing weakness in the lower fibers of trapezius on the left side

6. Which of the following is the best reason for including the client's signature and date on an intake form
A. Rebooking with the client for future appointments
B. Determining potential medical contraindications
C. Keeping the client's information private and protected
D. Protection in malpractice or negligence lawsuits

7. During a visual assessment, a therapist notes that the client's shoulders appear to be in a protracted position. This may be indicative of weakness in which of the following
A. Supraspinatus
B. Serratus anterior
C. Rhomboids
D. Pectoralis minor

8. A cold sore around the mouth of a client would affect a massage in what way
A. Massage around the mouth would be beneficial to speed healing of the sore
B. Massage around the mouth is contraindicated
C. Massage would not be performed at all until the cold sore clears up
D. Massage around the mouth is indicated

9. Which of the following is the best way to visually assess excessive tightness and shortening of the hip flexor muscles
A. Observe the position of the patellae
B. Observe the position of the pes anserinus
C. Observe the position of the acetabulofemoral joint
D. Observe the position of the anterior superior iliac spines

10. A client arrives for a massage, and as they enter the massage establishment, they stumble through the door. As they get to their feet, the client says they are fine with slurred speech, and walks towards the business desk with a slight stagger. Which of the following is not something the massage therapist should determine before proceeding with the massage appointment
A. If the client has a medical condition that may affect speech and gait such as cerebral palsy
B. If the client has sustained an injury upon entering the establishment, and if the fall was caused by anything relating to the physical building structure or ground
C. If the client is able to sufficiently pay for the scheduled appointment
D. If the client is intoxicated, or potentially taking medications that may affect speech or gait

11. Josh is a professional football kicker. His team has just scored a touchdown, and he has to kick an extra point. Josh lines up, the ball is snapped and placed by the holder, and Josh kicks the ball with the medial surface of his right foot. What actions are occurring in Josh's right lower limb that allow him to kick the extra point
A. Hip flexion and lateral rotation
B. Hip extension and adduction
C. Knee extension, hip adduction
D. Knee extension, hip medial rotation

12. A client states on an intake form that they ride a bicycle as a hobby, and have also been experiencing pain in the quadriceps recently due to riding their bicycle on a steeper incline. Which of the following is not a treatment modification the massage therapist should implement to assist this client
A. The massage therapist should attempt to perform proprioceptive neuromuscular facilitation on the quadriceps
B. The massage therapist should perform deep tissue massage on the quadriceps to break up adhesions that may have formed between the individual muscles
C. The massage therapist should perform petrissage on the quadriceps to remove waste from the muscles that may be stagnant in the area
D. The massage therapist should perform contrast therapy on the area to help reduce inflammation and bring fresh blood into the area to assist in healing

13. After a massage, the massage therapist notifies the client of stretches that the therapist thinks might help with a client's range-of-motion. This information would be documented under which section of SOAP notes
A. Plan
B. Objective
C. Subjective
D. Assessment

14. A client explains to a massage therapist in a pre-massage interview that they commonly experience severe headaches that seem to originate in the posterior neck. The therapist observes the client from a lateral view, and notices the head and neck appear to be in a pronounced anterior position with a severely flattened lordotic curvature in the cervical spine. Which of the following is the most likely cause of the head and neck being placed into this position
A. The trapezius muscles are experiencing unilateral hypertonicity
B. The levator scapulae muscles are experiencing bilateral hypertonicity
C. The sternocleidomastoid muscles are experiencing bilateral hypertonicity
D. The pectoralis minor muscles are experiencing bilateral hypertonicity

15. A massage therapist is working on a client's upper limb when they reach the elbow. The therapist notices the elbow feels warmer to the touch. While the therapist palpates the area, the client exclaims that they feel a dull ache in the area. What recommendation should the therapist give to the client after the session has ended
A. The therapist should recommend the client perform PRICE on the area and visit a physician if the condition persists
B. The therapist should attempt to stretch the joint to reduce adhesions that have formed in the area that may be contributing to pain
C. The therapist should ask the client to perform a resistive joint mobilization to help the biceps brachii and brachialis relax and take pressure off the joint
D. The therapist should apply a compression bandage to the area to stimulate lymph to flow out of the area to allow range-of-motion to return to a normal state

16. All of the following should be detailed in a client intake form except
A. Informed consent
B. HIPAA
C. Health history
D. Income

17. A client states they have been diagnosed with a low blood count. With this information, how should a massage therapist proceed
A. The massage therapist should perform the massage and take precautions when the client is getting off the table after the session has ended
B. The massage therapist should offer the client two aspirin to help thin the blood to make circulation more efficient
C. The massage therapist should perform the massage and work vigorously over the abdomen to stimulate peristalsis
D. The massage therapist should reschedule the appointment to prevent a potentially contagious disease from spreading

18. If a client is experiencing tightness in the iliopsoas, what may be an effect experienced in the hamstrings as a result
A. The hamstrings may develop adhesions
B. The hamstrings may be shortened
C. The hamstrings would experience no effects
D. The hamstrings may be stretched

19. A client informs their massage therapist that they were playing basketball two days prior and suffered an injury to the ankle that has inhibited movement and causes the client acute pain while walking. The therapist asks to view the area, and observes substantial inflammation and bruising in the area. Which of the following is an appropriate response from the massage therapist
A. The therapist should proceed with the massage and work gently on the area to assist in reducing inflammation
B. The therapist should proceed with the massage as scheduled and treat the injured area as a local contraindication
C. The therapist should proceed with the massage and apply heat to the area to bring oxygenated blood to the area to aid in tissue repair
D. The therapist should reschedule the appointment and refer the client to their primary care physician for proper treatment

20. During a massage, a massage therapist finds a contusion on the client's anterior thigh. What should the massage therapist do in this situation
A. The massage therapist should notify the client of the location of the bruise and document the bruise under the objective section of SOAP notes
B. The massage therapist should notify the client of the location of the bruise and document the bruise under the subjective section of SOAP notes
C. The massage therapist should notify the client of the location of the bruise and document the bruise under the plan section of SOAP notes
D. The massage therapist should notify the client of the location of the bruise and document the bruise under the assessment section of SOAP notes

21. Posture, desk height, and computer monitor placement are all important factors to consider in regards to
A. Trips and falls
B. Ergonomics
C. Safety signs
D. Compliance

22. A client details on an intake form that their occupation requires them to use a computer for several hours a day and answer phones. After consulting with the massage therapist, it is determined that the client holds the phone between their ear and shoulder the majority of the time while typing on a keyboard and inputting data. What type of muscle contraction is required to hold a phone between the ear and shoulder
A. Isotonic contraction of scalenes
B. Eccentric contraction of splenius capitis
C. Isometric contraction of levator scapulae
D. Isometric contraction of sternocleidomastoid

23. A client has recently received a C-section, and it is their first massage since the procedure. Which of the following is not a piece of information the therapist should obtain before proceeding with the massage
A. How long ago the client had the procedure
B. If the client is experiencing any pain or discomfort resulting from the procedure
C. The length of time the entire procedure took to complete
D. If the client is currently taking any medication to aid in the surgical site healing properly

24. All of the following may be experienced in a client who has an elevated right pelvis except
A. The iliotibial band may be stretched on the right side
B. The quadratus lumborum may be hypertonic on the right side
C. The latissimus dorsi may be stretched on the left side
D. The sartorius may be stretched on the left side

25. During the course of a massage, a client discloses he has pain in his shoulders and mid-back. This information would be documented under which section of SOAP notes
A. Objective
B. Assessment
C. Subjective
D. Plan

Answer Key on Page 322

You're not lost. You're just early in the process.

- Gary Vaynerchuk

Business

Business

Even if you aren't planning on becoming a business owner, understanding how businesses operate is knowledge everyone should have. It can help in retaining clientele, business relationships, and even keep you out of trouble from things like HIPAA violations.

Business for a massage therapist, in most locations, begins with a **certification**. A certification is a credential obtained by completing a certification course, usually in a **school setting**. It also may involve completing a certification exam. Certifications show that you have gained enough knowledge in a given subject to be able to perform that task. In this case, you gain a certificate after completing massage school.

A **license** is a jurisdictional requirement, which is used to **regulate** the practice of massage therapy. Licensing boards set rules and laws that a person is required to follow if they wish to be a licensed massage therapist. In most jurisdictions, a license allows a massage therapist to practice massage therapy and receive money as compensation.

Reciprocity refers to the ability for a massage license in one jurisdiction to be recognized as **valid in another jurisdiction**. Some jurisdictions may require a new license to be obtained, but no more schooling required. Others may require more schooling in addition to paying for a new license.

Business Management

Business Plan

A **business plan** is a document prepared to state the **objectives** of a future business, and its **means of achieving them**. Business plans are often utilized to obtain a business loan as a way to show a bank how the business will operate, turn a profit, and how the loan will be repaid. Business plans often include a business objective and summary, marketing strategies and planning, financial information and planning, and a prediction of company growth over an extended period of time, often five to ten years.

Mission Statement

A **mission statement** may be included in a business plan. A mission statement is a statement that defines the **overall objective and values of the business**. The mission statement often consists of the product being offered, with an over-arching vision of the business, such as the quality of service provided, who the clientele is, and what the clientele can expect to receive from the business.

Financial Planning

Financial planning is used to state **long-term objectives** in regards to **money**. These objectives can include the amount of money expended, the amount of money saved, repayment of loans, etc. Financial planning is useful in helping to guide a business towards achieving monetary goals that they have set, without straying from the plan they have laid out. This allows for proper budgeting for products, employees, utilities, and rent.

Market Analysis

Market analysis is utilized to **assess a market**, helping determine things such as customer volume, money spent in specific locations, money spent on specific products, the competition, and more. Market analysis can help determine the kind of business to launch, where to launch it, when to launch it, who to market it to, how much to price the product or service, and how to properly advertise the product or service.

Accounts Receivable

When money is owed to a business, such as credit or debt from a vendor, it is known as **accounts receivable**. This money is charged to another company for services or products the charging company has performed, and the other company is responsible for paying these charges. An example of accounts receivable is a massage business shipping a crate of body scrubs to a store, who will then sell them. The store will then owe the massage business payment for the body scrubs, and is usually given a time frame in which to deliver payment. Once payment is received, accounts receivable for that transaction returns to a zero balance.

Accounts Payable

When the business owes money to another company, however, it is known as **accounts payable**. An example of accounts payable is a business accruing credit card debt. The money owed by the business to the credit card company is accounts payable. Once the credit card debt is paid off by the business, the amount in accounts payable returns to a zero balance.

Taxpayer Identification Numbers

Taxpayer Identification Numbers, or TINs, are used to **identify a taxpayer** to the IRS and courts in legal proceedings. When submitting documentation to the IRS or courts, the TIN required must be **completely furnished** to allow proper identification to occur.

Social security numbers are issued by the Social Security Administration, and are used to **record wages and self-employed earnings** for collecting Social Security benefits.

An **Employer Identification Number**, or EIN, is used to **identify a business entity** in tax related documents, such as a W-2.

Individual Taxpayer Identity Numbers, or ITINs, are numbers given to people who otherwise **cannot obtain a social security number**, such as nonresidents and resident aliens, spouses, and dependents.

Liability Insurance

When operating a business at a physical location where there is customer exposure, liability insurance is often required. There are two types of liability insurance: General liability insurance, and Professional liability insurance.

General liability insurance protects the massage therapist in cases such as **accidental falls** by the client that result in bodily injury. **Professional liability insurance** is similar, but instead of protecting the therapist from workplace accidents, it protects the therapist from lawsuits regarding **malpractice or negligence**. If a massage therapist knowingly performs a service or treatment they are not authorized, licensed, or certified to perform, this is known as malpractice. If a client tells a therapist not to work on a specific part of the body(say, the feet), and the therapist forgets and works on that area, and injury results, this is considered negligence.

Types of Employment

There are many different types of employment you may encounter as a massage therapist. These are among the most common.

An **independent contractor** is a massage therapist that works independently, for themselves, but **contracts** with another person or company to perform work. Independent contractors are not beholden to the same limitations as employees, however. Independent contractors may work whatever schedule they want, charge their own prices, and wear their own uniform. Independent contractors do not receive benefits from an employer.

Sole proprietors are often categorized similarly to independent contractors. Sole proprietorships are businesses owned by **one person**. Sole proprietors may differ from independent contractors in licensing requirements.

A **partnership** is a business owned by **two or more people**. Ownership may be split differently depending on variables such as money entering into a business relationship, assets, etc.

S Corporations are corporations that pass income and taxes onto the **shareholders**. This requires the shareholders to shoulder the responsibility of reporting income and taxes to the IRS.

Tax Forms

A **W-2** is filed by **employees**, detailing earnings and money withheld for social security taxes, medicaid, state and federal income taxes. Gratuity may also be reported on the W-2, if the gratuity is added to the employee's paycheck.

		Department of the Treasury - Internal Revenue Service	
Form W-2 Wage and Tax Statement Copy B - To Be Filed With Employee's FEDERAL Tax Return. This information is being furnished to the Internal Revenue Service.	**2017** OMB No. 1545-0008	1 Wages, tips, other compensation 32340.00	2 Federal income tax withheld 455.00
	7 Social security tips	3 Social security wages 32340.00	4 Social security tax withheld 200.88
c Employer's name, address, and ZIP code WASHOE COUNTY SCHOOL DISTRICT PO BOX RENO, NV	8 Allocated tips	5 Medicare wages and tips 32340.00	6 Medicare tax withheld 47.00
	9 Verification code	10 Dependent care benefits	11 Nonqualified plans
	12a See instructions for box 12	12b	12c
e Employee's name, address, and ZIP code MEGHAN KENDRICK 123 FOUR FIVE SIX ST RENO, NV 89511	12d	13 Statutory emp Retirement plan Third-party sick pay	14 Other
	b Employer Identification Number (EIN) 88-9943740	a Employee's social security number 000-00-0001	
15 State Employer's state ID number	16 State wages, tips, etc.	17 State income tax	18 Local wages, tips, etc. 19 Local income tax 20 Locality name

A **1099** is issued to an **independent contractor** by the company they contract with. This statement details the amount of income accrued by the independent contractor through the year. There are many different types of 1099's. A 1099-MISC is used when a person has earned at least $600 in things such as rents, prizes and awards, and other income. 1099-INT details interest earned during the year. 1099-G covers monies received from the government, such as taxable grants. 1099-R is used when a person receives a disbursement on retirement funds from an IRA or 401(k).

☐ CORRECTED (if checked)		
PAYER'S name, street address, city or town, province or state, country, ZIP or foreign postal code, and telephone no. Business! 890 One Two Three Street Seattle, WA 00002	1 Rents $	2 Royalties $ 99,999.99	OMB No. 1545-0115 **2016** Form **1099-MISC** Miscellaneous Income
	3 Other income $	4 Federal income tax withheld $	
PAYER'S federal identification number 01-0000001	RECIPIENT'S identification number XXX-XX-5555	5 Fishing boat proceeds $	6 Medical & health care payments $
		7 Nonemployee compensation $	8 Substitute payments in lieu of dividends or interest $
RECIPIENT'S name Billy Bob 1234 Five Six Seven Street New York, NY 00001		9 Payer made direct sales of $5,000 or more of consumer products to a buyer (recipient) for resale ☐	10 Crop insurance proceeds $
		11	12
		13 Excess golden parachute payments $	14 Gross proceeds paid to an attorney $
		15a Section 409A deferrals $	15b Section 409A income $
Account number (see instructions) FATCA filing requirement ☐		16 State tax withheld $	17 State/Payer's state no. 18 State income $
Form **1099-MISC** (keep for your records)	www.irs.gov/form1099misc	Department of the Treasury - Internal Revenue Service	

A **Schedule C**, an attachment to form 1040, is filed to the IRS by **sole proprietors**, detailing the amount of money the business made during the previous year. Barter is also reported on a Schedule C, and the amount reported is 100% of the cost of service provided by the massage therapist, usually a massage session.

A **Schedule SE** is an attachment to form 1040 that details Social Security tax information for self employed individuals.

A **Schedule K-1** is a form filed by **individual partnership members**. It is similar to a W-2, detailing the amount of money each partnership member made during the previous year.

Profit and Loss(income and expense) statements are forms filed by businesses that show how much money was made(**profit**) and how much money was expended(**loss**) during the year.

Gift taxes may be used as deductions on taxes. If a business buys a gift for a customer, no more than **$25** may be claimed as a deduction for that specific client. Other gifts for different clients may also be reported, but each gift reported cannot exceed $25.

Medicolegal Terms

Subpoena

When a court requires a person to attend a hearing or trial and testify in some way, the person is issued a writ by the court known as a **subpoena**. Subpoena literally translates to "**under penalty**", and if the person does not appear, they will be in violation of law. There are two separate types of subpoenae. A **subpoena duces tecum** is a court summons in which the person being summoned is required to appear in court with documentation or other evidence used in a trial or hearing. A **subpoena ad testificandum** is a court summons in which the person being summoned is required to appear in court and testify.

Plaintiff and Defendant

In cases of trials, there are two sides: plaintiffs and defendants. A **plaintiff** is a person or company that brings a lawsuit against another person or company. The **defendant** is the person or company whom the lawsuit is brought against. It is the responsibility of the plaintiff to prove their case against the defendant.

Respondeat Superior

Respondeat superior refers to an **employer** being held **legally responsible** for the actions of an **employee**. Plaintiffs who bring lawsuits will commonly try to hold both the employer and employee responsible for any damages the plaintiff has suffered. Independent contractors and federal employees are not included.

Res Ipsa Loquitur

When a plaintiff sets out to prove that **harm** that has been done would not have occurred without **negligence**, it is known as **res ipsa loquitur**, which translates to "the thing speaks for itself". The plaintiff will set out to show that harm was the direct result of the defendant's actions and whatever instrument the defendant used was under their complete control, and nothing else could have caused the harm.

Pro Bono

Shortening of the term "pro bono publico" or "**for the public good**", refers to a lawyer performing work for a client or entity **without being compensated**. Commonly, pro bono work is given to non-profit organizations or low-income citizens who cannot otherwise afford an attorney.

Deposition

A **deposition** is a **statement given under oath** and **outside of court**. Depositions are used to determine what the person specifically knows about the case, and to document testimony for trial. Depositions are commonly used when there is a chance the witness will not appear in court. These cases are typically approved by a judge beforehand.

Arbitration

In some cases, two parties in a court dispute may not wish to go to trial, and instead begin **alternative dispute resolution(ADR)**. **Arbitration** is a form of ADR in which an **intermediary** is used. This intermediary is an impartial party who will hear both sides of the argument, and then make a **binding decision** on the outcome. This decision is typically not able to be appealed.

Mediation

Mediation is another form of ADR, in which both sides agree to come together and **negotiate** a form of settlement. It differs from arbitration in that there is no third party that makes a final decision. A **mediator** is a third party, and used to interpret and define information, and try to help both sides develop a resolution to the conflict.

Good Samaritan Laws

Good Samaritan Laws were developed in order to protect anyone who is helping a person they believe are in immediate danger or peril, are ill, or are in some way incapacitated. These laws **prevent** the good samaritan from being **sued for alleged wrongdoing**.

Business Matching

_____: Determining customer volume, products or treatments to offer, where to spend money, and competition

_____: Form filed to the IRS by sole proprietors detailing income for a business from the previous year

_____: Money owed to a business from an outside party for services rendered or products provided

_____: Jurisdictional requirement used to regulate the practice of massage therapy

_____: Insurance used to protect a business in cases such as accidental falls by a client that result in injury

_____: Form of alternate dispute resolution in which a third party is used to determine a binding outcome

_____: Lawyer performing work without being compensated

_____: A massage license in one jurisdiction being recognized as valid in another jurisdiction

_____: Employer being held legally responsible for the actions of an employee

_____: Form submitted to the IRS detailing income and expenses for a business from the previous year

_____: Statement defining the overall objectives and values of a business

_____: Credential obtained by completing a course in a school setting

_____: Statement given under oath outside of a courtroom setting for use as testimony in trial

_____: Form of alternate dispute resolution in which both parties come together to form a settlement

_____: Document created to state objectives of a business and how the objectives will be achieved

_____: Writ issued by a court requiring a person to attend a court proceeding and testify in some way

_____: Money owed by one business to another for services or products rendered such as credit card debt

_____: Law created to protect any person who is providing aid to another that may be in immediate danger, are ill, or in some way incapacitated

_____: Determining how to spend money, save money, and repay loans

_____: Form issued to independent contractors detailing income or royalties earned during the previous year

_____: Insurance used to protect a business in cases such as malpractice or negligence

_____: Form issued to partnership members detailing income from the previous year

A: Professional Liability Insurance
B: 1099
C: Accounts Receivable
D: Subpoena
E: Business Plan
F: Mediation
G: Respondeat Superior
H: Deposition
I: Good Samaritan Law
J: Reciprocity
K: Schedule K1

L: Pro Bono
M: Financial Planning
N: Arbitration
O: Mission Statement
P: Schedule C
Q: General Liability Insurance
R: Profit and Loss Statement
S: Market Analysis
T: Accounts Payable
U: License
V: Certification

Answer Key on Page 308

Business Crossword

Across

3. Tax form submitted to the IRS by sole proprietors
6. A person who brings a lawsuit against another person or company
11. A business that has two or more owners
12. Number used to identify an employer or business entity in tax related documents, abbv.
14. A person whom a lawsuit is brought against
15. Form of liability insurance used to protect against malpractice or negligence lawsuits
16. A lawyer performing work without receiving compensation
17. A written command issued by a court such as a subpoena

Down

1. The main thing independent contractors do not receive from the contracting agent
2. Form of alternate dispute resolution in which a third party is used to determine a binding outcome
4. A corporation that passes income and expenses on to its shareholders, who then must report this information to the IRS
5. A W-2 is a form given to this person, detailing income and taxes for the previous year
6. Statement submitted to the IRS detailing income and expenses for a business from the previous year
7. Number given to a person who cannot obtain a social security number such as a nonresident, abbv.
8. Determining budgeting for employees, products, rent, and utilities
9. A plaintiff setting out to prove harm would not have occurred without negligence
10. Number used to record wages and self-employed earnings for collecting Social Security benefits
13. A person who helps two parties negotiate some form of settlement in lawsuits

Answer Key on Page 309

Business Practice Test

1. A massage therapist agrees to exchange services with a tattoo artist. The massage therapist's treatment costs $100 per hour, while the tattoo artist charges $150 per hour, for a difference of $50 between the two. How much would the massage therapist be required to report to the IRS for tax purposes after exchanging these services
A. $150, or the full amount of the tattoo session
B. $100, or the full amount of the massage session
C. $0, because no money exchanged hands, only services
D. $50, or half the amount of the massage session

2. Which of the following is an example of a circumstance covered by general liability insurance
A. A massage therapist causes an injury to the client due to hyper-extending the knee while stretching the hamstrings
B. A client becomes enraged with a treatment they are receiving and intentionally breaks a window in the massage establishment
C. A massage therapist knowingly performs a treatment that they are not trained or certified in, resulting in injury to the client
D. A client develops an allergic reaction to detergent used to clean massage linens

3. A massage therapist owns a business and has decided to add hot towel treatments into the services provided. The therapist purchases a hot towel cabinet, and begins using the hot towel cabinet during massage to heat hand towels and washcloths. For tax purposes, what is the hot towel cabinet considered
A. Taxable income
B. Asset
C. Liability
D. Tax exemption

4. On tax documents such as a W-2 or 1099, an EIN is used to
A. Determine the amount of money withheld for social security tax
B. Detail royalties or gratuity earned
C. Identify a business entity
D. Estimate tax rate based on marital status

5. A massage therapist creates and sells body scrubs as an additional means of income for their business. A local beauty supply shop has shown an interest in the product, and the therapist agrees to sell 50 body scrub units to the beauty supply shop. The therapist mails the body scrubs in a box and includes an invoice, stating the amount of money the shop owes to the therapist for the body scrubs. Which of the following is the money owed to the massage therapist categorized as
A. Accounts receivable
B. Business assets
C. Accounts payable
D. Liabilities

6. A Schedule C is a tax form utilized to report gross income, net income, and deductions for whom
A. Sole proprietors
B. Partnership members
C. Independent contractors
D. Members of an S corporation

7. A massage therapist decides at the end of the year to purchase gifts for their clients who they see on a regular basis to show appreciation for their continued patronage. The therapist decides the best way to go about giving gifts is to buy gift cards. The therapist purchases gift cards for their clients, and saves the receipts of the gift card purchases for use in filing taxes. How much money may the therapist deduct from their taxes per client for the gifts
A. $35 per client
B. $10 per client
C. $50 per client
D. $25 per client

8. Which of the following is not reported on taxes as income
A. Gratuity received from clients
B. Referral fees paid by the massage therapist to scheduling websites
C. Payments for massage services made by clients
D. Product purchases by the client for bath bombs the therapist has made

9. During a massage shift, a therapist is approached by their manager. The manager explains to the therapist that their next client is specifically requesting a hot stone massage. The therapist states to the manager that they have never performed or been trained in hot stone massage. The manager says it'll be fine, and books the appointment without getting the therapist's approval. The therapist attempts to perform the hot stone massage, but fails to properly cool a stone to a tolerable temperature, and the client is burned. The client proceeds to sue the massage therapist due to the burn. The therapist responds by stating their manager forced them to perform the treatment even though the therapist did not have any training, and therefore it is the fault of the manager and not the therapist. Which medicolegal term describes this assumption on the part of the therapist
A. Subpoena duces tecum
B. Res ipsa loquitur
C. Respondeat superior
D. Pro bono

10. A massage therapist's client is suing their doctor for negligence. The client states to the court that the doctor recommended massage therapy for the client's condition, despite the condition being contraindicated for massage therapy. The massage therapist is issued a subpoena duces testificandum by the court. When responding to the subpoena, the massage therapist submits a form agreeing to appear. To verify the massage therapist's identity, the therapist's social security number is requested. How should the massage therapist provide their social security number when responding to the subpoena
A. The massage therapist should provide only the last four digits, for example, XXX-XX-1234
B. The massage therapist should provide only the first three digits, for example, 123-XX-XXXX
C. The massage therapist should provide the entire number, for example, 123-45-6789
D. The massage therapist should provide only the last six digits, for example, XXX-12-3456

11. A business is owned by two people. At the end of the year, the business owners are both required to file the following tax form to the IRS, detailing income and expenses each owner has incurred during the previous tax year
A. 1099
B. W-2
C. Schedule C
D. Schedule K-1

12. Which of the following is obtained to regulate the practice of massage therapy and allow a massage therapist to perform massage and receive monetary compensation
A. Insurance
B. Scope of practice
C. Certification
D. License

13. A massage therapist owns a business and is the sole therapist on staff. The therapist typically sees five or six clients every day, and is beginning to experience burn-out. The therapist has decided it may be ideal to add another massage therapist to the staff to ease some of the burden the therapist is experiencing. Which of the following should the therapist perform to determine if this is a wise business decision
A. The therapist should perform financial planning to determine the cost of hiring another therapist and how the therapist's income will be affected
B. The therapist should perform a market analysis to determine if the competition also has multiple massage therapists on staff
C. The therapist should develop a business plan to present to a bank to acquire a loan in order to expand the business by adding a second massage room
D. The therapist should perform a survey of all existing clients to determine the types of treatments the clients prefer, so the therapist can specifically hire someone who is certified in each service desired

14. A massage therapist is involved in a legal dispute with a client over assumed negligence. The therapist and client agree to have their cases heard by an impartial third party, who will make a binding decision to solve the dispute that typically cannot be appealed. Which of the following are the two parties using
A. Deposition
B. Res ipsa loquitur
C. Arbitration
D. Mediation

15. Business expenses include all of the following except
A. Massages
B. Advertising
C. Credit card fees
D. Electricity

16. A W-2 details net income for an employee. Which of the following describes net income
A. Income before taxes and expenses
B. Income received due to royalties
C. Income after expenses
D. Income produced by gratuity only

17. A massage therapist has decided to open a business, offering massage out of an office, but they need financial backing of some sort to begin operations. Which of the following should the massage therapist produce to present to a lender in the hopes of obtaining a loan
A. Market analysis
B. Business plan
C. Mission statement
D. Down payment

18. The cost of linen service, equipment purchases, utilities, and licensure can all be reported to the IRS as which of the following
A. Income
B. Tax credits
C. Tax exemptions
D. Deductions

19. Which of the following types of employment offers the most forms of protection and benefits
A. Employee
B. Sole proprietorship
C. Partnership
D. Independent contractor

20. A client receives a deep tissue massage, and the next day the client is experiencing discomfort in areas the massage therapist specifically massaged. The client files a lawsuit, alleging the massage therapist was negligent in the session and caused injury to the client. Which of the following forms of insurance provides coverage in this sort of circumstance
A. General liability insurance
B. Personal liability insurance
C. Professional liability insurance
D. Certified liability insurance

21. Of the following, which is not an item that can typically be used as a tax deduction for a sole proprietor
A. Massage lubricant purchases
B. Advertising expenses
C. Subscriptions to music services
D. Meal purchases for the sole proprietor

22. A massage therapist owns a business and income has plateaued. The therapist is looking at new ways to bring in more clients. What is the first step the therapist should take
A. The therapist should drop the prices of all of their treatments permanently to consistently bring in more clientele
B. The therapist should hire another massage therapist to perform the same types of massage treatments that are currently being offered by the therapist
C. The therapist should perform a market analysis to determine what the competition is doing and what treatments may be popular that the therapist is not currently offering
D. The therapist should close the business and work for the competition, because if you can't beat 'em, join 'em

23. A massage student has told their fellow classmates that they are interested in starting a massage therapy business once they are done with school. Three other students think it's a great idea, and they all agree that they should open a business together. If they were all follow through with the plan and open the business together, what type of business would it be categorized as
A. Sole proprietorship
B. Partnership
C. Limited liability corporation
D. S corporation

24. A massage student is granted which of the following after completing a massage therapy education course
A. Certification
B. Insurance
C. License
D. Reciprocity

25. A massage therapist calls a vendor and places an order for a crate of hypoallergenic massage lubricant. The therapist does not pay immediately, but is mailed an invoice with the crate to make payment at a later date. The money owed to the vendor by the massage therapist is categorized as which of the following
A. Accounts receivable
B. Financial analysis
C. Debt consolidation
D. Accounts payable

Answer Key on Page 322

Do as little as needed, not as much as possible.

- Henk Kraaijenhof

Ethics

Ethics

Ethics are **guiding moral principles**. These guiding moral principles are used to direct a massage therapist in proper course of action in ethical dilemmas. There are many different ethical dilemmas that may arise in the practice of massage therapy. Examples include becoming sexually attracted to a client(refer the client to another therapist) and attempting to sell products or merchandise to a client outside the scope of massage(don't do it).

Scope of Practice

Scope of practice is performing treatments and techniques you are **qualified to perform**. Working outside of the scope of practice can lead to malpractice lawsuits. Examples of working outside of the scope of practice include performing treatments such as acupuncture or chiropractic work without proper licensing. Stay within your scope of practice at all times!

Boundaries

Boundaries are **limitations** that can be set by the massage therapist and the client. They can be verbally set, such as a client asking a massage therapist to avoid working on a specific part of the body, or non-verbal, such as a client leaving an article of clothing on, which typically means they might not want to have that part of the body worked on. The best way to identify boundaries is to communicate with the client. Ask questions, reinforce the boundaries you or the client have set.

Permeable boundaries are boundaries that allow conversation, information, and emotions to **flow freely** between the therapist and client. No topic is deemed off-limits by either party, with neither the therapist nor the client being reserved in conversation.

Semi-permeable boundaries allow a therapist to be **open or distant** with the client **depending on the situation**. This allows the massage therapist to be reserved in certain conversations and withhold information deemed too personal or controversial, but still allow appropriate conversation to take place. In most cases, this is the appropriate boundary to establish in a massage setting, because it allows conversation but keeps the conversation from crossing the limits of comfort for both parties.

Impermeable boundaries severely limit the exchange of information between the therapist and client. Impermeable boundaries are useful when a client is asking too much information about the therapist, if the client makes sexual advances towards the therapist, or other similar situations. The massage therapist can stop verbal communication to establish an impermeable boundary.

Confidentiality is keeping client information **private and protected**. Client information includes anything that happens or is said during a massage session, client files, intake forms, SOAP notes, and even something as simple as names. This information needs to be kept private. Releasing this information is a violation of HIPAA.

Communication

Communication is extremely important in the client/therapist relationship. One of the main ways we communicate with clients is by asking questions.

An **open-ended question** is a question used when asking for **feedback** from clients. Often, open-ended questions are meant to extract more detail or information. It allows the answer to be more open and abstract.

A **close-ended question** is a question used when asking for a **yes-or-no response** only. These questions are used to extract important pieces of information in a short amount of time. When time is a factor, close-ended questions are primarily used to gather the important information without sacrificing too much time.

Self disclosure is when the **client** shares information about **themselves**. This information, which may be documented if relevant, needs to be kept confidential.

Active listening is listening to what the client is saying, and **actively interpreting** the information being given. The client's statements are being paid attention to, and the client has the full focus of the massage therapist while they are speaking. This allows the massage therapist to respond to and remember what is being said.

Passive listening is listening to a client **without responding**. Passive listening does not require the listener to engage the talker in conversation or ask questions in response. This can result in the mind wandering, and details being provided by the client to be forgotten.

Body language is a form of **unspoken communication** in which a person is able to communicate through conscious or subconscious gestures. Facial expression can convey a person's current emotion, such as happiness. Posture can express whether a person is open and willing to engage or closed and hostile or anxious. Eye contact, avoiding eye contact, the space a person leaves between others while communicating, and crossing the arms across the chest are all other examples of body language, and can be interpreted in many different ways. Paying attention to the client's body language can also be extremely important in certain situations, such as a client experiencing a flashback. The client may not communicate verbally, but the therapist should be aware of cues the body gives that something is not right, such as labored or rapid breathing. In this case, the therapist should stop the massage, communicate with the client verbally by saying their name to try to bring them out of the flashback, and listen to the client to figure out why the flashback occurred. Referring the client to a mental health specialist may also be accepted.

During conversation, a person may exhibit empathy or sympathy in response to another person and their situation. **Empathy** is when a person puts themselves in the shoes of another, viewing a situation from the other person's point of view. **Sympathy** is when a person feels compassion or pity for the other person and the situation they are in.

Transference and counter-transference occur when one person in the therapeutic relationship begins viewing the other as more than just their client or therapist. **Transference** is when the **client** begins viewing the massage therapist **similarly to a person in their own personal life**. They develop an emotional attachment to the massage therapist. **Counter-transference** is the opposite: a **massage therapist** develops an **emotional attachment to a client**. If either of these occur, it's best to refer the client to another massage therapist, separating the massage therapist from any possible ethical dilemmas.

Defense Mechanisms

A massage may leave a client in a psychologically vulnerable place, and they may exhibit defense mechanisms to help cope with their internal struggles.

Denial, a common defense mechanism, is a **refusal to acknowledge** a given situation, or acting as if something didn't happen.

Displacement is often negative. Displacement is **satisfying an impulse by substitution**. An example could be, you have a very bad day at work or school, you go home, and instead of being upset at school or work, you lash out at a significant other. Releasing your pent-up emotions at something other than what is causing the emotions.

Projection is placing one's own **internal feelings onto someone else**. An example could be my wife: when she gets hungry, she becomes easily agitated. She'll then accuse me of being in a bad mood, even though I'm feeling great. This is projection. For the record, this happens a lot.

Regression is **taking a step back psychologically** when faced with stress. An example could be quitting smoking. A person doesn't smoke for a few days, and then they are presented with a stressful situation, which causes them to regress and smoke again.

Repression is **subconsciously blocking out** unwanted emotions. Not even knowing you have something to be upset about. The mind can erase certain memories to help protect a person from stress.

Therapeutic Relationship

The relationship a massage therapist shares with a client is known as the **therapeutic relationship**. The relationship between a therapist and client has many complexities. The primary goal of the therapist in the therapeutic relationship is to help the clients achieve goals they may be seeking, whether it be physical or emotional.

The therapeutic relationship is the responsibility of the therapist to guide and cultivate. Ensuring the client is happy with the service received in turn gives the therapist confidence in helping treat the client, which may increase therapist happiness and satisfaction in the job they are performing.

In the therapeutic relationship, there exists a **power differential**. The client, while in control of the session in most aspects, gives the therapist the power to perform massage, trusting that they have obtained sufficient training and working knowledge to help achieve the client's goals. The power differential can shift back to the client if the client feels their goals aren't being met, or their boundaries are being violated, such is the drape revealing more of the client than they are comfortable with.

An extremely important part of the therapeutic relationship is **communication on both ends**, between the client and therapist. If the client does not properly communicate their goals, it becomes difficult for the therapist to design an effective treatment plan. On the other hand, if the therapist fails to communicate reasons for developing a treatment plan based on client goals, the client may feel as if their needs are not being met. It is incumbent on the therapist to direct the flow of communication. The therapist should not be afraid to ask questions or explain reasons for performing specific massage strokes, stretches, or techniques if the client may not understand the reasoning for them.

Dual Relationships

A **dual relationship** is a relationship between two people that consists of a **professional aspect and a personal aspect**. An example in massage therapy is a massage therapist's friend becoming a regular client. While this situation isn't out of the ordinary, it can lead to several ethical issues, from time and financial abuse to breach of confidentiality. For example, a friend may book a massage and no-show the appointment, thinking that because they are friends with the therapist, the therapist will understand and there will be no issues. Another example, the therapist gives their friend a massage and then they meet up later that week and the therapist asks the friend about their treatment progress in front of others. This is a breach of confidentiality. When dealing with dual relationships, it may be appropriate to define the therapeutic relationship to the friend, explaining that during the massage session they are considered a client first. The friend should also view the therapist as their massage therapist first and foremost, and friend second. Making this known to both parties can help prevent any ethical dilemmas from arising in the future.

Ethical Dilemmas

An **ethical dilemma** is any situation a person finds themselves in which offers **differing choices that conflict with a person's ethics**. Ethics are guiding moral principles, and a person may find themselves in conflict with ethical choices in certain circumstances. Ethical dilemmas arise when there are conflicts regarding duties or rights. **Duties** are often categorized as **nonmaleficence**, or doing no harm, and **beneficence**, or acting in good faith. **Rights** refer to the client having the ability to make **informed consent**, and having autonomy in making decisions that are in their best interest.

The ability to resolve ethical dilemmas can be tricky, and is often confusing. When approached with an ethical dilemma, questions a person can ask themselves are "Is this situation a potential problem?", "What do the Code of Ethics say regarding this situation?", and "What do other people think of this situation and how would they handle it?"

Here is an example of an ethical dilemma: A client states they are looking to buy a car for their child who has just graduated from high school. The massage therapist has a car for sale. Let's break down this dilemma using one of the questions listed above:

Is this situation a potential problem?

- Can you think of any reasons this situation could be considered a problem?
- Are there any ways the therapist's behavior, or the client's behavior, might change as a result of this situation if the therapist were to tell the client they were selling their car?
- Could the client potentially seek favors from the therapist to try to influence the therapist to sell the car to the client?
- Could the therapist give the client more massage time or treat the client more favorably than other clients because the client may want to purchase the car from the therapist?

These are all questions that a therapist must ask themselves when confronted with an ethical dilemma. My personal approach is, if I even have to question whether a certain situation is ethical or not, it's not a situation I want to be a part of. The question I always ask myself is, "What would I do if I wanted to keep my job or license? Would my employer or the state board approve or not?"

Sexual Misconduct

Sexual misconduct is any act that has a **sexual undertone or overtone** that is **inappropriate in a professional setting**. Sexual misconduct may involve making sexually charged comments and/or gestures, physically touching another person in an inappropriate way, and sexually harassing another person, among others. Sexual misconduct may even take place between two consenting adults, such as between a therapist and client. Sexual misconduct in any form can lead to the loss of employment, loss of licensure, lawsuits, and potential legal ramifications up to incarceration. Sexual misconduct in a professional setting may also lead to a negative view on the profession as a whole, which can be detrimental to the entire industry.

Sexual misconduct in massage therapy may be considered **abuse of the power differential** that the therapist has with the client.

In massage therapy, a massage therapist and client may develop an attraction to one another. If this is the case, the therapist needs to take charge of the situation, **identify the problem**, and **refer the client to another therapist**. If the therapist and client decide to begin dating, the therapist should no longer see the client. Taking these steps can help prevent allegations of sexual misconduct, keeping the therapist out of civil and legal trouble.

Massage therapy is an inherently intimate form of treatment. It is important for the massage therapist to **normalize and desexualize touch** associated with massage therapy to discourage the client from developing thoughts, feelings, and attraction to the massage therapist. Behaving in a **professional manner**, wearing clean and professional uniforms, and talking to the client in a professional manner are all ways to normalize the massage session and help the client understand it is not a sexual encounter, but a therapeutic service.

Accepting and Declining Clients

The act of accepting and declining clients can also have ethical associations. In general, any client should be accepted by the massage therapist **unless there are circumstances** preventing the therapist from booking with the client. Examples include the following:

- If the therapist's schedule is completely booked, they cannot fit the client in to their schedule so they'd have to refer the client out to another therapist.
- If the client is underage, the therapist may not be willing to work on the client without parental consent.
- If the client is exhibiting medical conditions that may be contraindicated, or if the client appears to be intoxicated, it may be appropriate to refuse to treat the client.
- If the client is exhibiting transference, or the therapist is exhibiting counter-transference, the client should be referred to another therapist.

There are instances where it is not just ethically but legally wrong to refuse to book a client. **Title VII of the Civil Rights Act of 1964** states it is **illegal to discriminate** against a person in a place of business based on age, race, religion, gender, or sexual preference. A therapist may refuse service to any person for any justifiable reason, unless it is a reason covered in Title VII of the Civil Rights Act of 1964. This act also applies to employment. For example, a male massage therapist cannot be denied a position at a large chain massage establishment based solely on being a male. This specific example is known as **gender discrimination**.

Ending the Client Relationship

Ending a client relationship can be tricky, and the client may not understand the reasoning for it. Approaching the situation with care is required. The therapist has the right to end the relationship with the client for any reason, as long as the reason does not fall under Title VII of the Civil Rights Act of 1964. Common reasons a therapist might end the client relationship:

- The therapist feels as if they are unable to help the client, and the therapist feels as if the client would obtain better results with another therapist.
- If the therapist feels as if the client's goals with treatment have been accomplished.
- If the client is exhibiting transference, or the therapist is exhibiting counter-transference.
- If the client or therapist are exhibiting any form of sexual attraction.
- If the client is behaving inappropriately during the massage session, either verbally or physically.
- If the client continuously abuses the therapist's time by no-showing appointments or arriving late.

A therapist should **refer the client to another therapist** or establishment, and **calmly explain** the reason why they are ending the client relationship. Once the decision is made, it should be final, and the therapist should not go back on their stance. This can strain the relationship a therapist has with the client and make every session after uncomfortable for both parties, becoming a detriment.

Business Practices

A massage therapist should strive to run an **ethical business** in all aspects. There are several factors that play in to being ethical in business, such as handling money, marketing, and filing taxes.

Money can be a driving force in making unethical decisions in business. If a person is at risk of losing money, or has the opportunity to gain a vast amount of money, they may be more willing to behave unethically to achieve these goals. Behaving unethically based on money can not only damage the business's reputation, but the reputation of the entire industry.

Set Fee Structure

In most circumstances, a therapist should create a **set fee structure** for each service they provide and have it posted where a client can view it. The price of the service should generally **remain the same for every appointment**, with adjustments made for certain people like return clients, or if offering pre-paid treatment packages. A set fee structure assures the client that they aren't being taken advantage of based on factors such as the amount of money they make. If a therapist were to change the price of their service for one client based on the client's income being higher than average, it is unethical and known as **financial abuse**.

Gratuity

Gratuity is something a therapist may choose to accept or not accept. In general, clients do leave gratuity to massage therapists for their service. The amount the client leaves is usually **up to the client**. The client may ask a therapist how much a standard gratuity is. The therapist may answer **honestly**, but always preface the answer by telling the client tips are always **appreciated but not expected**. The therapist should provide a **general price range or percentage for the gratuity**, and be honest in the number they are providing the client.

Barter

Barter is simply **trading one thing for another**, with no money exchanging hands. In massage therapy, it is common practice to trade massages with other therapists. Massage therapists may barter with other professionals such as hair stylists, car mechanics, and tattoo artists to exchange services, or they can barter with vendors or other business owners to obtain products for use in the therapist's practice. Despite no money exchanging hands, bartering is still considered **taxable income**. If a massage therapist charges $75 for one massage, and they barter with an esthetician for a manicure and pedicure that costs $100, the therapist would be responsible for **reporting the full cost of the massage**, $75, as income on their taxes. The esthetician would be responsible for reporting the full cost of the manicure and pedicure, $100, as taxable income on their taxes.

Workplace Issues

There may be unethical situations arising throughout the workplace. If a business owner or manager gives preferential treatment to a friend or family member in instances such as promotions or hiring over others who are more or equally qualified based on nothing but their personal relationship, this is known as **nepotism**. Booking only clients of one gender with therapists of the same gender, despite the therapists being equally qualified, is a form of **gender discrimination**. These are only two examples. Therapists should set examples for everyone in the business setting, showing ethical behavior, and bringing unethical or illegal activity to the attention of the appropriate parties, whether it be direct supervisors, owners, or government agencies.

Other businesses or professionals may attempt to get a massage therapist to behave unethically in hopes of advancing their own business. For example, a chiropractor may attempt enticing a massage therapist to send them referrals by offering a small referral fee for each client. This example is known as a **kickback**. This can lead to the therapist thinking only of the referral fee being offered, and ignoring whether or not the client can actually benefit from seeing this specific chiropractor. This is not in the best interest of the client, or beneficence.

Marketing

Ethical marketing is essential in **gaining a good reputation** in the community and with potential customers and clients. A therapist should never misrepresent their business or credentials, and be as honest as possible when discussing the product or service offered. Any marketing should **refrain from misleading images or statements**, as this leads to lack of trust in the business. Marketing should not exaggerate the purpose or benefits of the business. This can lead to client dissatisfaction, and a lack of trust in the business.

Torts, Slander, and Libel

A **tort** is a **wrongful act** by one person that is responsible for an **injury or harm to another person**, and is considered a civil wrong that bears liability. Torts are often used to provide monetary compensation to a person who has been injured or harmed in some way by the offending party or parties.

Intentional torts are the result of one party **intentionally causing injury or harm** to another in some way, be it physical, emotional, or damaging a person's standing or reputation. Examples of intentional torts that do not physically harm a person are slander and libel. **Slander** is a person **intentionally using false statements verbally** in order to discredit or harm the reputation of a person. **Libel** is similar, but instead of the false statement being spoken, it is **written**. These are only considered intentional torts when the person saying the false claim knows the statement is false and will harm a person's reputation.

Ethics Matching

_____: Satisfying an impulse by substitution

_____: Type of question used when seeking a yes-or-no response

_____: Listening to information the client is providing and interpreting the information given

_____: Information and conversation between the massage therapist and client flowing freely

_____: Guiding moral principles used to guide a massage therapist in proper professional course of action

_____: A massage therapist performing treatments and techniques they are qualified to perform

_____: Information the client shares about themselves during a massage session

_____: Refusal to acknowledge a given situation

_____: Possible lawsuit that could arise against a massage therapist if the therapist works outside their scope of practice

_____: Severely limiting communication between the massage therapist and client

_____: Subconsciously blocking out any unwanted emotions

_____: Limitations set by the client or massage therapist which can be either verbal or physical

_____: Unspoken communication using conscious or subconscious gestures

_____: Keeping client information private and protected

_____: Placing one's own internal feelings onto another person

_____: A client personalizing the relationship with a massage therapist, building an emotional attachment

_____: Limiting the flow of communication and being selective in topics discussed between the massage therapist and client

_____: The relationship shared between a massage therapist and the client

_____: The client conceding control of the massage session to the therapist based on the therapist's education and experience

_____: Type of question used when seeking feedback from a client

_____: Taking a step back psychologically when faced with emotional stress

_____: A massage therapist personalizing the relationship with a client, building an emotional attachment

A: Impermeable Boundary
B: Denial
C: Body Language
D: Repression
E: Confidentiality
F: Projection
G: Open-Ended Question
H: Semi-Permeable Boundary
I: Counter-Transference
J: Active Listening
K: Power Differential

L: Regression
M: Close-Ended Question
N: Self Disclosure
O: Permeable Boundary
P: Displacement
Q: Ethics
R: Boundaries
S: Transference
T: Malpractice
U: Scope of Practice
V: Therapeutic Relationship

Answer Key on Page 308

Ethics Crossword

Across

7. A client developing an emotional attachment to a massage therapist
8. Form of question utilized when seeking a yes-or-no response only
9. Form of question utilized when asking for feedback from a client
10. Breaking confidentiality may be a violation of this
12. Form of boundary in which conversation is essentially stopped, such as when a client makes a sexual advance towards a massage therapist
15. A massage therapist developing an emotional attachment to a client
17. Satisfying an impulse by substitution

Down

1. A form of psychological protection exhibited when a person is confronted with stress or other internal struggles
2. Placing one's own internal feelings onto someone else
3. Form of listening in which the therapist does not respond or actively interpret the information being shared
4. A massage therapist performing treatments they are qualified to perform
5. Form of boundary in which conversation is somewhat limited in scope to avoid certain topics that may be controversial
6. Form of boundary in which conversation flows freely between the massage therapist and client
11. Limitations set by a massage therapist or client that may be verbal or physical
13. Self disclosure is when the following person shares information about themselves in a massage session
14. A person refusing to acknowledge a given situation
16. Unspoken communication that may be conscious or subconscious
18. Guiding moral principles

Answer Key on Page 309

Ethics Practice Test

1. A client and massage therapist are chatting during a massage session. The client begins a story about an experience they had in church, and during the story, the client asks the therapist if the they attend church. The therapist says yes, and lets the client know which church they attend. The client exclaims that they know where that church is, and then continues the story. Which of the following best describes this situation
A. The therapist and client have established transference
B. The therapist and client have established an impermeable boundary
C. The therapist and client have established a dual relationship
D. The therapist and client have established a permeable boundary

2. A massage therapist gives a friend a massage. After the massage, the client realizes they are short on money by $20. The client hands the massage therapist the money they have, and tells the massage therapist they will pay them the rest the next time they come in for a massage. Which of the following best describes this situation
A. The massage therapist has a dual relationship with the client and the therapist's friendship is potentially being exploited by the client
B. The massage therapist is exhibiting counter-transference with the client by allowing the client to not pay full price for the appointment
C. The massage therapist is exhibiting a power differential in the therapeutic relationship
D. The massage therapist is experiencing financial abuse on behalf of the client by encouraging the client not to pay for the treatment they have received

3. A client calls a large chain massage establishment to schedule a massage. Immediately the receptionist identifies that the client is a male, and notifies the client that due to previous instances of problems with male clients, they are not booking male clients. Which of the following is the massage establishment in violation of for refusing the client based solely on their gender
A. Health Insurance Portability and Accountability Act
B. Civil Rights Act of 1964
C. Omnibus Reconciliation Act
D. Emergency Medical Treatment and Active Labor Act

4. A massage therapist arrives to work for their scheduled shift, and looks at their scheduled appointments for the day. The therapist notices one name in particular, a client the therapist has been working with for the past year on a biweekly basis. The therapist has come to really enjoy seeing this client, feeling as if they connect on a personal level that the therapist doesn't experience with other clients. Which of the following best describes this situation
A. The massage therapist and client have developed a sexual attraction between each other
B. The massage therapist has developed a dual relationship with the client
C. The massage therapist has displayed an impermeable boundary with the client
D. The massage therapist is exhibiting counter-transference towards the client

5. A massage therapist is chatting with a client during a massage, and the client reveals that they are a hairstylist. The client, wanting to save money, asks the therapist if they'd be interested in trading a massage for a haircut some day. Trading services is known as
A. Gifting
B. Gratuity
C. Bartering
D. Negotiating

6. During a massage session, a client experiences a flashback of a traumatizing event. The client begins openly weeping while on the table. Which of the following is the most appropriate response from the massage therapist
A. The massage therapist should continue the massage and put a blanket atop the client
B. The massage therapist should immediately end the massage and give the client psychological advice on how to deal with their trauma
C. The massage therapist should end the massage and refer the client to another massage therapist who is more equipped to handle the client's issues
D. The massage therapist should stop the massage, say the client's name to try and connect with the client, and ask the client if they'd like to continue with the massage after the flashback has passed

7. A client has been coming in to a chain massage establishment for a year, usually once a month. After every appointment, the client calls management and complains about the massage they have received, coming up with various reasons they are unhappy. After the first few times this happens and the client receives discounts for the next appointments, management notices it's become a problem. All of the following may be appropriate responses to the situation except
A. Document every instance of the client complaint and read each SOAP note to identify patterns in the treatments that may be causing the client to be unhappy
B. Explain to the client that the massage establishment may not be the right place for them, and they should seek treatment elsewhere
C. Offer the client a free massage to help improve the client's satisfaction with the business
D. Notify the client that illegitimate complaints after every appointment need to stop if they'd like to remain a client of the establishment

8. A client receives a massage. The massage therapist and client have been working together for some time, and have always been flirtatious in conversation during the treatment. During the treatment, the client states they have always felt a physical attraction toward the therapist. The therapist pauses for a moment, then admits to the client they have felt the same. Passions overtake the therapist and client, and the two engage in sexual activities during the session. Describe what is occurring in this situation
A. The client is displaying a semi-permeable boundary
B. The massage therapist is working outside of their scope of practice
C. The client is violating the massage therapist's physical boundaries
D. The massage therapist is engaging in sexual misconduct

9. A well known celebrity is staying at a resort and calls the spa to book a massage appointment. The receptionist at the spa books the appointment and notices the client's name. The receptionist quickly informs all of the massage therapists in the spa that the celebrity will be coming in for a massage. A guest overhears the receptionist, and asks if it's the celebrity from the latest hit TV show. The receptionist says yes, it's the same person. Which of the following describes this situation
A. The customer asking about the celebrity should be removed from the spa for risking the celebrity's confidentiality and violating HIPAA
B. The celebrity's confidentiality has been breached due to the receptionist sharing their name with people who aren't directly involved with the massage session
C. The receptionist is displaying strong managerial practices by informing the entire staff to expect this celebrity
D. The massage therapists are in an ethical dilemma due to perceived importance of this client in relation to other clients they see who are not famous

10. Adjusting the amount of money a client pays based on income level
A. Sliding fee scale
B. Preferred service discount
C. Adjustable credit
D. Prepaid plan

11. A massage therapist is massaging a client, and the client complains of general discomfort in the back not due to the massage. The therapist tries stretching the client's back and working on muscles that may be producing the discomfort, but the client states nothing is helping. The client then asks the massage therapist if they can try popping the back, because the client feels that will help relieve much of the discomfort. Which of the following is the appropriate response from the massage therapist to the client's request
A. The massage therapist should comply with the client's request, and charge extra for the additional treatment being performed
B. The massage therapist should abruptly end the session and ask the client to leave for inappropriate behavior
C. The massage therapist should deny the client's request and explain that what the client is requesting is outside of the therapist's scope of practice
D. The massage therapist should comply with the client's request, and document the additional work in SOAP notes

12. A client makes an appointment with a massage therapist for a one hour deep tissue massage at 12:00 PM. The time comes for the appointment, but the client has not arrived for the appointment. The massage therapist attempts to contact the client via telephone, but the client does not answer. The client finally arrives for the appointment at 12:45 PM. The client requests the full massage, but the massage therapist has a 1:15 appointment scheduled. Which of the following is the best course of action for the massage therapist to take in this situation
A. The massage therapist should explain to the client that they have another appointment booked and cannot give the client the full massage, but they can massage the client for the remaining time in the scheduled appointment
B. The massage therapist should reschedule the 1:15 appointment to make room for the client to receive their full treatment
C. The massage therapist should refuse to massage the client because the appointment start time is 45 minutes late and the client is being disrespectful
D. The massage therapist should apologize to the client and offer the client a discount on their next appointment for not being able to fit them in for their entire scheduled time

13. A massage establishment posts a job listing for a massage therapist. The establishment receives several applications. As one of the managers skims through the applications, they recognize a name as that of a friend of theirs. The manager pulls out the application from the stack and puts the others away. The manager sends a text message to their friend and tells the friend they're hired, even without an interview. What does this situation detail
A. The manager is displaying nepotism
B. The manager is violating the Civil Rights Act of 1964
C. The manager is engaging in kickbacks
D. The manager is establishing a dual relationship

14. A massage therapist has been working with a client for several months. The client has noticed significant improvement with the range-of-motion they have in the neck now compared to the beginning of the treatments. After the massage ends and the client pays for the treatment, the client is feeling especially grateful, and gives the massage therapist a hug. The massage therapist was not expecting a hug, as they had always parted with a handshake. The therapist becomes slightly uncomfortable, but lightly embraces the client, and sends the client on their way. Which best describes this situation
A. The therapist has established a dual relationship with the client
B. The client has violated the therapist's physical boundaries
C. The client has exhibited counter-transference towards the massage therapist
D. The therapist has established a permeable boundary with the client

15. During a massage, a client feels as if the massage therapist's pressure is going to deep and is causing the client pain and discomfort. The client politely asks the massage therapist to lighten the pressure. The massage therapist agrees to lighten the pressure, but feels as if the client needs deeper pressure to reach the muscles deeper in the body and help treat the client better. The massage therapist temporarily lightens the pressure, then goes back to using the deeper pressure. Which of the following is this an example of
A. Financial abuse
B. Good Samaritan Law
C. Semi-permeable boundary
D. Physical abuse

16. A client is receiving a massage, and is enjoying the treatment very much. It is the client's first massage, and they are unfamiliar with tipping etiquette. The client asks how much they should leave as gratuity. Which of the following is the most appropriate response from the massage therapist to the client's question
A. The massage therapist should explain that tipping is always expected and clients always tip 50% of each service
B. The massage therapist should explain that tipping is not mandatory or even expected, but when people do tip they tip a percentage of the service cost
C. The massage therapist should explain that they do not accept gratuity but will accept gifts instead
D. The massage therapist should explain that tipping is not customary in the massage industry and that the client should never tip a massage therapist

17. A client and therapist are chatting during a massage. The client tells the therapist that they saw someone leave the establishment as the client was entering, and thought that they recognized the person. The client asks the therapist what the person's name was, but the massage therapist simply says "I can't give out personal information like names, I'm sorry." The client understands. Which of the following best describes this situation
A. The client is violating the previous client's HIPAA rights
B. The therapist is protecting the previous client's confidentiality
C. The therapist is establishing a permeable boundary with the client
D. The client is creating an ethical dilemma for the therapist

18. All of the following describe reasons dual relationships may be problematic in a business setting except
A. The therapist's friend may feel as if they are owed special treatment and/or pricing because they know each other outside the business
B. The therapist's friend may fail to show up to a scheduled appointment because they are friends with the therapist and don't think it's a big deal
C. The therapist's friend respects the therapist and their work and supports the therapist by paying full price and not requesting a discount
D. The therapist may give preferential treatment to their friend and offer additional treatments such as body scrubs without charging the friend more than they would another client

19. A client has been seeing a massage therapist for two months to work on a problem with the client's low back. The therapist has told the client to call the therapist's work phone number to schedule appointments, but the client has begun calling the therapist on their home phone number and reaching out on the therapist's personal social media page. The client thinks it is no big deal because they have been doing treatments together for a while, and the client considers the therapist as something of a friend. Which of the following best describes this situation
A. The client is showing signs of transference towards the massage therapist
B. The client is displaying a permeable boundary towards the massage therapist
C. The client is taking control of the power differential in the therapeutic relationship
D. The client is violating the massage therapist's time boundaries

20. A massage therapist is at work, and a friend of theirs sends them a text message saying they'd like to get in for a massage later that day. The massage therapist checks the schedule and sees that they are completely booked. The therapist thinks for a moment, and decides to cancel one of the appointments they have scheduled later in the day to make room for their friend. Which of the following describes this situation
A. The massage therapist is making a savvy business decision and avoiding the potential of a no-show by the original client
B. The massage therapist is performing financial abuse by forcing the client to reschedule the appointment
C. The massage therapist is displaying a negative trait of dual relationships
D. The massage therapist is violating HIPAA in regards to the client whose appointment is being canceled

21. A massage therapist has been working with a client to address a client's back issues for an extended period of time. After numerous appointments, the client's back issues have not improved. Of the following, which is not an appropriate strategy in response to the lack of improvement
A. The massage therapist may ask the client to detail their daily activities to determine if there is anything preventing treatment from helping
B. The massage therapist may refer the client to another therapist who may be able to help
C. The massage therapist may explain to the client that there is no way to help the client's issues
D. The massage therapist may research new techniques that specifically target the issue

22. A chiropractor enters a massage establishment and asks to speak with the massage therapist. The therapist asks what they can do for the chiropractor, and the chiropractor informs the therapist that they are looking to increase their number of patients, and they would be willing to give the massage therapist compensation for every patient the therapist refers to the chiropractor. The massage therapist declines the proposal. Which describes this situation
A. The chiropractor is offering a kickback
B. The massage therapist is engaging in nepotism
C. The chiropractor is attempting to establish a dual relationship with the therapist
D. The massage therapist is rejecting the chiropractor's proposal due to the possibility of HIPAA violations

23. A massage therapist receives a phone call from a potential client whose name she recognizes. The therapist believes the client is a wealthy member of the community who owns several used car dealerships. The client asks for the price of a one hour Swedish massage. The massage therapist normally charges $70 for one hour, but knowing the client is wealthy and can afford it, tells the client the price is $100. Which of the following describes this situation
A. The massage therapist is exhibiting a dual relationship and hoping they can get a discount on a new car by giving the client a great massage
B. The massage therapist is performing financial abuse by charging one client more than another based on their perceived income
C. The massage therapist is up-selling the client in the hopes that the client enjoys the service and returns again
D. The massage therapist is rewarding the client for being more wealthy than the therapist's other clients

24. A massage therapist is working on a client's back. The client has only engaged in minimal small talk to this point. Unexpectedly, the client asks the therapist if they are dating anyone. The therapist reluctantly answers no, and the client asks if the client would be interested in going on a date. The therapist politely declines, and stops talking altogether. Which of the following describes this situation
A. The client has engaged in sexual misconduct
B. The massage therapist has established counter-transference
C. The client has established a dual relationship
D. The massage therapist has established an impermeable boundary

25. A client and massage therapist have developed a long-term working relationship lasting several years. The client and therapist enjoy the sessions together because they feel as if they get a lot accomplished. Over the past few months, the client has begun bringing the massage therapist a small gift before each session. Which of the following is the best response on behalf of the massage therapist
A. The massage therapist should begin bringing the client gifts in return so the client does not feel unappreciated and taken advantage of
B. The massage therapist should keep accepting gifts from the client as there is no ethical problem with the client bringing gifts
C. The massage therapist should let the client know that they appreciate the gifts but they are not necessary as payment for the service is more than enough
D. The massage therapist should tell the client what to get for them next time

Answer Key on Page 322

Today I will do what others won't, so tomorrow I can accomplish what others can't.

- Jerry Rice

Medical Terminology

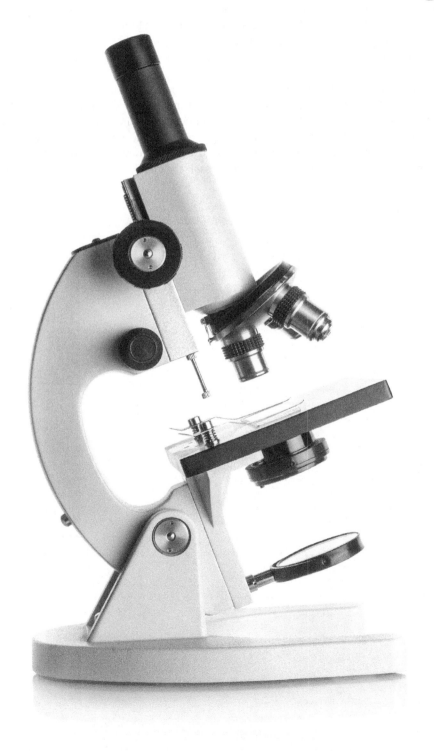

Medical Terminology

Medical terminology can be divided into three primary components: word roots, prefixes, and suffixes.

The word root of a medical term is the primary structure involved. It gives us a starting point when breaking down a word. An example is the word root "hepat/o", which means "liver".

A prefix is used to modify a word root, and is attached at the beginning of the word root. An example is "a-", which means "without". A disease that uses "a-" is "arrhythmia", which means "without rhythm".

A suffix is used to add description to, or alter, a word root, and is attached at the end of the word root. An example is "-itis", which means "inflammation". A disease that uses "-itis" is "hepatitis". As stated before, the word root "hepat/o" means "liver". If we attach "-itis", it becomes "inflammation of the liver".

Many different medical terms, prefixes, suffixes, and word roots have the same meaning. The reason for different terms having the same meaning can be traced back to the origin languages. Modern medical terminology originated in both Latin and Greek, with the majority of the words being Greek. When people like Celsus, a Roman physician, began creating medical terminology, they often used Greek terms, but conformed them to be Latin in origin. This is the reason for many terms sharing the same definition.

Medical terminology is especially useful when studying not only anatomy and physiology, but pathology as well. Knowing medical terminology can help you figure out what the general medical condition is just by looking at the name. First start by identifying the word root. We'll use the term "bursitis". The word root in "bursitis" is "burs/o", which means "bursa/bursa sac". This way, we know the condition has something to do with a bursa sac. Then we try to identify any prefixes. "Bursitis" does not contain any prefixes. Therefore, we move to suffixes. We know that "-itis" is a suffix, and it means "inflammation". We can then combine the two meanings together, and reach the conclusion that "bursitis" is inflammation of a bursa sac.

Word Roots

Cardiovascular Word Roots

angi/o: vessel(ex: **Angio**plasty)
aort/o: aorta(ex: **Aor**tic arch)
arteriol/o: arteriole(ex: **Arteriolo**sclerosis)
arteri/o: artery(ex: **Arterio**sclerosis)
ather/o: fatty plaque(ex: **Athero**sclerosis)
atri/o: atrium(ex: **Atri**al fibrillation)
bas/o: alkaline(ex: **Baso**phil)
cardi/o: heart(ex: Echo**cardio**gram)
chrom/o: color(ex: **Chromo**some)
eosin/o: rose colored(ex: **Eosino**phil)
erythr/o: red(ex: **Erythro**cyte)
granul/o: granule(ex: **Granulo**cyte)
hemangi/o: blood vessel(ex: **Hemangi**oma)
hem/o: blood(ex: **Hemo**globin)
kary/o: nucleus(ex: **Karyo**type)
leuk/o: white(ex: **Leuko**cyte)
lymph/o: lymph(ex: **Lymph**angitis)
morph/o: form(ex: **Morph**ology)
nucle/o: nucleus(ex: **Nucleo**lus)
phag/o: eat(ex: **Phago**cytosis)
phleb/o: vein(ex: **Phleb**itis)
poikil/o: irregular(ex: **Poikilo**cytosis)
reticul/o: mesh(ex: **Reticulo**cyte)
scler/o: hard(ex: Athero**scler**osis)
sider/o: iron(ex: **Sidero**blastic anemia)
sphygm/o: pulse(ex: **Sphygmo**manometer)
thromb/o: clot(ex: **Thrombo**cyte)
vascul/o: vessel(ex: A**vascul**ar)
ven/o: vein(ex: **Ven**ipuncture)
ventricul/o: ventricle(ex: **Ventriculo**megaly)

Digestive Word Roots

append/o: appendix(ex: **Append**ectomy)
appendic/o: appendix(ex: **Appendic**itis)
bucc/o: cheek(ex: **Bucc**inator)
cheil/o: lip(ex: **Cheil**itis)
chol/e: bile(ex: **Chole**cystitis)
col/o: large intestine(ex: **Col**itis)
colon/o: large intestine(ex: **Colono**scopy)
dont/o: teeth(ex: Perio**dont**al abscess)
duoden/o: duodenum(ex: **Duoden**al ulcer)
enter/o: small intestine(ex: Gastro**enter**itis)
esophag/o: esophagus(ex: **Esophag**itis)
gastr/o: stomach(ex: **Gastr**itis)
gingiv/o: gums(ex: **Gingiv**itis)
gloss/o: tongue(ex: Hypo**gloss**al nerve)
hepat/o: liver(ex: **Hepat**itis)
ile/o: ileum(ex: **Ileo**cecal sphincter)
jejun/o: jejunum(ex: **Jejuno**stomy)
labi/o: lip(ex: **Labio**mental groove)
lingu/o: tongue(ex: Bi**lingu**al)
odont/o: teeth(ex: **Odonto**blast)
or/o: mouth(ex: **Or**al cavity)
pancreat/o: pancreas(ex: **Pancreat**itis)
pharyng/o: pharynx(ex: **Pharyng**itis)
proct/o: anus(ex: **Procto**logy)

pylor/o: pylorus(ex: **Pyloro**stenosis)
rect/o: rectum(ex: **Recto**rrhagia)
sial/o: saliva(ex: **Sialo**rrhea)
sigmoid/o: sigmoid(ex: **Sigmoid**ectomy)
stomat/o: mouth(ex: **Stomat**itis)

Endocrine Word Roots

aden/o: gland(ex: **Aden**oma)
adren/o: adrenal glands(ex: **Adren**aline)
adrenal/o: adrenal glands(ex: **Adrenal**ine)
calc/o: calcium(ex: Hyper**calc**emia)
gluc/o: sugar(ex: **Gluc**agon)
glyc/o: sugar(ex: Hyper**glyc**emia)
gonad/o: gonads(ex: **Gonado**tropin)
home/o: same(ex: **Home**ostasis)
kal/i: potassium(ex: Hyper**kal**emia)
thyr/o: thyroid(ex: Hyper**thyr**oidism)
toxic/o: poison(ex: In**toxic**ation)
thalam/o: thalamus(ex: **Thalam**otomy)

Integumentary Word Roots

adip/o: fat(ex: **Adip**ose)
albin/o: white(ex: **Albin**ism)
carcin/o: cancer(ex: **Carcino**gen)
cirrh/o: yellow(ex: **Cirrh**osis)
cutane/o: skin(ex: Sub**cutane**ous)
cyan/o: blue(ex: **Cyan**osis)
derm/o: skin(ex: Sclero**derm**a)
dermat/o: skin(ex: **Dermat**itis)
erythem/o: red(ex: Lupus **erythem**atosus)
hidr/o: sweat(ex: Hyper**hidr**osis)
hist/o: tissue(ex: **Hist**ology)
ichthy/o: scaly(ex: **Ichthy**osis)
jaund/o: yellow(ex: **Jaund**ice)
kerat/o: hard(ex: **Kerat**in)
lip/o: fat(ex: **Lip**oma)
melan/o: black(ex: **Melan**oma)
myc/o: fungi(ex: Onycho**myc**osis)
onych/o: nail(ex: **Onycho**mycosis)
pil/o: hair(ex: Arrector **pil**i)
phyt/o: plant(ex: Dermato**phyt**osis)
seb/o: sebum(ex: **Seb**aceous cyst)
squam/o: scale(ex: **Squam**ous suture)
sudor/o: sweat(ex: **Sudor**iferous gland)
trich/o: hair(ex: **Tricho**moniasis)
ungu/o: nail(ex: Tinua **ungu**ium)
xanth/o: yellow(ex: **Xanth**oma)
xer/o: dry(ex: **Xer**ophthalmia)

Lymphatic Word Roots

adenoid/o: adenoids(ex: **Adenoid**ectomy)
immun/o: immune(ex: **Immun**ology)
lymph/o: lymph(ex: **Lymph**angitis)
splen/o: spleen(ex: **Splen**ectomy)
tonsill/o: tonsils(ex: **Tonsill**itis)
thym/o: thymus(ex: **Thym**ectomy)

Muscular Word Roots

adhes/o: stick to(ex: **Adhes**ion)
duct/o: carry(ex: **Duct**openia)
erg/o: work(ex: **Ergo**nomic)
fasci/o: fascia(ex: Tensor **fasci**ae latae)
fibr/o: fiber(ex: **Fibro**myalgia)
fibros/o: fiber(ex: **Fibros**is)
flex/o: bend(ex: **Flex**ion)
is/o: same(ex: **Iso**metric)
kinesi/o: movement(ex: **Kinesi**ology)
lei/o: smooth(ex: **Leio**myoma)
lev/o: lift(ex: **Lev**ator scapulae)
levat/o: lift(ex: **Lev**ator scapulae)
metr/o: length(ex: Iso**metr**ic)
quadr/i: four(ex: **Quadr**iceps)
rect/o: straight(ex: **Rect**us abdominis)
ten/o: tendon(ex: **Teno**periosteal)
tend/o: tendon(ex: **Tend**onitis)
tendin/o: tendon(ex: **Tendin**itis)
tens/o: strain(ex: **Tens**or fasciae latae)
ton/o: tension(ex: Iso**ton**ic)
tort/i: twisted(ex: **Tort**icollis)

Nervous Word Roots

astr/o: star(ex: **Astro**cytoma)
ax/o: axon(ex: **Ax**on)
cephal/o: head(ex: En**cephal**itis)
cerebell/o: cerebellum(ex: **Cerebell**um)
clon/o: clonus(ex: **Clon**us)
cortic/o: cortex(ex: **Cortico**steroid)
crani/o: skull(ex: **Crani**um)
dendr/o: tree(ex: **Dendr**ite)
dur/o: dura mater(ex: Epi**dur**al)
encephal/o: brain(ex: **Encephal**itis)
esthesi/o: sensation(ex: An**esthesic**)
gangli/o: ganglion(ex: **Gangli**on cyst)
gli/o: glue(ex: **Gli**oblastoma)
lex/o: word(ex: **Lex**icon)
lob/o: lobe(ex: **Lob**otomy)
mening/o: meninges(ex: **Mening**itis)
ment/o: mind(ex: **Ment**ality)
mot/o: move(ex: Loco**mot**ion)
myel/o: canal(ex: Osteo**myel**itis)
narc/o: stupor(ex: **Narc**olepsy)
neur/o: nerve(ex: **Neur**algia)
olig/o: few(ex: **Oligo**dendrocyte)
phas/o: speech(ex: Dys**phas**ia)
phren/o: mind(ex: **Phren**ology)
psych/o: mind(ex: **Psych**osis)
spin/o: spine(ex: Semi**spin**alis)
synapt/o: point of contact(ex: **Synap**se)
tax/o: order(ex: **Tax**onomy)

Reproductive Word Roots

amni/o: amnion(ex: **Amnio**centesis)

andr/o: male(ex: **Andro**gen)

cervic/o: neck(ex: **Cervix**)

colp/o: vagina(ex: **Colpo**scopy)

embry/o: embryo(ex: **Embryo**nic stage)

epididym/o: epididymis(ex: **Epididym**itis)

episi/o: vulva(ex: **Episio**tomy)

fet/o: fetus(ex: **Fetal** development)

galact/o: milk(ex: **Galactor**rhea)

genit/o: genitalia(ex: **Genit**al herpes)

gynec/o: woman(ex: **Gynec**ology)

hyster/o: uterus(ex: **Hyster**ectomy)

hymen/o: hymen(ex: **Hymen**ectomy)

lact/o: milk(ex: **Lact**ation)

mamm/o: breast(ex: **Mamm**ary gland)

mast/o: breast(ex: **Mast**ectomy)

men/o: menstruation(ex: **Meno**pause)

metr/o: uterus(ex: **Metror**rhagia)

nat/o: birth(ex: Neo**nat**al)

o/o: egg(ex: **Oo**cyte)

oophor/o: ovary(ex: **Oophor**ectomy)

orch/o: testicle(ex: **Orch**iectomy)

ovari/o: ovary(ex: **Ovari**an tumor)

pen/o: penis(ex: **Peno**scrotal fusion)

perine/o: perineum(ex: **Perineo**tomy)

prostat/o: prostate(ex: **Prostat**itis)

salping/o: fallopian tube(ex: **Salping**itis)

sperm/o: sperm(ex: **Sperm**icide)

spermat/o: sperm(ex: **Spermat**ogenesis)

test/o: testicle(ex: **Test**icular tortion)

uter/o: uterus(ex: **Uter**ine lining)

vagin/o: vagina(ex: Bacterial **vagin**osis)

vesicul/o: seminal vesicle(ex: **Vesicul**itis)

vulv/o: vulva(ex: **Vulv**itis)

Respiratory Word Roots

alveol/o: alveolus(ex: **Alveoli**)

anthrac/o: black(ex: **Anthra**x)

bronch/o: bronchus(ex: **Bronch**itis)

bronchi/o: bronchus(ex: **Bronchi**ole)

con/i: dust(ex: **Coni**dium)

embol/o: plug(ex: **Embol**ism)

emphys/o: inflate(ex: **Emphys**ema)

epiglott/o: epiglottis(ex: **Epiglott**itis)

laryng/o: larynx(ex: **Laryng**itis)

muc/o: mucous(ex: Sub**muc**osa)

nas/o: nose(ex: **Nas**al cavity)

ox/o: oxygen(ex: Hyp**ox**ia)

pector/o: chest(ex: **Pector**alis major)

phon/o: sound(ex: Dys**phon**ia)

phren/o: diaphragm(ex: **Phren**ic nerve)

pleur/o: pleura(ex: **Pleur**al membrane)

pneum/o: lung(ex: **Pneum**onia)

pulm/o: lung(ex: **Pulm**onary edema)

rhin/o: nose(ex: **Rhin**itis)

sinus/o: sinus(ex: **Sinus**itis)

spir/o: breathe(ex: **Spiro**meter)

steth/o: chest(ex: **Steth**oscope)

thorac/o: chest(ex: **Thorac**ic vertebrae)

trache/o: trachea(ex: **Tracheo**tomy)

Skeletal Word Roots

acr/o: extremity(ex: **Acro**megaly)

acromi/o: acromion(ex: **Acromio**clavicular)

ankyl/o: crooked(ex: **Ankyl**osis)

arthr/o: joint(ex: **Arthr**itis)

brachi/o: arm(ex: Biceps **brachi**i)

calcane/o: calcaneus(ex: **Calcane**al tendon)

carp/o: carpals(ex: **Carpo**metacarpal joint)

chondr/o: cartilage(ex: Costo**chondr**itis)

clavicul/o: clavicle(ex: Sterno**clavicul**ar)

cleid/o: clavicle(ex: Sterno**cleido**mastoid)

condyl/o: condyle(ex: Epi**condyle**)

cost/o: ribs(ex: Inter**cost**al)

dactyl/o: fingers/toes(ex: Poly**dactyl**y)

femor/o: femur(ex: Rectus **femor**is)

fibul/o: fibula(ex: Tibio**fibul**ar joint)

humer/o: humerus(ex: Gleno**humer**al joint)

ili/o: ilium(ex: **Ili**acus)

ischi/o: ischium(ex: **Ischi**al tuberosity)

kyph/o: hill(ex: **Kyph**osis)

lamin/o: lamina(ex: **Lamino**tomy)

lord/o: curve(ex: **Lord**osis)

metacarp/o: metacarpals(ex: **Metacarpo**phalangeal)

metatars/o: metatarsals(ex: **Metatarso**phalangeal)

orth/o: straight(ex: **Ortho**pedic)

oste/o: bone(ex: **Osteo**arthritis)

patell/o: patella(ex: **Patell**ar tendon)

ped/i: foot(ex: **Ped**icure)

pelv/i: pelvis(ex: **Pelv**ic girdle)

phalang/o: phalanges(ex: Inter**phalange**al)

pod/o: foot(ex: **Pod**iatrist)

pub/o: pubis(ex: **Pub**ic symphysis)

rachi/o: spine(ex: **Rach**itis)

radi/o: radius(ex: **Radio**ulnar joint)

sacr/o: sacrum(ex: **Sacro**tuberous ligament)

scapul/o: scapula(ex: Sub**scapul**aris)

scoli/o: crooked(ex: **Scoli**osis)

spondyl/o: vertebrae(ex: **Spondyl**osis)

synov/o: synovium(ex: **Synov**ial fluid)

tal/o: talus(ex: **Talo**tibial joint)

tars/o: tarsals(ex: **Tarso**metatarsal)

uln/o: ulna(ex: Humero**uln**ar joint)

vertebr/o: vertebrae(ex: Inter**vertebr**al disc)

Urinary Word Roots

albumin/o: albumin(ex: **Albumin**uria)

azot/o: nitrogenous(ex: **Azot**emia)

cyst/o: bladder(ex: **Cyst**itis)

glomerul/o: glomerulus(ex: **Glomerul**onephritis)

ket/o: ketone bodies(ex: **Ket**osis)

nephr/o: kidney(ex: **Nephr**ologist)

pyel/o: renal pelvis(ex: **Pyelo**nephritis)

ren/o: kidney(ex: Ad**ren**al glands)

ur/o: urine(ex: **Ur**ic acid)

ureter/o: ureter(ex: **Uretero**scopy)

urethr/o: urethra(ex: **Urethr**itis)

urin/o: urine(ex: **Urin**ation)

vesic/o: bladder(ex: **Vesico**ureteral reflux)

Oncology Word Roots

blast/o: germ cell(ex: **Blast**oma)

carcin/o: cancer(ex: **Carcino**gen)

cauter/o: burn(ex: **Cauter**ize)

chem/o: chemical(ex:**Chemo**therapy)

cry/o: cold(ex: **Cryo**therapy)

mut/a: genetic change(ex: **Muta**tion)

onc/o: tumor(ex: **Onc**ology)

rhabdomy/o: skeletal muscle(ex: **Rhabdomyo**lysis)

sarc/o: connective tissue(ex: Kaposi's **sarc**oma)

Miscellaneous Word Roots

aur/i: ear(ex: **Aur**icle)

bi/o: life(ex: Micro**bio**logy)

burs/o: bursa(ex: **Burs**itis)

cerat/o: horn(ex: Tri**cerat**ops)

chir/o: hand(ex: **Chiro**practor)

corac/o: crow-like(ex: **Corac**oid)

coron/o: crown(ex: **Coron**oid)

dextr/o: right(ex: Ambi**dextr**ous)

dors/o: back(ex: **Dors**al body cavity)

dynam/o: power(ex: **Dynamo**meter)

ect/o: outside(ex: **Ecto**pic pregnancy)

faci/o: face(ex: **Faci**al nerve)

glauc/o: gray(ex: **Glauc**oma)

hydr/o: water(ex: **Hydro**therapy)

irid/o: iris(ex: **Irido**cyclitis)

kerat/o: cornea(ex: **Kerato**scope)

lacrim/o: tear(ex: **Lacrim**al duct)

lapar/o: abdominal wall(ex: **Laparot**omy)

myring/o: eardrum(ex: **Myring**itis)

omphal/o: navel(ex: **Omphalo**cele)

ophthalam/o: eye(ex: **Ophthalamo**scope)

phot/o: light(ex: **Photo**sensitivity)

py/o: pus(ex: **Pyo**derma)

pyr/o: heat(ex: Anti**pyr**etic)

therm/o: heat(ex: **Thermo**meter)

tympan/o: eardrum(ex:**Tympan**itis)

ventr/o: belly(ex: **Ventr**al body cavity)

viscer/o: internal organs(ex: **Viscer**optosis)

zo/o: animal(ex: **Zoo**notic)

Prefixes

a-: without(ex: **A**vascular)
ab-: away(ex: **Ab**duction)
ad-: towards(ex: **Ad**duction)
af-: towards(ex: **Af**ferent)
allo-: other(ex: **Allo**patric speciation)
an-: without(ex: **An**emia)
ana-: against(ex: **Ana**phylaxis)
ante-: before(ex: **Ante**cubital)
anti-: against(ex: **Anti**biotic)
auto-: self(ex: **Auto**nomy)
bi-: two(ex: **Bi**ceps femoris)
brady-: slow(ex: **Brady**cardia)
circum-: around(ex: **Circum**duction)
contra-: against(ex: **Contra**indication)
de-: cessation(ex: **De**generation)
di-: double(ex: **Di**encephalon)
dia-: through(ex: **Dia**lysis)
dipl-: double(ex: **Dipl**opia)
dys-: difficult(ex: **Dys**pnea)
ec-: out(ex: **Ec**topic pregnancy)
echo-: repeated sound(ex: **Echo**lalia)
ecto-: outside(ex: **Ecto**morph)
ef-: away(ex: **Ef**ferent)
en-: within(ex: **En**docrine)
end-: within(ex: **End**ometriosis)
endo-: within(ex: **Endo**scopy)
epi-: above(ex: **Epi**dermis)
eso-: inward(ex: **Eso**teric)
eu-: good(ex: **Eu**phoria)
ex-: outside(ex: **Ex**cretion)
exo-: outside(ex: **Exo**crine)
extra-: outside(ex: **Extra**corporial)
hemi-: half(ex: **Hemi**plegia)
hetero-: different(ex: **Hetero**chromia)
homo-: same(ex: **Homo**eostasis)
hyper-: excessive(ex: **Hyper**thyroidism)
hypo-: below(ex: **Hypo**xia)
im-: not(ex: **Im**potence)
infra-: below(ex: **Infra**spinatus)
inter-: between(ex: **Inter**osseous)
intra-: inside(ex: **Intra**venous)
iso-: same(ex: **Iso**tonic)
macro-: large(ex: **Macro**phage)
mal-: bad(ex: **Mal**ignant)
meso-: middle(ex: **Meso**thelioma)
meta-: change(ex: **Meta**physis)
micro-: small(ex: **Micro**organism)
mono-: one(ex: **Mono**nucleosis)
multi-: many(ex: **Multi**ple sclerosis)
neo-: new(ex: **Neo**natal)
nulli-: none(ex: **Nulli**fy)
oxy-: sharp(ex: **Oxy**tocin)
pan-: all(ex: **Pan**demic)
para-: beside(ex: **Para**thyroid)
per-: through(ex: **Per**itoneum)
peri-: around(ex: **Peri**osteum)
poly-: many(ex: **Poly**cythemia)
post-: after(ex: **Post**partum)

pre-: before(ex: **Pre**patellar bursitis)
pro-: before(ex: **Pro**gesterone)
pseudo-: false(ex: **Pseudo**ephedrine)
quadri-: four(ex: **Quadri**ceps)
retro-: behind(ex: **Retro**peritoneal)
semi-: half(ex: **Semi**membranosus)
sub-: under(ex: **Sub**scapularis)
super-: above(ex: **Super**ior)
supra-: above(ex: **Supra**spinatus)
sym-: together(ex: Pubic **sym**physis)
syn-: together(ex: **Syn**ergist)
tachy-: rapid(ex: **Tachy**cardia)
torti-: twisted(ex: **Torti**collis)
trans-: through(ex: **Trans**dermal)
tri-: three(ex: **Tri**ceps brachii)
ultra-: excessive(ex: **Ultra**sound)
uni-: one(ex: **Uni**lateral)

Suffixes

-ac: referring to(ex: Hypochondri**ac**)
-acusis: hearing(ex: Hyper**acusis**)
-al: referring to(ex: Iliofemor**al**)
-algia: pain(ex: Fibromy**algia**)
-ar: referring to(ex: Alveol**ar**)
-ary: referring to(ex: Coron**ary**)
-ate: form of(ex: Acet**ate**)
-ation: process(ex: Replic**ation**)
-asthenia: weakness(ex: My**asthenia**)
-blast: germ cell(ex: Osteo**blast**)
-capnia: carbon dioxide(ex: Hyper**capnia**)
-cele: hernia(ex: Meningo**cele**)
-centesis: puncture(ex: Amnio**centesis**)
-cision: cutting(ex: In**cision**)
-clast: break(ex: Osteo**clast**)
-crine: secrete(ex: Endo**crine**)
-cusis: hearing(ex: Dysa**cusis**)
-cyte: cell(ex: Erythro**cyte**)
-derma: skin(ex: Sclero**derma**)
-duction: bringing(ex: Ab**duction**)
-dynia: pain(ex: Gastro**dynia**)
-eal: referring to(ex: Corpor**eal**)
-ectasis: dilation(ex: Bronchi**ectasis**)
-ectomy: removal(ex: Append**ectomy**)
-edema: swelling(ex: Lymph**edema**)
-emesis: vomiting(ex: Hyper**emesis**)
-emia: blood(ex: Leuk**emia**)
-esis: condition(ex: Cent**esis**)
-esthesia: sensation(ex: An**esthesia**)
-ferent: to carry(ex: Af**ferent**)
-gen: produce(ex: Carcino**gen**)
-globin: protein(ex: Hemo**globin**)
-gnosis: knowing(ex: Dia**gnosis**)
-gram: record(ex: Echocardio**gram**)
-graph: recording(ex: Electrocardio**graph**)
-ia: condition(ex: Hypox**ia**)
-iasis: abnormal condition(ex: Lith**iasis**)
-iatry: medicine(ex: Ped**iatry**)
-ic: referring to(ex: Idiopath**ic**)
-ician: specialist(ex: Phys**ician**)
-icle: small(ex: Ventr**icle**)

-ile: referring to(ex: Juven**ile**)
-ine: referring to(ex: Medic**ine**)
-ism: condition(ex: Gigant**ism**)
-ist: specialist(ex: Dent**ist**)
-itis: inflammation(ex: Hepat**itis**)
-kinesia: movement(ex: Hypo**kinesia**)
-lalia: speech(ex: Dys**lalia**)
-lampsia: shine(ex: Preec**lampsia**)
-lepsy: seizure(ex: Epi**lepsy**)
-lith: stone(ex: Mono**lith**)
-logist: specializing in(ex: Cardio**logist**)
-logy: study of(ex: Neuro**logy**)
-lucent: clear(ex: Trans**lucent**)
-lysis: dissolve(ex: Dia**lysis**)
-malacia: soften(ex: Chondro**malacia**)
-mania: frenzy(ex: Pyro**mania**)
-megaly: enlargement(ex: Acro**megaly**)
-meter: measuring(ex: Thermo**meter**)
-metry: measuring(ex: Tele**metry**)
-oid: resembling(ex: Corac**oid**)
-ole: little(ex: Arteri**ole**)
-oma: tumor(ex: Carcin**oma**)
-orexia: appetite(ex: An**orexia**)
-ory: referring to(ex: Circulat**ory**)
-ose: referring to(ex: Coma**tose**)
-osis: condition(ex: Atheroscler**osis**)
-ous: referring to(ex: Por**ous**)
-pathy: disease(ex: Neo**pathy**)
-penia: deficiency(ex: Hydro**penia**)
-phagia: eat(ex: Dys**phagia**)
-phasia: speech(ex: Dys**phasia**)
-philia: attraction(ex: Hemo**philia**)
-phoria: feeling(ex: Eu**phoria**)
-phylaxis: protection(ex: Ana**phylaxis**)
-physis: growth(ex: Epi**physis**)
-plasia: formation(ex: Hyper**plasia**)
-plasm: growth(ex: Neo**plasm**)
-plasty: repair(ex: Rhino**plasty**)
-plegia: paralysis(ex: Quadri**plegia**)
-pnea: breathing(ex: A**pnea**)
-poiesis: formation(ex: Hemato**poiesis**)
-porosis: porous(ex: Osteo**porosis**)
-rrhage: bursting forth(ex: Hemo**rrhage**)
-rrhea: discharge(ex: Dia**rrhea**)
-rrhexis: rupture(ex: Entero**rrhexis**)
-scope: examining(ex: Endo**scope**)
-spasm: twitch(ex: Myo**spasm**)
-scopy: visual exam(ex: Arthro**scopy**)
-stasis: standing still(ex: Homeo**stasis**)
-stenosis: narrowing(ex: Arterio**stenosis**)
-stomy: opening(ex: Colo**stomy**)
-tension: stretch(ex: Hyper**tension**)
-thorax: chest(ex: Pneumo**thorax**)
-thymia: emotion(ex: Dys**thymia**)
-tomy: incision(ex: Ana**tomy**)
-toxic: poison(ex: Neuro**toxic**ity)
-tripsy: crushing(ex: Litho**tripsy**)
-trophy: nourishment(ex: A**trophy**)
-uria: urine(ex: Hyper**uria**)
-y: condition(ex: Acromegal**y**)

General Medical Terms

A

ABC: References things to check before administering resuscitation efforts, Airway, Breathing, Circulation.
Abscess: A localized collection of pus.
Acute: Sudden, severe onset of a medical condition or disease.
Adhesion: Stuck together.
Ambulant/Ambulatory: The ability to walk.
Arrest: Cessation of bodily activity or function.
Aseptic: Sterile.
Autonomy: Being self-governed.

B

Benign: Does not spread.
Biopsy: Surgically removing tissue to examine microscopically.

C

Cachexia: Loss of appetite, weight, with muscle atrophy, usually associated with a serious medical condition such as cancer.
Carcinogen: A substance that may cause cancer.
Chronic: A disease or condition that persists over a period of time.
Collis: Neck.

D

Diagnosis: Determination of the cause of a disease.

E

Edema: An excessive accumulation of fluid in an area.
Etiology: The study of the cause of a disease.
Excision: Surgically removing a structure or tissue.

F

Febrile: Presence of a fever.
Fistula: Location where an organ has developed an opening into another organ.

I

Idiopathic: An unknown cause of disease.
Incision: Cutting in to, typically with a scalpel.
Incontinence: Loss of control of the bladder and/or bowels.
In Situ: "In original place", commonly references cancer that is still in its place of origin, such as the epithelium of the skin.
Intravenous: Inside a vein, usually referencing injections.
Ischemia: Lack of blood flow to an area, which may result in necrosis.

M

Malaise: General unwell feeling or discomfort.
Malformation: A structure that is not formed properly.
Malignant: Spreading of cancer from one area to another.

N

Necrosis: Death of tissue.
Neopathy: A new disease.

P

Pallor: General paleness.
Palsy: Paralysis.
Peptic: Referring to the stomach.
Phlegm: Secretions expelled from the lungs, also known as sputum.
Phobia: Fear of a person, thing, or situation.
Prognosis: Predicted outcome of a disease and recovery rate.
Pulse: Expansion of an artery as blood passes through.
Pyrogenic: Producing fever.

S

Sepsis: An infection.
Sign: Observable indications of an illness.
Sinus: A cavity.
Sputum: Secretions expelled from the lungs, also known as phlegm.
Symptom: A physical manifestation of an illness.
Syndrome: Groups of symptoms caused by a disease.

T

Transient: Short duration.

Medical Terminology Matching

Word Roots

____: necr/o   ____: gloss/o

____: leuk/o   ____: my/o

____: melan/o   ____: nephr/o

____: cost/o   ____: brachi/o

____: spondyl/o   ____: phyt/o

____: gastr/o   ____: erythr/o

____: derm/o   ____: encephal/o

____: chondr/o   ____: hem/o

____: adip/o   ____: pneum/o

____: hepat/o   ____: phleb/o

____: cyst/o   ____: cardi/o

A. Muscle   L. Stomach
B. Liver   M. White
C. Bladder   N. Vein
D. Kidney   O. Lung
E. Arm   P. Skin
F. Blood   Q. Cartilage
G. Black   R. Death
H. Tongue   S. Red
I. Brain   T. Heart
J. Rib   U. Fat
K. Vertebrae   V. Plant

Prefixes

____: auto-   ____: bi-

____: a-   ____: macro-

____: tachy-   ____: brady-

____: meta-   ____: torti-

____: mal-   ____: anti-

____: syn-   ____: iso-

____: homeo-   ____: circum-

____: hypo-   ____: endo-

____: inter-   ____: ad-

____: dia-   ____: epi-

____: micro-   ____: hyper-

A. Together   L. Towards
B. Change   M. Small
C. Without   N. Around
D. Two   O. Twisted
E. Against   P. Excessive
F. Rapid   Q. Inside
G. Through   R. Below
H. Equal   S. Self
I. Slow   T. Between
J. Same   U. Bad
K. Large   V. Above

Suffixes

____: -ferent   ____: -plegia

____: -blast   ____: -gen

____: -duction   ____: -phagia

____: -crine   ____: -globin

____: -cision   ____: -clast

____: -trophy   ____: -edema

____: -algia   ____: -osis

____: -stasis   ____: -cyte

____: -emia   ____: -oid

____: -derma   ____: -lysis

____: -pnea   ____: -ectomy

A. Nourishment   L. Germ Cell
B. Blood   M. Removal
C. Production   N. Dissolve
D. Swelling   O. Cutting
E. Resembling   P. Pain
F. Condition   Q. Eating
G. Skin   R. Breathing
H. Standing Still S. Secrete
I. To Carry   T. Cell
J. Break   U. Paralysis
K. Bringing   V. Protein

Answer Key on Page 308

Medical Terminology Breaking Down/Building

Break down the following diseases by their word roots, prefixes, and suffixes, giving the definition of each part in the blank spaces.

1. Arteriosclerosis: _____/_____/_____
2. Pyelonephritis: _____/_____/_____
3. Encephalitis: _____/_____
4. Lymphedema: _____/_____
5. Hyperthyroidism: _____/_____/_____
6. Cholecystitis: _____/_____/_____
7: Hepatitis: _____/_____
8: Phlebitis: _____/_____
9. Torticollis: _____/_____
10. Dermatophytosis: _____/_____/_____
11. Acromegaly: _____/_____
12. Myocardial Infarction: _____/_____/_____
13. Insomnia: _____/_____
14. Neuralgia: _____/_____
15. Tenosynovitis: _____/_____/_____

Build the name of the following diseases just using their definition. Remember, not every disease has a prefix or suffix!

1. Without blood: _____/_____
2. Fatty plaque hard condition: _____/_____/_____
3. Stomach inflammation: _____/_____
4. Black tumor: _____/_____
5. Fiber muscle pain: _____/_____/_____
6. Bone joint inflammation: _____/_____/_____
7. Bladder inflammation: _____/_____
8: Without breath: _____/_____
9. Nail fungus condition: _____/_____/_____
10. Skin inflammation: _____/_____
11. Above tension: _____/_____
12. Without rhythm: _____/_____
13. White blood condition: _____/_____
14. Hill condition: _____/_____
15. Cell inflammation: _____/_____

Answer Key on Page 308

Medical Terminology Crossword

Across

2. -algia
4. a-
6. encephal/o
8. pan-
10. brachi/o
11. scler/o
15. ad-
16. -osis
17. bi/o
19. ab-
20. intra-

Down

1. hepat/o
3. -itis
5. cardi/o
7. -stenosis
9. ecto-
12. angi/o
13. -duction
14. ren/o
18. -cep

Answer Key on Page 310

Medical Terminology Practice Test

1. The word root "ather/o" means
A. Fatty plaque
B. Ventricle
C. Canal
D. Artery

2. Which of the following prefixes means "without"
A. eso-
B. af-
C. iso-
D. an-

3. The suffix "-emia" means
A. Blood condition
B. Production
C. Inflammation
D. Death

4. The word root "lord/o" means
A. Hill
B. Lateral
C. Curve
D. Branch

5. The term "epinephrine" is defined as
A. Secreting into the mouth
B. Below the liver formation
C. Crooked spine condition
D. Secreting above the kidney

6. The word root "phag/o" means
A. White
B. Bile
C. Eat
D. Movement

7. Which prefix means "half"
A. semi-
B. ultra-
C. sub-
D. inter-

8. The suffix "-plegia" means
A. Deficiency
B. Nourishment
C. Paralysis
D. Vomiting

9. Which suffix means "to carry"
A. -rrhage
B. -uria
C. -ferent
D. -acusis

10. The term "encephalitis" is defined as
A. Liver inflammation
B. Skin inflammation
C. Tongue inflammation
D. Brain inflammation

11. The prefix "anti-" means
A. Against
B. Double
C. Around
D. Towards

12. "Removal of the gallbladder" is
A. Angioplasty
B. Cholecystectomy
C. Colostomy
D. Leiomyogram

13. A person diagnosed with "without rhythm" who has "slow heart" would have which conditions
A. Heart murmur and arrhythmia
B. Arrhythmia and bradycardia
C. Tachycardia and pericarditis
D. Heart murmur and tachycardia

14. The term "endocrine" means
A. Secreting outside
B. Secreting above
C. Secreting inside
D. Secreting below

15. The suffix "-itis" means
A. Disease
B. Growth
C. Condition
D. Inflammation

16. Which of the following describes a condition that has something to do with the kidneys
A. Pyelonephritis
B. Osteoporosis
C. Gastritis
D. Cystitis

17. What form of medication works "against heat"
A. Antibiotic
B. Antihistamine
C. Antifungal
D. Antipyretic

18. Injections that are "subcutaneous" go where
A. Above the nerve
B. Under the skin
C. Into the muscle
D. Into the skin

19. Which of the following terms means "crooked condition"
A. Kyphosis
B. Lordosis
C. Scoliosis
D. Osteoporosis

20. Which medication means "against life"
A. Antipyretic
B. Antibiotic
C. Antifungal
D. Antiviral

21. The term "coronoid" means
A. Head inflammation
B. Resembling a crow
C. Shoulder condition
D. Resembling a crown

22. Which term means "nerve pain"
A. Neuralgia
B. Neuritis
C. Neuroglia
D. Neuroma

23. Which of the following is "around the heart"
A. Epidural
B. Pericardium
C. Perineum
D. Epimysium

24. A person with "tinea pedis" is suffering from what
A. Virus on the face
B. Bacterial in the bone
C. Fungus on the foot
D. Parasite in the small intestine

25. The word root "flex/o" means
A. Strain
B. Tension
C. Lift
D. Bend

Answer Key on Page 322

Anatomy and Physiology

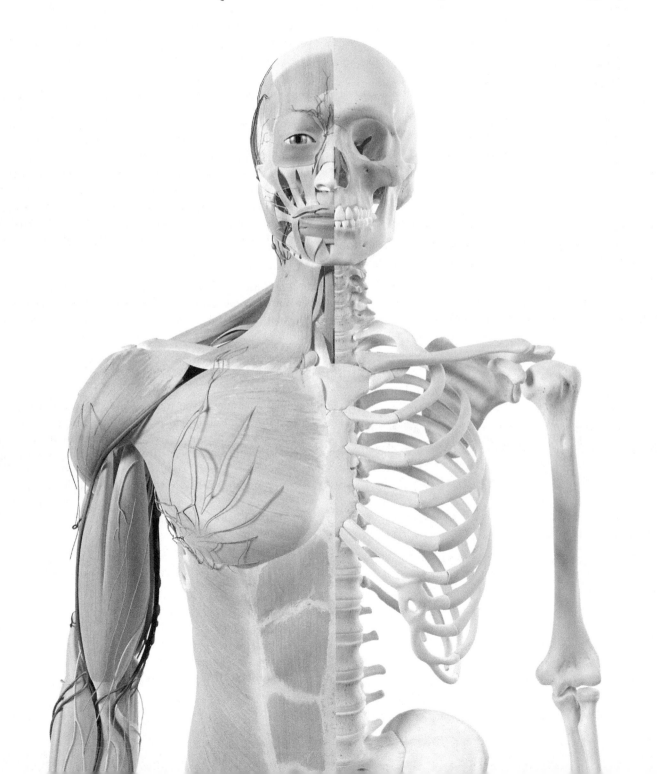

Anatomy and Physiology

Anatomy is the study of the **structure** of the human body. All of the parts that make up the body constitute anatomy, from bones, muscles, and nerves, to cells, tendons, ligaments, and everything in between.

Physiology is the study of the **function** of the body. How do the parts of the body that make up the body's anatomy function? What do they do? This is physiology. Anatomy and physiology go hand-in-hand.

Homeostasis

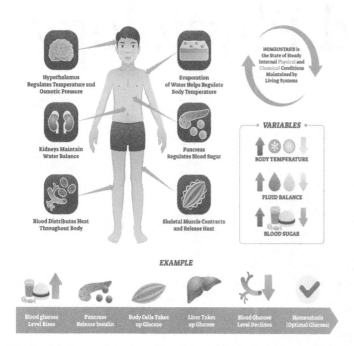

Homeostasis is the existence and maintenance of a **constant internal environment**. The body's internal environment is constantly changing and responding to various stimuli. Examples of stimuli are temperature, hormones, diet, and the body's pH level. These stimuli that change the body's internal environment in some way are known as **homeostatic variables**. As the variables change, so too does the internal environment.

The body responds to these changes by utilizing **homeostatic mechanisms**, such as sweating and shivering. An example, when body temperature gets too high, the body mechanically (physically) responds by sweating. Sweat evaporates off the skin, which cools the body down, lowering body temperature. When the body becomes too cold, the body responds by mechanically increasing the amount of twitching in the skeletal muscles. This increased twitching, which is normally undetectable, results in shivering, which produces body heat and raising body temperature.

The body's internal environment is constantly changing, and the body constantly adjusts certain aspects of itself to respond to these changes. If temperature is an example, the **set point**(normal range) of a body's temperature is 98.6 degrees Fahrenheit. The internal body temperature is never set right at 98.6 degrees. It is constantly fluctuating around it, maintaining a normal range of optimal body function.

Regional Anatomy

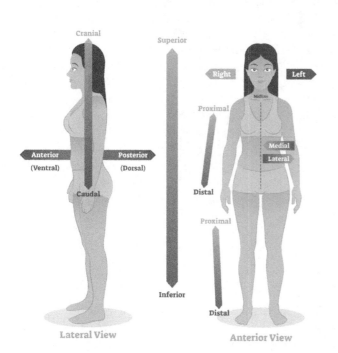

Regional Anatomy is the study of the structures of the body, broken down into different parts. When describing the position of one structure in the body in relation to another structure or structures, we use **directional terms**. An example, using the term "medial condyle" instead of just "condyle" lets us communicate effectively which condyle is being discussed.

The main directional terms are:
- **Superior**: Above.
- **Inferior**: Below.
- **Anterior**: Front.
- **Posterior**: Back.
- **Proximal**: Closer to the midline.
- **Distal**: Further from the midline.
- **Medial**: Middle.
- **Lateral**: Side.
- **Deep**: More internal.
- **Superficial**: Towards the surface.

Body Planes

Body planes are important for viewing structures from different aspects. These can be used when doing simple visual assessment, or in instances such as surgery or cadaver dissection.

There are four main body planes: A **midsagittal**, or **median plane**, runs down the **midline of the body**, splitting the body into **equal left and right sides**. This is the only location for a midsagittal plane.

 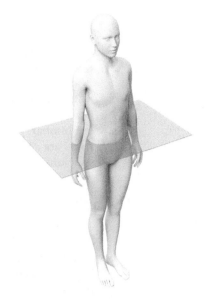 

A **sagittal plane** also splits the body into left or right sides, but **not equally**. It can be located anywhere along the body except down the midline. Pictured is a **midsagittal plane**, splitting the body into equal left and right sides.

A **transverse**, or **horizontal plane**, splits the body into **superior and inferior** portions. It does not have to be at the waist. It can split the body into superior and inferior at any point along the body.

A **frontal**, or **coronal plane**, splits the body into **anterior and posterior**. If a person wanted to dissect the heart and make all four chambers visible, they would cut the heart into a frontal or coronal plane. See photo on page 77.

Body Regions

The body can be broken down into different parts, or regions. There are three main body regions: the central body region, the upper limb, and the lower limb.

The **central body region** contains all of the structures located in the **center of the body**: the **head**, the **neck**, and the **trunk**. Take away the arms and legs, and you're left with the central body region.

The **trunk** can be further divided into three regions: the **thorax**, or **chest**, the **abdomen**, and the **pelvis**. The thorax contains the heart, lungs, esophagus, thymus, and major blood vessels connecting to the heart. The abdomen contains the majority of our digestive organs, including the stomach, liver, gallbladder, pancreas, small intestine, and large intestine. It also contains the kidneys and ureters. The pelvis contains the urinary bladder, urethra, and reproductive organs.

The **upper limb** can be broken down into four regions: the **arm, forearm, wrist**, and **hand**. The arm contains the humerus. The forearm contains the radius and ulna. The wrist contains the carpals. The hand contains the metacarpals and phalanges.

The **lower limb** can also be broken down into four regions: the **thigh, leg, ankle**, and **foot**. The thigh contains the femur. The leg contains the tibia and fibula. The ankle contains the tarsals. The foot contains the metatarsals and phalanges.

The abdomen specifically can be divided into **four quadrants**, or **nine regions**. Dividing the abdomen into these quadrants or regions helps pin-point exact locations a person may be experiencing pain or discomfort, or identify what structures are in a given area.

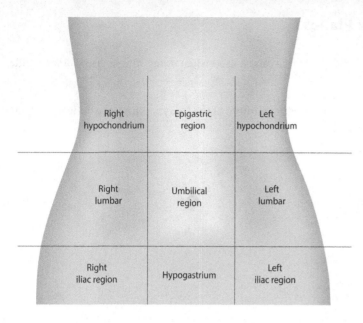

The four quadrants are the upper right, upper left, lower right, and lower left.

The **upper right quadrant** contains the liver, gallbladder, pancreas, right kidney, small intestine, and large intestine.

The **upper left quadrant** contains the stomach, spleen, pancreas, left kidney, small intestine, and large intestine.

The **lower right quadrant** contains the small intestine, large intestine, uterus, ovary, and urinary bladder.

The **lower left quadrant** contains the small intestine, large intestine, uterus, ovary, and urinary bladder.

The nine regions of the abdomen are the **right hypochondriac, epigastric, left hypochondriac, right lumbar, umbilical, left lumbar, right iliac, hypogastric, and left iliac.** These regions are smaller than the quadrants and allow very specific locations to be utilized.

Body Cavities

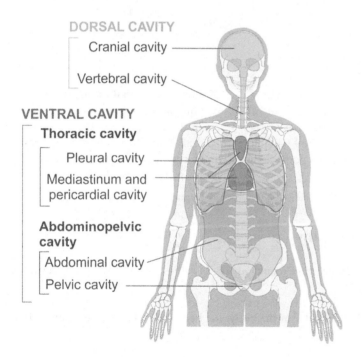

The **dorsal body cavity** is created by the **cranium and the vertebral column.** Its responsibility is to **protect the brain** via the bones of the cranium(frontal, parietal, temporal, occipital), and to **protect the spinal cord** via the vertebrae. The spinal cord passes through the spinal canal, a passageway created by the vertebral column. The brain and spinal cord are vital in body function, and are thus protected by bones to maximize their safety.

The **ventral body cavity** is divided into two separate cavities, the **thoracic cavity** and the **abdominopelvic cavity.** The thoracic cavity holds three more cavities inside of it, the pleural cavity, the mediastinum, and the pericardial cavity. The **pleural cavity** contains the **lungs.** The **mediastinum** is the area located **between the lungs** that contains major blood vessels such as the aorta and superior vena cava, the pulmonary arteries, the trachea, and the esophagus. The **pericardial cavity** contains the **heart.**

The **abdominopelvic cavity** can also be split into smaller cavities, the abdominal cavity and the pelvic cavity. The **abdominal cavity** houses all major digestive organs such as the stomach, liver, pancreas, gallbladder, small intestine, and large intestine, and also contains the kidneys. The **pelvic cavity** contains all internal reproductive organs and the urinary bladder.

Cells

Cells are the **functional units** of all tissues. Cells are responsible for performing all essential life functions, from synthesizing nutrients to destroying pathogens and debris. Cells **divide** via a process known as **mitosis.** During mitosis, the cell splits from one single mother cell into two separate daughter cells. These daughter cells then divide further into daughter cells of their own, and the cycle repeats until enough cells are present to form a tissue.

Inside each cell are **organelles,** structures that help regulate function of the cell.

The **nucleus** regulates the **overall function** of the cell. Inside the nucleus is **DNA**(deoxyribonucleic acid), which is the building block for life. Also inside the nucleus is the **nucleolus**, which contains **RNA**(ribonucleic acid). RNA is vital in transmitting signals from DNA to ribosomes for protein synthesis.

Golgi apparatus allows proteins and lipids to be bundled and **transported** within the cell itself.

Lysosomes are responsible for **breaking down** several different substances inside the cell, including protein and waste products.

Mitochondria are responsible for the production of **adenosine triphosphate(ATP)**, the molecule that provides **energy** to the body by transporting chemical energy to parts of the body that require it.

Ribosomes, which contain protein and RNA, are responsible for **synthesizing cell proteins**.

Smooth endoplasmic reticulum is responsible for synthesizing **carbohydrates and lipids** for use in producing new cell membranes.

Cytoplasm is found inside the cell, and is a **gel-like substance**. It allows organelles, nutrients, and waste products to move throughout the cell.

Mitosis

Replication

Cell Division

2N Daughter Cell

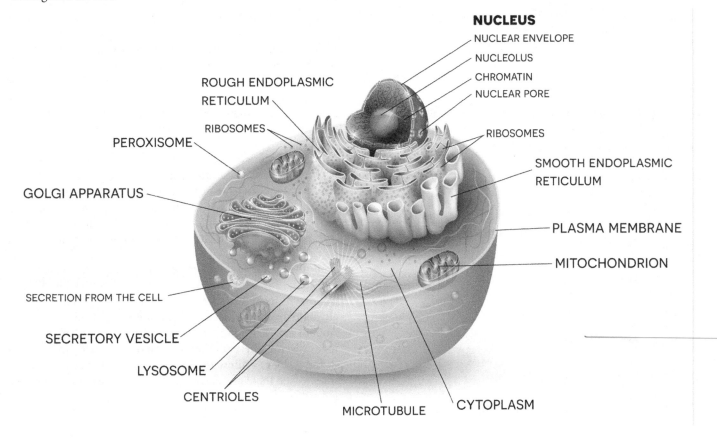

Tissue

The body is constructed by smaller parts making bigger parts, until we have an organism. The organization of the body is: cells > tissues > organ > organ system > organism. A **tissue** is made of a **group of cells** with **similar function and structure**. When these cells, all formed roughly the same way, which perform the same action, come together, they form a tissue. There are **four** types of tissue in the human body: epithelial, muscular, nervous, and connective.

Epithelial Tissue

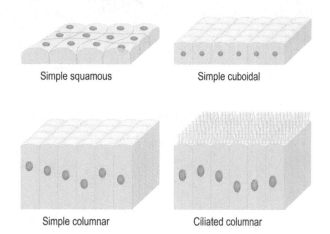

Simple squamous

Simple cuboidal

Simple columnar

Ciliated columnar

Epithelial tissue forms most **glands**, the **digestive tract**, the **respiratory tract**, and the **epidermis**. Anywhere there is a mucous membrane, there is epithelium. Epithelial tissue is responsible for **protection**(the epidermis protects the body from pathogens and trauma), **secretion**(glands secrete substances, from hormones to mucous), and **absorption of nutrients**(the linings of the small intestine are made of epithelium, which allows nutrients to be absorbed into the blood stream). Epithelial tissue is also **avascular**, which means there is no direct blood supply to the tissue. This is what allows layers of the epidermis to be peeled away without any bleeding.

Muscular Tissue

Muscular tissue creates **muscles**. There are three types of muscles: skeletal muscles, so named because they connect to the skeleton, cardiac muscles, which create the heart, and smooth muscles, which are abundant in several locations in the body.

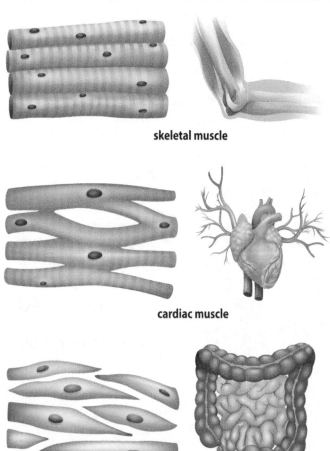

skeletal muscle

cardiac muscle

smooth muscle

Skeletal muscles attach to the **skeleton**. Another name for skeletal muscle is "**striated**" muscle, due to its appearance under a microscope. These muscles are **voluntary**, meaning they can be controlled. When these muscles contract, they pull on the bones they attach to, which allows movement.

Skeletal muscles are always in a state of **twitching**, even if it can't be felt. It's this twitching, very fine contractions, that produces **body heat**. When body temperature drops, the skeletal muscles increase the amount of contraction, which produces high body temperature, with the twitching of the muscles becoming more apparent. This is what happens when a person shivers.

Cardiac muscle is the muscle that makes the **heart**. Another name for cardiac muscle is "**branching**" muscle, due to its appearance under a microscope. Cardiac muscle is **involuntary**, meaning it cannot be controlled. Cardiac muscle is powerful, shooting **blood** out of the heart with each contraction. The only function of cardiac muscle is to send blood from one place to another.

Smooth muscle is found in several locations throughout the body. Another name for smooth muscle is "**non-striated**" muscle, due to its appearance under a microscope. Smooth muscle is **involuntary**, meaning it cannot be controlled. Because smooth muscle is found in several different regions of the body, it has several different functions. Smooth muscle can be found in the **walls of hollow organs** such as the stomach and intestines. When these muscles contract, they force food through the Digestive System, which is known as **peristalsis**.

Other locations smooth muscle can be found are in the skin, and in the eyes. In the skin, smooth muscle attaches to hair. When these muscles contract, they stand hair up, producing goosebumps. These muscles are known as the **arrector pili** muscles. In the eyes, smooth muscles help to dilate the iris and pupil.

Nervous Tissue

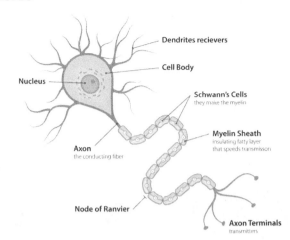

Nervous tissue forms the **brain**, **spinal cord**, and **nerves**. The primary cell of nervous tissue is known as a **neuron**. Neurons process nervous impulses, sending these impulses to other tissues, such as muscles, or between other neurons.

Neurons receive **action potentials**(electric impulses), which are brought into the cell by **dendrites**, branch-like projections coming off the cell body of the neuron. Once the nucleus processes the information coming into the cell, it sends the impulse out of the cell to its destination by way of the **axon**, a long projection coming off the cell body. The axons terminate at other neurons, or help innervate muscles.

Surrounding the axons are sheaths of protein and fat known as **myelin**. Myelin sheaths allow efficient and rapid transmission of impulses traveling along an axon, and help provide protection for the axon. Myelin sheaths in the peripheral nervous system are produced by **Schwann cells**.

Connective Tissue

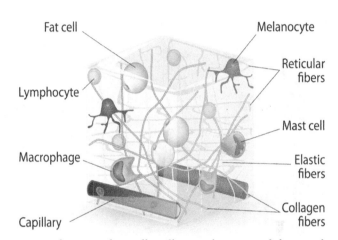

Connective tissue is the most abundant form of tissue in the body. There are several different structures made by connective tissue, including **tendons**, **ligaments**, **fascia**, **bones**, **lymph**, **cartilage, and blood**. Connective tissue is responsible for **connecting** tissues. In addition to connecting tissues, it helps to **separate** tissues, as seen in serous membranes and cartilage.

Connective tissue contains two specific types of cells known as blast cells and clast cells. These cells play a very important role in the health of connective tissue. **Blast cells** are germ cells that are responsible for **building connective tissue**. Blast cells divide and build tissue until the structure is complete. Once the structure is complete, the blast cells mature, and stop dividing. **Clast cells** are responsible for **breaking down tissue**, which is very important in keeping the tissue healthy. If a person suffers an injury such as a sprain or a fracture, clast cells will enter the area and destroy the dead tissue, cleaning the area, which allows blast cells a clean surface to build new tissue on.

Blood

Blood is the **most abundant** form of connective tissue in the body. Blood is mainly a mode of **transportation** for blood cells, hormones, nutrients, and waste products. There are four parts of blood: erythrocytes, leukocytes, thrombocytes, and plasma.

Erythrocytes, also known as **red blood cells**, are responsible for **transporting oxygen and carbon dioxide** throughout the body. The cytoplasm of erythrocytes is made of a protein known as **hemoglobin**, which is primarily made of iron. Hemoglobin is what oxygen and carbon dioxide attach to. In the lungs, when the erythrocytes are exposed to the alveoli, carbon dioxide detaches from the erythrocytes, and oxygen then attaches in its place. In all other areas of the body where gas exchange occurs, oxygen detaches first from erythrocytes, and carbon dioxide takes its place. This is how gas exchange occurs in erythrocytes.

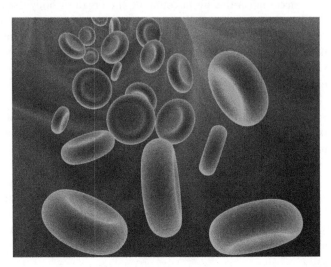

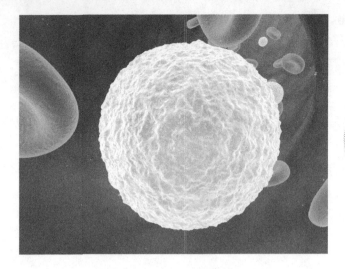

Leukocytes, also known as **white blood cells**, are the body's primary **defense against pathogens**. There are several different types of leukocytes, ranging from T-cells to basophils. These cells eat pathogens(such as bacteria), dead cells, and debris floating in the blood stream.

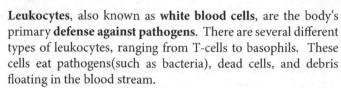

Leukocytes have an average lifespan of 2-3 weeks, and are then destroyed by the Lymphatic System!

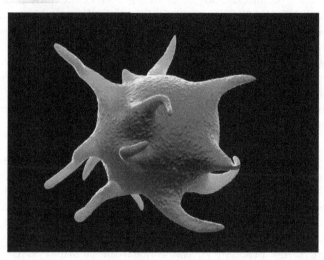

Thrombocytes, also known as **platelets**, have one function: to **clot the blood**. This is vitally important when a person is bleeding. If the blood does not clot, the person could continue bleeding until they lose too much blood.

Plasma is the **fluid** portion of blood. The majority of blood, around 56%, is made of plasma. Plasma is what allows all of the blood cells, hormones, nutrients, and waste to move throughout the body. Without plasma, these substances would go nowhere.

Serous Membranes

Serous membranes are forms of connective tissue that are used to **separate organs from one another**, preventing friction. They accomplish this by surrounding the organ or body cavity.

Inside the thorax, there are two serous membranes: the **pericardium**, which **surrounds the heart**, and the **pleural membranes**, which **surround the lungs**. These membranes help protect these organs from injury.

Inside the abdomen and pelvis, there is one serous membrane: the **peritoneum**. This membrane keeps the organs inside the abdomen and pelvis from being injured, and provides a pathway for many blood vessels, lymph vessels, and nerves to travel.

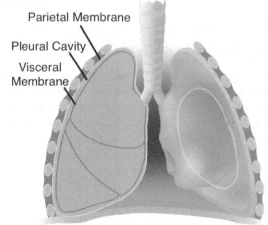

Parietal Membrane

Pleural Cavity

Visceral Membrane

Inside of a serous membrane is a thick fluid, known as **serous fluid**. This fluid helps the membranes absorb shock. Holding the fluid in place are two walls. The **inner wall**, which comes into contact with the organs, is known as the **visceral serous membrane**. The **outer wall**, which comes into contact with other structures such as bones or other organs, is known as the **parietal serous membrane**.

Cardiovascular System

The Cardiovascular System is one of the most important organ systems in the body, responsible for **transportation** of nutrients such as oxygen and hormones to tissues. It also allows for waste to be moved to areas of the body where it can be eliminated, such as the lungs, liver, and kidneys. Wastes include carbon dioxide and urea.

Heart

The primary organ of the Cardiovascular System is the heart. The heart, a large, powerful muscle, has one function: to **pump blood** throughout the body.

Blood is sent to the body to exchange oxygen and carbon dioxide. When gas exchange occurs in the body in areas other than the lungs, oxygen detaches from the erythrocytes, and carbon dioxide takes its place. Deoxygenated blood is returned to the heart via the **largest veins** in the body, the vena cavae(1). The **superior vena cava** returns blood to the heart from the head and upper limbs, while the **inferior vena cava** returns blood to the heart from the trunk and lower limbs. When blood first enters the heart, it is deoxygenated, and enters into the **right atrium**(2). It then passes through the **tricuspid valve**(which separates the right atrium from the right ventricle), into the **right ventricle**(3). The cardiac muscle in the right ventricle contracts, and it sends the deoxygenated blood out of the heart to the lungs through the **pulmonary arteries**(4[main pulmonary artery], 5[left and right branches]). Despite carrying deoxygenated blood, these vessels are still called arteries because they carry blood away from the heart. After blood cycles through the lungs, exchanging oxygen and carbon dioxide, the blood returns back to the heart through the **pulmonary veins**(6[left and right branches]). Again, despite carrying oxygenated blood, these vessels are called veins because they carry blood towards the heart. The blood re-enters the heart into the **left atrium**(7). It passes through the **bicuspid/mitral valve**(which separates the left atrium and left ventricle), into the **left ventricle**(8). An extremely powerful contraction occurs in the left ventricle, which shoots blood out of the heart to the rest of the body through the **aorta**(9), the **largest artery** in the body. The aorta has three branches that emerge from the **aortic arch**(10), sending blood to regions such as the head and upper limbs.

The pathway of blood flow through the heart

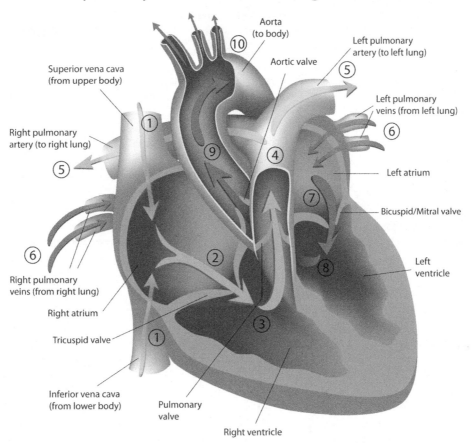

 Easy to Remember: Each side of the heart is made of the same structures, just with different names! Remember "VAVVA": Vein, Atrium, Valve, Ventricle, Artery!

Blood Vessels

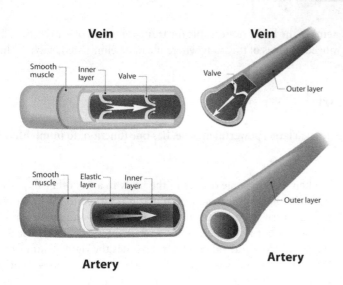

Blood vessels are the main mode of transportation for not only blood, but other substances, such as hormones. These substances are carried throughout the body in blood vessels. The largest types of blood vessels are known as arteries. **Arteries** primarily carry oxygenated blood **away from the heart**, to tissues. Arteries are the deepest blood vessels due to their size and importance. Tissues surrounding the arteries help to protect them from damage, which could result in severe bleeding and loss of oxygen.

Veins are blood vessels that primarily carry deoxygenated blood **towards the heart**, where it can replace carbon dioxide with oxygen. Veins are much more superficial than arteries, often visible under the skin, whereas most arteries cannot be seen.

Capillaries are microscopic arteries, and are where gas exchange takes place between blood vessels and tissues. Capillaries branch off from arterioles, exchange gas, and then return blood to veins through the smallest type of vein known as a **venule**.

Major arteries and veins are often named after their location in the body, such as the brachial artery/vein(in the arm), femoral artery/vein(in the thigh), abdominal aorta(in the abdomen), etc.

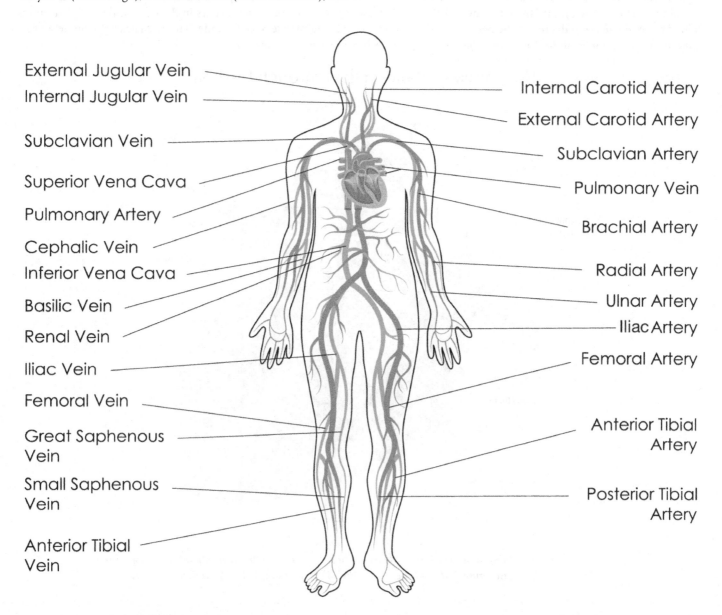

Digestive System

The Digestive System has many structures, organs, and functions. It is one of the most important systems in the body, responsible for **bringing nutrients into the body**, **digestion of food**, **absorption of nutrients** into the body's tissues, and **elimination of waste products**.

Structures of the Digestive System include the mouth, pharynx, esophagus, stomach, liver, gallbladder, pancreas, small intestine, and large intestine.

Digestion

The **mouth**, also known as the **oral cavity**, is the first place digestion begins taking place. The **teeth** manually break down food by **chewing**, or **mastication**. The food mixes with **saliva**, which contains digestive enzymes such as **amylase**, that help to break down carbohydrates. The **tongue** assists with mastication by pressing food against the teeth. Once food has been properly chewed, it is swallowed.

After food is swallowed, it moves from the mouth into the **pharynx**, also known as the **throat**. The pharynx is simply a passageway for food, water, and air on the way to their respective destinations. Food leaves the pharynx and enters the esophagus.

The **esophagus** is a long tube that runs from the pharynx inferiorly, passes through the diaphragm, and connects to the **stomach**. The esophagus, much like the pharynx, has one function: transporting food. The esophagus, and every hollow organ of the Digestive System, is lined with smooth muscle. When the smooth muscle rhythmically contracts, it forces food further along in the organ. This is known as **peristalsis**.

Once food reaches the **stomach**, both ends of the stomach close off, and the stomach begins **digesting** the food. Powerfully, it churns the food, breaking it down manually. Stomach acids like **hydrochloric acid** and **pepsin** mix with the food inside the stomach and further help to break down the food. Once food is properly digested, the stomach opens at the pylorus, the bottom of the stomach, and food exits the stomach and enters into the small intestine.

The small intestine is where the majority of absorption of nutrients occurs. Accessory organs produce substances that help aid the small intestine in digestion. These accessory organs are the liver, gallbladder, and pancreas.

The **liver**, the heaviest internal organ, mainly acts as a **blood detoxifier**. It filters harmful substances from the blood. However, it aids in digestion by **producing bile**, a yellowish substance that aids in the emulsification of fats. Connecting to the liver is the gallbladder. Once the liver produces bile, it empties the bile into the gallbladder, where it is stored until it is needed.

The **gallbladder** has one function: to **store bile** and empty bile into the small intestine through the bile duct, which connects to the duodenum, the first section of the small intestine.

The **pancreas** creates **pancreatic juice**, which aids in the digestion of proteins, lipids, and carbohydrates. These substances empty into the small intestine through the same path as bile, the bile duct.

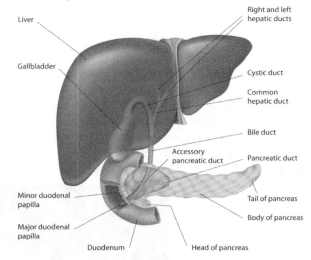

Food moves from the stomach into the **small intestine**. The first section of the small intestine is known as the **duodenum**. The duodenum is the last section of the Digestive System that digestion of food takes place. Bile and pancreatic juice mix with food in the duodenum and further break down substances. Peristalsis forces the food from the duodenum further into the small intestine, into the middle portion, known as the **jejunum**. The jejunum is where the majority of nutrient absorption takes place in the small intestine. As the food is forced through the small intestine, it moves into the final section, known as the **ileum**. Final absorption occurs in the ileum. Food moves through the ileum and into the large intestine.

The **large intestine** has two primary functions: **absorption of water**, and **elimination of waste**. As feces moves through the large intestine, water is absorbed. If too much water is absorbed, constipation may result. If not enough water is absorbed, diarrhea may result. The large intestine has four sections: the **ascending colon**, the **transverse colon**, the **descending colon**, and the **sigmoid colon**. As the feces leaves the sigmoid colon, it enters the rectum, where it is ready to be eliminated from the body.

Stages of Digestion

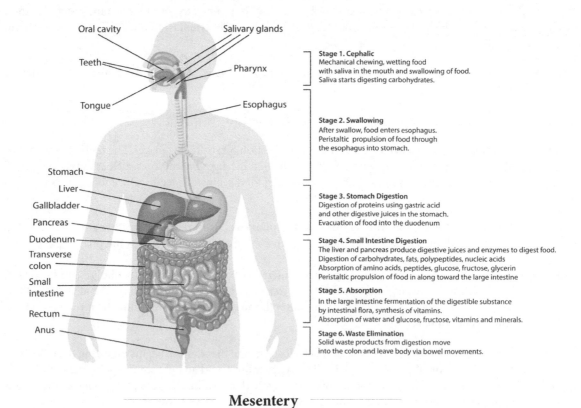

Oral cavity

Teeth

Tongue

Salivary glands

Pharynx

Esophagus

Stage 1. Cephalic
Mechanical chewing, wetting food
with saliva in the mouth and swallowing of food.
Saliva starts digesting carbohydrates.

Stage 2. Swallowing
After swallow, food enters esophagus.
Peristaltic propulsion of food through
the esophagus into stomach.

Stomach
Liver
Gallbladder
Pancreas
Duodenum
Transverse colon
Small intestine
Rectum
Anus

Stage 3. Stomach Digestion
Digestion of proteins using gastric acid
and other digestive juices in the stomach.
Evacuation of food into the duodenum

Stage 4. Small Intestine Digestion
The liver and pancreas produce digestive juices and enzymes to digest food.
Digestion of carbohydrates, fats, polypeptides, nucleic acids
Absorption of amino acids, peptides, glucose, fructose, glycerin
Peristaltic propulsion of food in along toward the large intestine

Stage 5. Absorption
In the large intestine fermentation of the digestible substance
by intestinal flora, synthesis of vitamins.
Absorption of water and glucose, fructose, vitamins and minerals.

Stage 6. Waste Elimination
Solid waste products from digestion move
into the colon and leave body via bowel movements.

Mesentery

The mesentery is a fan-shaped extension of the peritoneum that **suspends the small and large intestines** from the posterior abdominal wall, holding them in place. The point of attachment where the mesentery attaches to the posterior abdominal wall is known as the **mesenteric root**. The mesentery additionally allows a **conduit** for blood vessels, nerves, and lymphatic channels to pass in the abdomen.

Several blood vessels use the mesentery as a conduit. Arteries found in the mesentery include the superior mesenteric artery and inferior mesenteric artery. Veins found in the mesentery include the superior mesenteric vein and inferior mesenteric vein.

In a person with Crohn's disease, the mesentery often presents with an increased amount of fat. This fat is thicker than the fat of a person without Crohn's disease, and this may lead to future treatments for Crohn's disease that specifically target the mesentery. In addition, these fat cells produce a type of protein known as **C-reactive protein**, which is normally produced by the liver. C-reactive protein(CRP) levels typically increase when there is some sort of inflammation in the body. High levels of CRP in the blood may indicate infection, inflammation, and other conditions such as heart disease or cancer.

Sphincters

In the Digestive System, there are **ring-like bands of muscle** between digestive organs, known as **sphincters**. Sphincters function to allow food to enter into an organ, or to keep food from moving backwards.

There are four primary sphincters in the Digestive System:

The **esophageal sphincter** is located between the **pharynx** and the **esophagus**. It opens and allows food to move down into the esophagus. Another name for this sphincter is the upper esophageal sphincter.

The **cardiac sphincter** is located between the **esophagus** and the **stomach**. It is named after the region of the stomach it connects to, which is known as the cardia. When food enters the stomach, the cardiac sphincter closes, preventing food and stomach acid from ascending into the esophagus. Another name for this sphincter is the lower esophageal sphincter.

The **pyloric sphincter** is located between the **stomach** and the **small intestine**. It is named after the region of the stomach it connects to, which is known as the pylorus. When food enters the stomach, the pyloric sphincter closes, preventing food from leaving the stomach before digestion has taken place. When food has been properly digested, the pyloric sphincter opens, and food leaves the stomach and enters the small intestine.

The **ileocecal sphincter** is located between the **small intestine** and the **large intestine**. It is named after the parts of the two organs that come together, the ileum(small intestine) and cecum(large intestine).

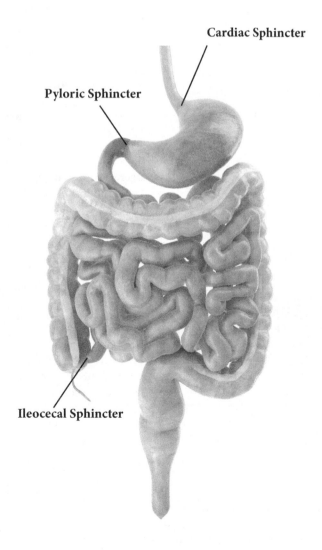

Cardiac Sphincter

Pyloric Sphincter

Ileocecal Sphincter

Endocrine System

The Endocrine System is responsible for coordinating specific activities of cells and tissues by releasing **hormones** into the body. Endocrine glands differ from exocrine glands in two specific ways: endocrine glands create and secrete hormones, while exocrine glands create and secrete things like sweat, saliva, and oil. Endocrine glands secrete hormones directly into the **blood stream**, while exocrine glands secrete their substances onto a **surface**(such as the surface of the mouth or skin). Endocrine glands have many different functions that help regulate body function and homeostasis.

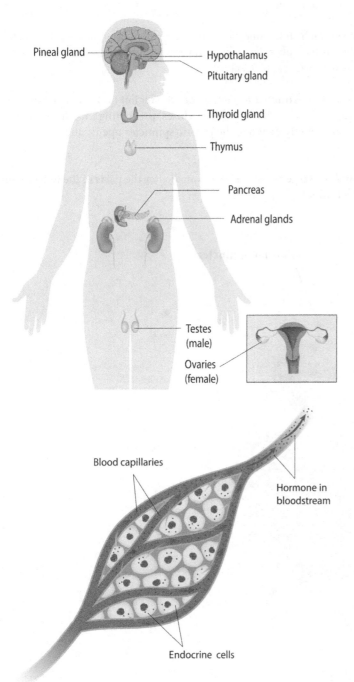

Hormone secretion into the blood stream

DID YOU KNOW?

While most hormones are made by these endocrine glands, other organs can also produce hormones! The placenta produces estrogen and progesterone, and the stomach produces ghrelin, the hormone that stimulates appetite!

Adrenal Glands

The adrenal glands, located **atop the kidneys**, secrete **epinephrine and norepinephrine**. These hormones help to elevate blood pressure, heart rate, and blood sugar. They are considered stress hormones, and are secreted when the body is under stress, or in the sympathetic nervous response.

Hypothalamus

The hypothalamus produces **dopamine**, an important hormone that increases blood pressure and heart rate. It is considered the **reward center hormone**. If you win at a game or contest, your hypothalamus may release dopamine, which gives a sensation of excitement.

Ovaries

The ovaries are the female gonads. They create **estrogen and progesterone**, two hormones important to female development and bone growth.

Pancreatic Islets

Pancreatic Islets are the parts of the pancreas that create **glucagon**, which **increases blood sugar levels**, and **insulin**, which **decreases blood sugar levels**. Glucagon is created by **alpha cells**, and insulin is created by **beta cells**.

Pineal Gland

The pineal gland is responsible for the production of **melatonin**, the hormone that regulates the body's wake/sleep cycle, also known as the **circadian rhythm**.

Pituitary Gland

The pituitary gland, which many consider the "master gland", secretes **growth hormone**, which regulates the amount of growth a person may experience. It also secretes **prolactin**, which stimulates milk production, and **follicle-stimulating hormone**, which influences production of female egg cells and male sperm cells.

Testes

The testes are the male gonads. The testes secrete **testosterone**, the primary male hormone, responsible for increasing bone and muscle mass.

Thyroid

The thyroid is a gland in the neck that produces **calcitonin**, which decreases the levels of calcium in the blood stream. Too much calcium may weaken bones and cause kidney stones.

Integumentary System

The Integumentary System is the body's first line of defense against pathogens and trauma. Its primary function is to protect the body. It also secretes substances, may absorb certain substances, and even eliminates waste.

Skin

The skin, which is the body's **largest organ**, is the main structure of the Integumentary System. The skin **protects the body** by creating a thick barrier that prevents pathogens from entering, and helps to cushion the body from blunt trauma.

Aiding the skin in protection are the **nails**. Finger and toe nails are made of **keratin**, the same cells that create thick layers in the skin called calluses. The nails prevent damage to the distal phalanges.

Hair also aids in protection, but in a different way. Hair is used to regulate temperature. When body temperature drops, smooth muscle that attaches to each hair, known as **arrector pili**, contract, forcing the hair to stand up. This creates an insulating layer, which is meant to trap warmth underneath the hair, much like a blanket. This does little for humans, but is utilized by animals to retain heat in cold environments.

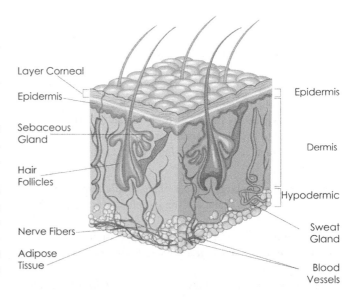

Glands

Inside the skin are glands, which also aid in protection. **Sudoriferous glands** emerge from deep in the skin to the surface directly through tubes. Sudoriferous glands create and secrete **sweat**. Sweat is mostly made of water, but may also contain salt and waste products such as ammonia. Sweat is used to lower body temperature by evaporating off the surface of the skin. The evaporation cools the skin, which helps lower the internal body temperature.

Sebaceous glands are glands that connect to hair, and produce **oil(sebum)**. Oil helps to protect the body from pathogens and debris in the air. Blockage of a sebaceous gland, however, may lead to a bacterial infection, and acne.

Sensory Receptors

Inside the skin, there are many types of receptors that detect certain sensations, relaying the information to the brain. Sensory receptors aren't exclusive to the skin, but there are an abundance of them in the skin.

Nociceptors are a type of sensory receptor that detects the sensation of **pain**. While unpleasant, pain is actually vital in protection of the body. The term "noci-" is Latin for "hurt".

Meissner's Corpuscles are sensory receptors that are very superficial in the skin, and detect **light pressure**. Massage strokes such as effleurage and feather strokes are detected by Meissner's Corpuscles.

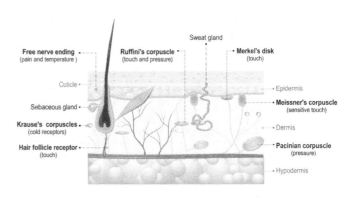

Pacinian Corpuscles are sensory receptors that are very deep in the skin, and detect **deep pressure**. Deep massage strokes, such as compression, are detected by Pacinian Corpuscles.

 Easy to Remember: Nociceptors detect pain. Remember the old saying "No pain, No gain".

 Easy to Remember: Pacinian Corpuscles detect deep pressure. Match up "Paci" of Pacinian with "Paci" of Pacific Ocean. The Pacific Ocean is deep!

Lymphatic System

The Lymphatic System is vital in the body's **defense against pathogens** and disease. Not only are leukocytes abundant in lymph, but antibodies are created in the Lymphatic System. The Lymphatic System contains lymph, lymph nodes, lymph vessels, and lymph organs.

Lymph, the primary structure of the Lymphatic System, is a **fluid** composed of water, protein, leukocytes, urea, salts, and glucose. Lymph allows transport of all of these substances through the body, ultimately dumping into the blood stream. Lymph is made of **interstitial fluid**, fluid found between cells.

Lymph travels throughout the body through **lymph vessels**. Lymph vessels are similar to blood vessels, but only flow in one direction, **towards the heart**. Lymph vessels absorb foreign bodies and nutrients from tissues, bringing them into the lymph to be transported to the blood stream or lymph nodes. The **largest lymph vessel** in the body is located in the trunk. It is known as the **Thoracic Duct**. The Thoracic Duct drains lymph into the **left subclavian vein**, where it joins with blood.

Lymph nodes are **large masses** of lymphatic tissue. They are responsible for production of **antibodies**, and help **filter and destroy** any foreign objects that enter the lymph. During an infection, lymph nodes may become tender and swollen.

The **thymus**, located in the chest, is responsible for production of **T-lymphocytes**, or T-cells. T-cells are vital in regulation of the body's immune system. If a person contracts HIV, the virus destroys the T-cells, which essentially disables the immune system.

The **spleen** is an organ of the Lymphatic System responsible for **destroying** dead or dying **red blood cells** from the blood stream, in addition to destroying pathogens and debris.

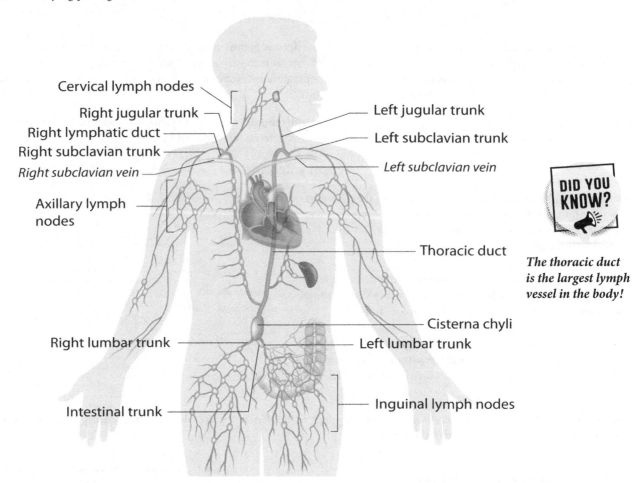

DID YOU KNOW?

The thoracic duct is the largest lymph vessel in the body!

Muscular System

Muscles have numerous actions in the body, primarily **producing body heat**, contracting to **allow movements**, and **constricting organs and blood vessels**.

Muscle Structure

Skeletal muscles are broken down into the following components:

- **Sarcomeres** are the functional units of skeletal muscle. When they shorten, the muscle contracts.
- **Actin** is part of a sarcomere, known as the **thin filament**. Actin is what myosin attaches to during a muscle contraction. Actin anchors to the **Z-Line** in a sarcomere.
- **Myosin** is part of a sarcomere, known as the **thick filament**. Myosin resembles a golf club head, and attaches to actin during a muscle contraction. The entire span of the thick filaments in one sarcomere is known as the **A-Band**.
- **Tropomyosin** is a protein that covers the attachment sites where myosin attaches to actin during a contraction. **Calcium ions** are responsible for removing the tropomyosin from the actin, allowing the myosin to attach to the actin and initiate a contraction.

Muscle contractions begin with **action potentials** sent from the brain. Action potentials terminate at the **neuromuscular junction**, releasing **acetylcholine(aCh)** into the synapse. This results in the aCh binding to certain receptors in the muscle fiber, which in turn allows sodium ions to enter the muscle fiber. The sodium ions come into contact with the sarcoplasmic reticulum, which causes a release of **calcium ions**. The calcium ions enter into the working unit of muscles, known as sarcomeres. A sarcomere contains thick filaments, known as myosin, and thin filaments, known as actin. When a muscle isn't in a state of contraction, the myosin and actin do not interact due to the presence of tropomyosin preventing myosin from attaching to actin. When the body wants to allow the muscle to contract, calcium ions bind to tropomyosin, causing them to reveal the attachment sites on the actin for the myosin. Once the tropomyosin is removed, the myosin attaches to the actin, pulling the Z-lines closer together. This causes the sarcomere to shorten. The shortening of all the sarcomeres in a muscle fiber result in the entire muscle contracting.

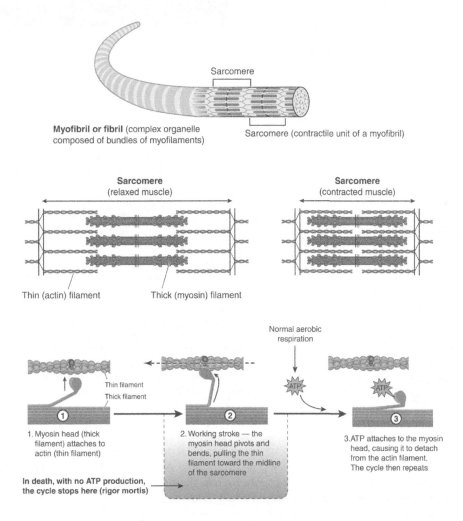

Muscle Contractions

When there is **tension** in a muscle, it is **contracting**. A muscle can contract without causing movement, though. There are four types of muscle contractions.

Isometric Contraction

Iso means "**same**" or "**equal**". Metric means "**length**". When an isometric contraction occurs, as the name implies, the **length** of the muscle **stays the same**, but **tension** in the muscle **changes**. An example: imagine trying to lift something that is too heavy for you to lift. The muscles required to lift the object increase in tension, but because the muscles aren't strong enough, the length of the muscles doesn't change.

Isotonic Contraction

Iso means "**same**" or "**equal**". Tonic means "**tension**". When an isotonic contraction occurs, as the name implies, the **tension** in the muscle **stays the same**, but the muscle **length changes**. There are two separate types of isotonic contractions:

Concentric Contraction

When a concentric contraction occurs, several things take place. The tension in the muscle **initially increases** until the amount of tension required to perform the action is reached, then the tension **remains constant**. While the tension remains constant, the muscle **length decreases**. An example is performing a biceps curl.

Eccentric Contraction

When an eccentric contraction occurs, several things take place. The tension in the muscle **initially decreases** until the amount of tension required to perform the action is reached, then the tension **remains constant**. While the tension remains constant, the muscle length **increases**. An example is extending the elbow and lowering the weight down after the biceps curl in a concentric contraction.

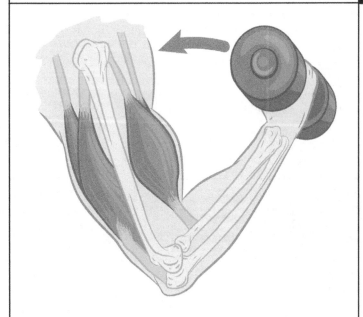

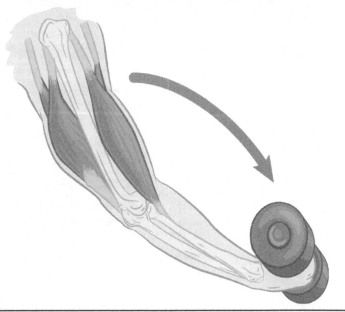

General Rule of Thumb: With concentric contractions, the muscle length decreases. With eccentric contractions, the muscle length increases.

Proprioceptors

Proprioceptors are structures in the body that are responsible for detection of the body's **position in space**. Proprioceptors allow the location of the parts of the body, the body's weight, and center of gravity to be known even on a subconscious level. Proprioceptors can be found in several locations in the body, such as the skin, muscles, tendons, and ears. The two main types of proprioceptors in the muscles are **muscle spindles**, and **Golgi tendon organs**.

Muscle Spindles

Muscle spindles, also known as **stretch receptors**, are able to detect when a muscle is stretching or elongating. When muscle spindles detect the muscle is stretching too far, they send a sensory impulse to the spinal cord, which responds by sending a motor impulse to the muscle that stimulates the muscle to **produce tension**. This counteracts the stretch and prevents damage to the muscle.

Golgi Tendon Organs

Golgi tendon organs are able to **detect the amount of tension** in a muscle. They are located at the origin and insertion of muscle fibers and tendons, also known as the **musculotendinous junction**. Golgi tendon organs detect when the muscle

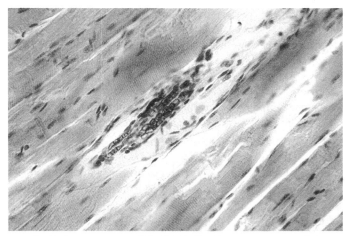

Muscle spindles

is producing tension, and if the tension is too great, Golgi tendon organs will **prevent the muscle from producing additional force**. This is done to prevent injury to muscles. An example is during weight lifting, when performing repetitions at the end of a set. The muscle may become more difficult to contract when lifting the weight due to the Golgi tendon organ preventing further force from being exerted by the muscle.

Muscle Shapes

Muscles have several different shapes. These include:

Circular: Circular muscles are arranged in a **circular** manner. Examples include orbicularis oris and orbicularis oculi.

Convergent: Convergent muscles are **spread out** on one end and **merge together** at another end. An example is pectoralis major.

Fusiform: Fusiform muscles are **thin** at the **attachment sites** and **wider in the middle**. An example is biceps brachii.

Parallel: Parallel muscles have muscle fibers that all run in the **same direction**. Examples include sartorius and coracobrachialis.

Pennate: Pennate muscles have an appearance resembling a **feather**. These muscles can be **unipennate**(one feather), **bipennate**(two feathers), or **multipennate**(multiple feathers). Examples include flexor pollicis longus(unipennate), rectus femoris(bipennate), and deltoid(multipennate).

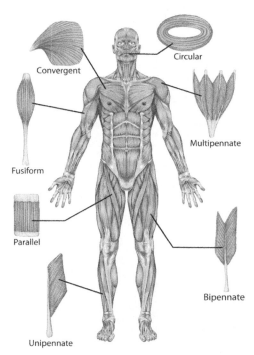

Muscle Actions

Muscles perform numerous actions on the body, depending on which muscle is contracting. To see examples of all of these actions, refer to page 214. Muscle actions include the following:

Flexion: **Decreasing the angle** of a joint.
Extension: **Increasing the angle** of a joint.
Adduction: Moving a structure **towards the midline**.
Abduction: Moving a structure **away from the midline**.
Protraction: Moving a structure **anteriorly**.
Retraction: Moving a structure **posteriorly**.
Inversion: Turning the sole of the foot **in towards the midline**.
Eversion: Turning the sole of the foot **out away from the midline**.
Elevation: Moving a structure **superiorly**.
Depression: Moving a structure **inferiorly**.

Supination: **Rotating the palm** so it is facing **upwards**.
Pronation: **Rotating the palm** so it is facing **downwards**.
Rotation: **Turning a structure** around its **long axis**.
Circumduction: **Turning a structure** around the **circumference** of a joint.
Opposition: Moving structures in **opposite directions**.
Lateral Deviation: Moving a structure from **side-to-side**.
Plantarflexion: Pointing toes **down**.
Dorsiflexion: Pointing toes **up**.

When a muscle performs an action, other muscles associate with the muscle in different ways.

A **prime mover/agonist** is the muscle that primarily performs a specific action. An example: when plantarflexion is performed, the **strongest muscle** performing it is the gastrocnemius. That means gastrocnemius is the prime mover/agonist.

A **synergist** is the muscle that **assists the prime mover/agonist** in performing the action. Synergists are not as strong as prime movers. An example: when plantarflexion is performed, soleus contracts to allow more strength, assisting gastrocnemius in performing the action. That means soleus is the synergist.

An **antagonist** is a muscle that performs the **opposite action** of the prime mover/agonist. Every muscle has an antagonist. An example: gastrocnemius contracts, performing plantarflexion. To return the foot to the starting position, gastrocnemius relaxes, and tibialis anterior contracts, which performs dorsiflexion. This makes tibialis anterior the antagonist to gastrocnemius.

A **fixator** is a muscle that **stabilizes an area** or joint while an action is being performed. Stabilizing the joint prevents things like injury and allows optimal movement to occur. An example: supraspinatus stabilizes the head of the humerus in the glenoid fossa, keeping the joint together during the numerous movements the glenohumeral joint performs.

Easy to Remember: Just think of it like this: Batman is the Agonist, the main character, Robin is the Synergist, the helper, and The Joker is the Antagonist, who does the opposite of Batman!

Nervous System

Nerves are structures in the Nervous System, made of nervous tissue. Nerves have many functions, from regulating vital functions within the body, to controlling muscles.

There are two divisions of the Nervous System: the **Central Nervous System**, and the **Peripheral Nervous System**. The Central Nervous System consists of the **brain and spinal cord**. The Central Nervous System is under involuntary control, responsible for interpretation of sensations and mental activity.

Nerve impulses are categorized as **sensory or motor**. **Sensory impulses** are detected by sensory receptors throughout the body (such as nociceptors, olfactory receptors, etc), and travel **to the brain** and/or spinal cord for processing. These impulses are called **afferent impulses**. In the case of reflexes, these impulses only reach the spinal cord, due to the immediacy of the required response. This is why reflexes are involuntary! Once the impulse reaches the brain and/or spinal cord, the brain and/or spinal cord interpret the sensation, and send a **motor impulse** back down the body to tell the body how to respond to the stimulus. These impulses are called **efferent impulses**.

Easy to Remember: Just remember "SAME". You can pair up "Sensory" with "Afferent", and "Motor" with "Efferent"!

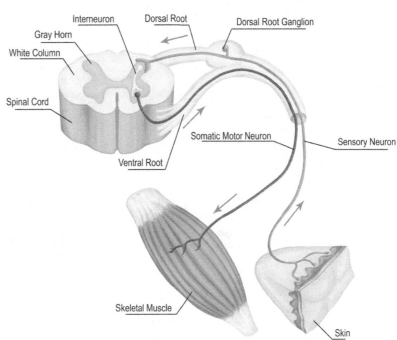

Central Nervous System

The brain consists of three parts: the **cerebrum**, which is the largest part of the brain and split into left and right hemispheres, the **cerebellum**, located at the back and bottom of the brain, and the **brain stem**, which connects the brain to the spinal cord.

Each side of the **cerebrum** is divided into **lobes**, named after the bones atop them: **frontal lobe**(processes motivation, aggression, mood), **temporal lobe**(processes memory, hearing, and smell), **parietal lobe**(processes most sensory information), and **occipital lobe**(processes vision).

The **cerebellum** is responsible for regulation of **muscle tone, balance**, **coordination**, and control of **general body movements**.

The **brain stem**, which consists of(in descending order) the **midbrain**, the **pons**, and the **medulla oblongata**, controls the **vital functions** of the body, such as breathing, heart rate, coughing, sneezing, vomiting, and blood vessel diameter.

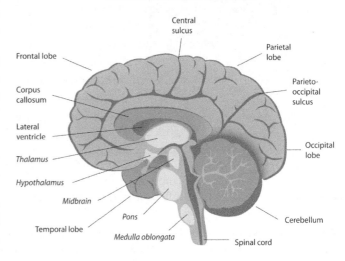

Median section of the brain

Meninges

Surrounding the brain and spinal cord are three layers of connective tissue known as the **meninges**. The deepest layer that comes into contact with the brain is known as the pia mater. The intermediate layer is known as the arachnoid. The most superficial layer, which comes into contact with the bones of the cranium, is known as the dura mater.

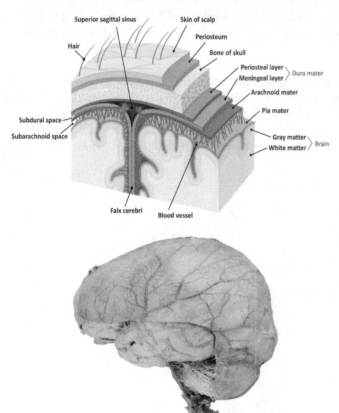

Pia Mater

The **pia mater**(tender mother), the **deepest layer**, is responsible for helping to protect the brain and spinal cord by containing cerebrospinal fluid. This fluid provides a cushion for the brain and spinal cord to help prevent injury. The pia mater is very delicate, and covers the brain completely by extending into the folds.

Arachnoid

The **arachnoid**, which is the **intermediate layer** of the meninges, is separated from the pia mater by subarachnoid space. The subarachnoid space contains cerebrospinal fluid, which helps to cushion and protect the brain and spinal cord. The arachnoid resembles cob webs or spider webs, which is where it gets its name. It is made of fibrous material that fluid is easily able to pass through. Unlike the pia mater, the arachnoid does not extend into the folds of the brain. The arachnoid is wrapped loosely around the brain.

Dura Mater

The **dura mater**(tough mother) is the **most superficial and strongest layer** of the meninges. The dura mater is responsible for protecting the brain by providing a thick padding around it. The dura mater is made of fibrous tissue, giving it the ability to properly protect the brain and spinal cord. It contains large blood vessels than branch off into capillaries that go into the pia mater.

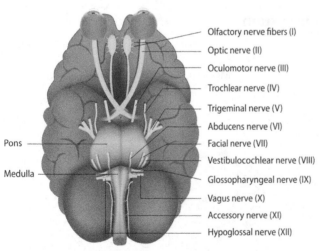

Brain covered with dura mater

Peripheral Nervous System

The Peripheral Nervous System consists of the body's **nerves**. There are two divisions of the Peripheral Nervous System: **Cranial Nerves** and **Spinal Nerves**. Cranial Nerves emerge from the brain, and help to regulate the functions of the head and face. There are **twelve pairs of Cranial Nerves**, each numbered in Roman Numerals:

- Olfactory(I)
- Optic(II)
- Oculomotor(III)
- Trochlear(IV)
- Trigeminal(V)
- Abducens(VI)
- Facial(VII)
- Vestibulocochlear(VIII)
- Glossopharyngeal(IX)
- Vagus(X)
- Accessory(XI)
- Hypoglossal(XII)

Spinal Nerves are much more numerous than Cranial Nerves. There are **31 pairs of Spinal Nerves**. The Spinal Nerves emerge from the spinal cord, and are responsible for controlling skeletal muscle.

A bundle of Spinal Nerves that emerge from the spinal cord is known as a **plexus**. There are three plexi in the body: **Cervical Plexus**, **Brachial Plexus**, **Lumbosacral Plexus**. The Cervical Plexus emerges from the spinal cord in the range of **C1-C4**. The primary nerve of the Cervical Plexus is known as the **Phrenic Nerve**. The Phrenic Nerve descends inferiorly from the cervical vertebrae and innervates(provides nervous stimulation to) the **diaphragm**.

Brachial Plexus

The Brachial Plexus emerges from the spinal cord at **C5-T1**. The nerves of the Brachial Plexus move distally, controlling the muscles of the **upper limb**. There are five primary nerves of the Brachial Plexus:

- Radial
- Musculocutaneous
- Axillary
- Median
- Ulnar

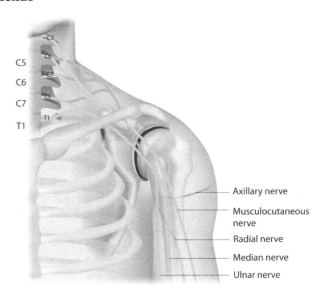

The **Radial Nerve** is located on the posterior arm and forearm, and innervates the triceps brachii, anconeus, brachioradialis, and wrist extensors.

The **Musculocutaneous Nerve** is located in the anterior arm, and innervates the biceps brachii, brachialis, and coracobrachialis.

The **Axillary Nerve** is primarily located in the armpit, and innervates the teres minor and deltoid.

The **Median Nerve** is located in the anterior arm, forearm, and hand, and innervates the wrist flexors, and most muscles on the lateral side of the hand.

The **Ulnar Nerve** is located on the anterior arm, medial forearm, and medial hand, and innervates the wrist flexors and most muscles on the medial side of the hand.

Lumbosacral Plexus

The Lumbosacral Plexus emerges from the **entire span** of the lumbar and sacral vertebrae. The major nerves of the Lumbosacral Plexus include:

- Sciatic
- Femoral
- Obturator
- Tibial
- Common Peroneal
- Deep Peroneal
- Superficial Peroneal

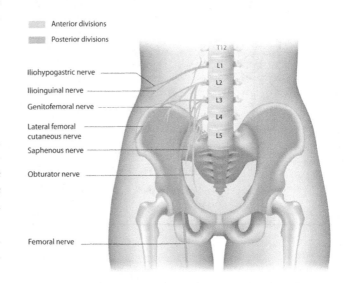

The **Sciatic Nerve** is a large nerve located on the posterior thigh. The Sciatic Nerve is actually both the Tibial Nerve and the Common Peroneal Nerve bundled together. Once the Sciatic Nerve reaches the back of the knee, it branches off into two separate nerves. The Sciatic Nerve innervates the Hamstring muscle group.

The **Femoral Nerve** is located on the anterior thigh, and innervates the quadriceps muscle group, iliacus, sartorius, and pectineus.

The **Obturator Nerve** is located on the medial portion of the thigh, and innervates the adductor muscle group.

The **Tibial Nerve**, after branching off the Sciatic nerve, runs down the posterior leg, and innervates the gastrocnemius, soleus, tibialis posterior, and plantaris.

The **Common Peroneal Nerve**, after branching off the Sciatic Nerve, actually branches off into two other nerves of its own: The Deep Peroneal and Superficial Peroneal Nerves.

The **Deep Peroneal Nerve** is located on the anterior leg, and innervates the tibialis anterior.

The **Superficial Peroneal Nerve** is located on the lateral portion of the leg, along the fibula, and innervates the peroneus longus.

Autonomic Nervous System

The autonomic nervous system helps to **regulate homeostasis** by release of hormones, controlling heart rate, breathing rate, and other bodily functions. There are two divisions of the autonomic nervous system: the **Sympathetic Nervous System**, and the **Parasympathetic Nervous System**.

Sympathetic Response

The Sympathetic Nervous System is also known as "**fight-or-flight**". When the body is in a state of **stress**, the Sympathetic Nervous System helps the body respond by releasing **norepinephrine** into the blood stream, which **increases heart rate and blood sugar**. The digestive organs will also shut down, and blood will be pulled from these organs and supplied to the muscles for use.

Parasympathetic Response

The Parasympathetic Nervous System is also known as "**rest-and-digest**". When the body is in a state of **relaxation**, the Parasympathetic Nervous System helps the body to calm itself. It decreases the body's heart rate, and increases blood flow to the digestive organs to **increase peristalsis**. The Parasympathetic Nervous System, decreasing heart rate, and peristalsis are all controlled by Cranial Nerve X, the **Vagus Nerve**.

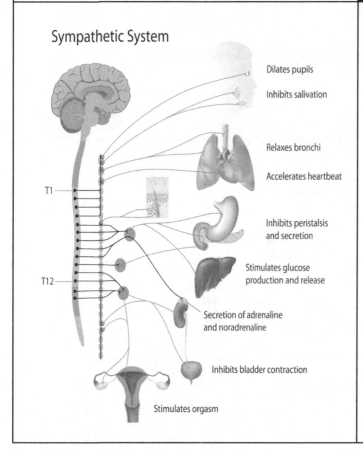

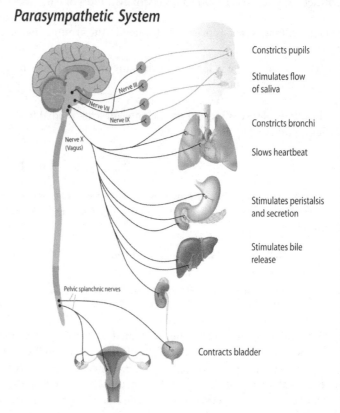

Reproductive System

The Reproductive System is responsible for **reproduction**, or the creation of offspring. Many organs and structures in the Reproductive System are shared with other body systems, such as the urethra, testes, and ovaries. There are two subcategories: the **Male Reproductive System** and **Female Reproductive System**. Each vary in structures and function.

Male Reproductive System

The Male Reproductive System is responsible for the production of **spermatozoa**(sperm) and male hormones, such as testosterone. Major structures of the Male Reproductive System include the penis, testes, scrotum, and ducts that carry sperm.

The **penis** is the primary organ of the Male Reproductive System, responsible for **sexual intercourse**, which allows passage of sperm outside the body through the urethra. The penis also allows urine to leave the body. During sexual arousal, nerves cause blood vessels in the penis to dilate, which then causes the penis to fill with blood. This results in an erection.

The **testes** are responsible for the production of **testosterone**. They are also responsible for **spermatogenesis**, or sperm production. After the testes produce sperm, it is stored in a tube located atop each testicle, known as the **epididymis**. Upon ejaculation, the sperm leaves the epididymis and enters the vas deferens.

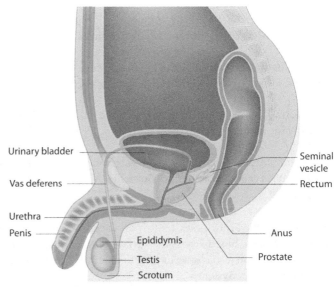

The **vas deferens** are tubes that connect the **epididymis to the urethra**. During ejaculation, smooth muscle in the walls of the vas deferens contract rhythmically(known as peristalsis), forcing sperm into the urethra. The sperm mixes with secretions from structures such as the prostate, which creates semen.

The **prostate** is a gland located near the bladder that produces secretions that join with sperm to create **semen**.

Female Reproductive System

The Female Reproductive System is responsible for the production of **egg cells**, estrogen, progesterone, and **fetal development**. Major structures of the Female Reproductive System include the vagina, ovaries, fallopian tubes, uterus, and cervix.

The **vagina** is the **passageway** located between the cervix and the opening to the outside of the body. The vagina is often confused with the outer, visible portion, known as the vulva. The vagina allows a passageway for the penis during sexual intercourse.

The **ovaries** are responsible for the production of **estrogen and progesterone**. The ovaries are also the structures that produce and release **egg cells**(oocytes) in women. Eggs are typically released once a month from one ovary.

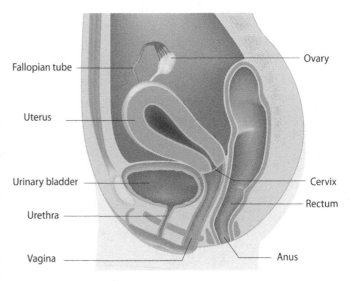

The **fallopian tubes** allow **passage of oocytes** from the ovaries to the uterus. Fertilization most commonly occurs in the fallopian tubes.

The **uterus** is an inverted pear-shaped organ responsible for the **development of a fetus**. Upon fertilization, the embryo attaches to the wall of the uterus. The placenta develops, which connects to the embryo, providing it with blood flow and nutrients to help it grow. During childbirth, the placenta detaches from the uterus and exits through the cervix and vagina.

The **cervix** is a narrow, circular passage that connects the **vagina to the uterus**. During pregnancy, the cervix is closed by a thick layer of mucous. During childbirth, the cervix dilates widely, which allows a passage for the child to pass through.

Respiratory System

The Respiratory System has one essential function: to **bring oxygen into the body**, and **eliminate wastes such as carbon dioxide** from the body. The main organs of the Respiratory System are the **lungs**. The left lung has two lobes and is smaller than the right lung, which has three lobes. This is due to the presence of the heart on the left side of the chest.

Conduction of air is controlled by the **nose**. Air enters the body through the nose, and is filtered by **hair and mucous**. The nose also warms the air as it enters the body.

The **larynx**, also known as the voice box, is a short tube located inferior to the pharynx. As air passes over the vocal cords in the larynx, the **vocal cords vibrate**, which **produces sound** used with the tongue to create speech.

Sitting atop the larynx is a flap of tissue known as the **epiglottis**. Upon swallowing, the epiglottis lies on top of the larynx, blocking any food or fluid from entering the larynx, which **prevents choking**.

Connecting to the larynx inferiorly is a tube of cartilage known as the **trachea**, or the wind pipe. The trachea is the primary passageway for air to enter into the lungs.

Once air enters the lungs, it goes into each lung through **bronchial tubes**, which branch off of the trachea. These tubes branch into smaller tubes called bronchioles. Bronchial tubes **secrete mucous**, which helps to trap any dirt or debris that have made it into the lungs.

At the end of the bronchioles are tiny **air sacs**, known as **alveoli**. The alveoli resemble a cluster of grapes. Capillaries attach to the alveoli and move blood across the surface of the alveoli. This allows carbon dioxide to detach from the erythrocytes and exit the blood stream, and also allows oxygen to enter the blood stream and attach to erythrocytes. Alveoli are where **gas exchange** occurs in the Respiratory System.

Respiration is accomplished by contraction of the **diaphragm**, a large muscle connected to the rib cage that separates the chest from the abdomen. The diaphragm creates a vacuum inside the chest. When it contracts, it descends, pulling the chest down. This allows air to enter into the lungs. When the diaphragm relaxes, it ascends up into the chest, which forces air out of the lungs.

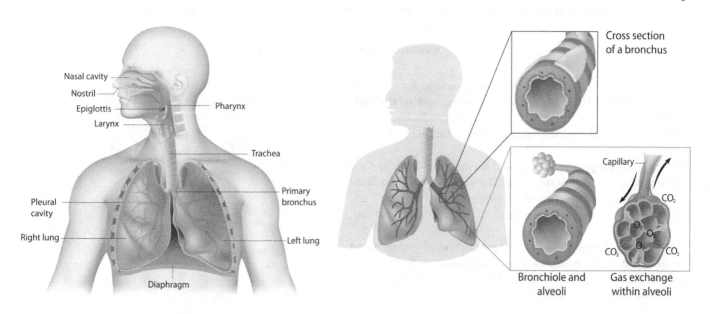

There are four major structures that pass through the diaphragm: the aorta, the inferior vena cava, the thoracic duct, and the esophagus!

Skeletal System

The Skeletal System is a vital component of movement. Muscles attach to bones, and when a muscle contracts, it pulls on a bone(or bones), which performs an action. Bones also produce blood cells, provide stability for the body, and protect structures and organs in the body.

There are **206 bones** in the human body. Each bone can be classified as one of the following: Long bone, Short bone, Irregular bone, Flat bone, Sesamoid bone.

Long bones appear **longer than they are wide**. There are numerous long bones in the body, including, but not limited to, the clavicle, humerus, femur, metatarsals, and phalanges.

Short bones are **as long as they are wide**. Examples include the carpals and tarsals.

Irregular bones are bones that have generally **unusual shapes**. Examples include the mandible, vertebrae, and pubis.

Flat bones are named after how they look: **flat**. They are typically thin and flat. Examples include the scapula, ribs, and cranial bones.

Sesamoid bones are bones **embedded inside tendons**, and named after what they look like. They are rounded, and resemble **sesame seeds**. The primary examples are the patella and pisiform.

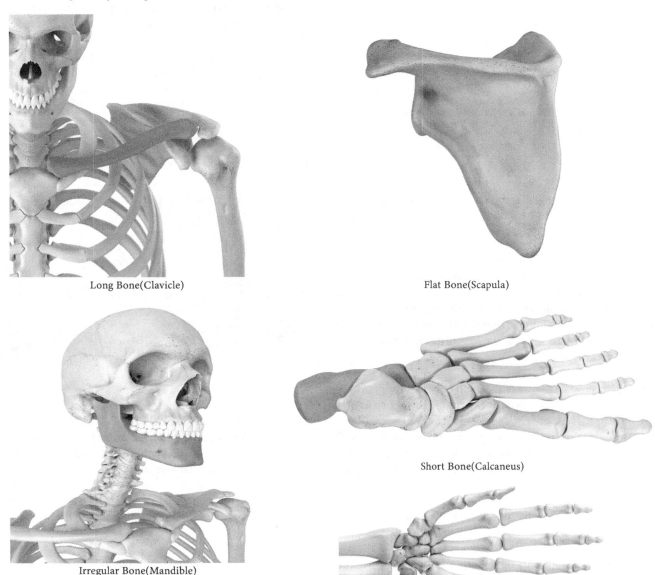

Long Bone(Clavicle)

Flat Bone(Scapula)

Irregular Bone(Mandible)

Short Bone(Calcaneus)

Sesamoid Bone(Pisiform)

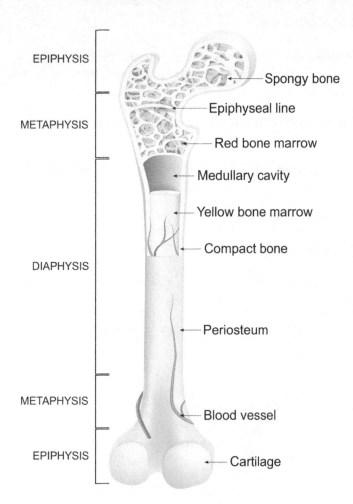

EPIPHYSIS

METAPHYSIS

DIAPHYSIS

METAPHYSIS

EPIPHYSIS

Spongy bone

Epiphyseal line

Red bone marrow

Medullary cavity

Yellow bone marrow

Compact bone

Periosteum

Blood vessel

Cartilage

Long Bone Structure

Long bones consist of three main parts: the epiphyses, the metaphyses, and the diaphysis. The **epiphyses** can be found on the **ends of the long bone**, where the bone articulates with other bones. The epiphyses are **covered with cartilage** to prevent friction between the articulating bone surfaces. The epiphyses are primarily made of spongy bone, which allows certain bones to withstand extreme pressure without fracturing, such as the femur.

The **metaphyses** are the sections between the epiphyses and the diaphysis. Inside the metaphyses, there is a line of cartilage called the **epiphyseal plate/line**, and it is where **growth in the bone** takes place during childhood and adolescence. As a person grows, eventually the cartilage ossifies and becomes part of the bone, and growth in the bone no longer occurs.

The **diaphysis** is the **shaft of the bone**. Inside the shaft of the bone is the medullary cavity. The medullary cavity contains **red bone marrow** during childhood, which is the site of **red blood cell formation**. When the child ages, the red bone marrow is converted into yellow bone marrow, which is mainly just fat. The diaphysis is made of compact bone to provide as much strength as possible around the medullary cavity, while still giving enough space for the cavity itself to fill with marrow.

Joints

Where bones come together is known as an **articulation**. Another name for articulation is "joint". Joints are where **movements occur**. We don't flex muscles, we flex joints!

All joints are classified as one of the following: Synarthrotic, Amphiarthrotic, or Diarthrotic. **Synarthrotic joints** are joints with **little to no movement** in them, such as the sutures in the skull. **Amphiarthrotic joints** are joints that are **slightly movable**, such as the intervertebral joints. **Diarthrotic joints** are **freely movable** joints, and have no real movement restrictions, such as in the shoulder or hip.

Joints have several structures that help create and support them. Between bones that articulate, on the epiphyses, there is **articular cartilage**. This type of cartilage is known as **hyaline cartilage**. It is a dense form of cartilage, very thick, and is a shock-absorber. Hyaline cartilage also **prevents friction** between the articulating bones, so bones don't rub against each other during movement.

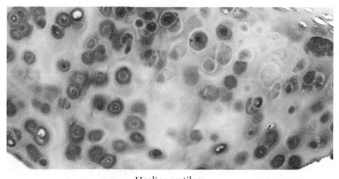

Hyaline cartilage

Easy to Remember: To remember the joint classifications, just think of "SAD". This tells you the joint classifications in order from least movable joint to most movable joint. Synarthrosis, Amphiarthrosis, Diarthrosis.

Certain joints have a specific type of cartilage in them known as a **labrum**. The labrum, found in the glenohumeral joint and acetabulofemoral joint, is used to **deepen the joint**, providing a deeper socket for these ball-and-socket joints. This provides more **strength and stability** for the joint.

Bones are held together by **ligaments**. Ligaments are avascular, meaning they are not supplied with blood by blood vessels. Ligaments are strong, but do not stretch very far before injury can occur. Tearing of ligaments such as the Anterior Cruciate Ligament is common in activities such as sports, or in car accidents.

Four of the most important joints joined together by ligaments are located in the skull, between the cranial bones. These synarthrotic joints are called **sutures**. The **sagittal suture** runs along a sagittal plane on the top of the head, connecting the **two parietal bones**. The **coronal suture** runs on a coronal plane, connecting the **frontal bone** to the **parietal bones**. The **squamous suture** runs on a sagittal plane, but is located on the side of the skull, connecting the **parietal and temporal bones** together. Finally, the **lambdoid suture**, named for its resemblance to the Greek letter "lambda", connects the **occipital bone** to the **parietal bones**.

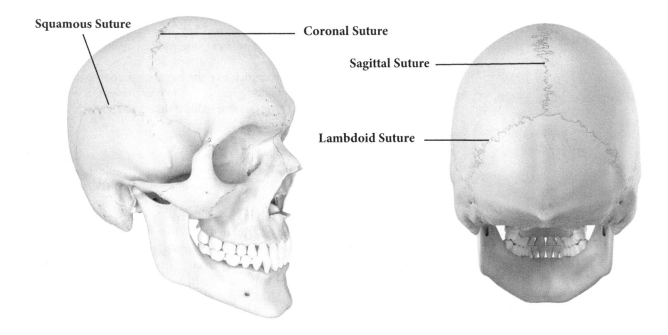

Muscles are held to bones via **tendons**. Tendons are similar to ligaments, but have a much more rich blood supply, and are able to stretch further before injury occurs.

Inside the joint itself, a membrane is present, known as the **synovial membrane**. The synovial membrane produces a fluid that helps to **lubricate the joint**, known as the **synovial fluid**. Lubrication of the joint is key in keeping the joint functioning optimally. Surrounding the entire joint is thick, dense connective tissue known as the **joint capsule**. The joint capsule keeps everything inside the joint, such as the synovial fluid, and provides even more strength and support for the joint.

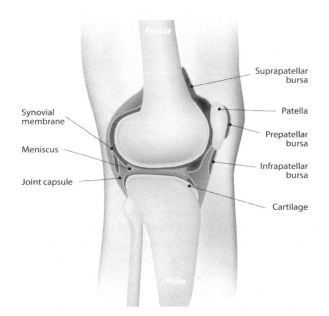

There are 360 joints in an average adult's body!

Types of Synovial Joints

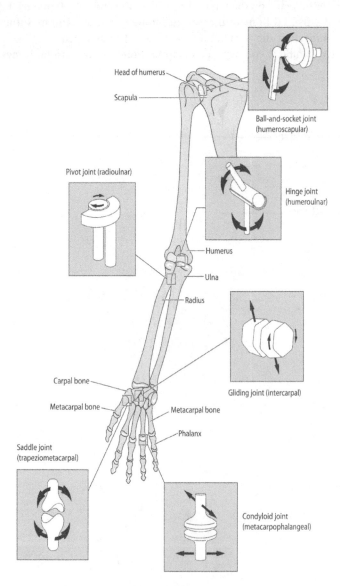

Head of humerus
Scapula
Ball-and-socket joint (humeroscapular)

Pivot joint (radioulnar)

Hinge joint (humeroulnar)

Humerus
Ulna
Radius

Gliding joint (intercarpal)

Carpal bone
Metacarpal bone
Metacarpal bone
Phalanx

Saddle joint (trapeziometacarpal)

Condyloid joint (metacarpophalangeal)

There are six different types of synovial joints.

Ball-and-Socket joints feature one bone with a **ball** at the epiphysis, and another bone with a **socket**. The ball fits in the socket, creating a ball-and-socket joint. Examples include the shoulder and hip joints. Ball-and-socket joints have the most amount of movement, able to move the joint in really any direction.

Hinge joints act much like the hinge on a door, only opening and closing. Hinge joints only allow movement in **one plane**, allowing only **flexion and extension**. Examples include the elbow and knee joints.

Pivot joints allow only one type of movement: **rotation**. All they do is allow structures to turn. An example is the atlantoaxial joint, which lets us shake our head "no". This is rotation.

Plane/gliding joints are produced when the articulating bones have **flat surfaces**, and there is a **disc of cartilage** between the bones. This allows the joint to move, or glide, in any direction, although with slight movement. Examples include the joints between the carpals and tarsals.

Saddle joints are only located in one part of the body: the **carpometacarpal joint of the thumb**. Saddle joints are named after the appearance of the articulating bones. The articulating surfaces are both shaped like saddles. The two bones that create the saddle joint are the **first metacarpal and the trapezium**.

Ellipsoid/condyloid joints are extremely similar to ball-and-socket joints. On one bone, there is a **condyle**, which resembles a ball, but isn't as pronounced. This condyle fits into an **elliptical cavity** on another bone, which is similar to a socket, but not as deep. This allows movements such as flexion, extension, adduction, abduction, and circumduction. An example is the radiocarpal joint.

Anatomical Laws

Davis's Law is an anatomical law described by Henry Davis, examining the **remodeling of soft tissue** due to outside factors. The law states that tissues such as muscle will **repair damage** done to the tissue to **strengthen the tissue** and prevent injury in the future. For example, if a person were to exercise and be sore the next day, the muscle will repair itself in a manner to increase muscle density and improve strength, leading to the person being stronger and not injuring the muscle the next time they exercise.

Hilton's Law is an anatomical law described by John Hilton, examining innervations of muscles and skin. The law states that **a nerve that innervates a muscle that crosses a joint** and acts on the joint **will also innervate the skin and joint atop the muscle**. An example, the tibial nerve innervates the gastrocnemius. The gastrocnemius crosses the popliteal region at the posterior knee, so the tibial nerve will also innervate the joint and skin at the back of the knee.

Wolff's Law is an anatomical law described by Julius Wolff, examining the **remodeling of bone tissue** due to outside factors. The law states that bone will **remodel itself to be more dense**, adding strength to the bone, **when the bone is placed under pressure**. For example, lifting a heavy object can place many pounds of pressure on the bones. The bones respond by remodeling to be able to support the increased demand on the bone, adding density and strength to the bone itself. If the bone is not placed under stress for a period of time, the bone will become less dense and weaken, which may lead to increased likelihood of fracture or the development of conditions such as osteoporosis. Weight bearing exercise such as weight lifting is vital in maintaining bone strength.

Easy to Remember: To remember Wolff's Law, just picture a wolf chewing on a bone that's so strong, it won't break!

Skeleton Divisions

There are two divisions of the skeleton: the Axial Skeleton and the Appendicular Skeleton.

The **Axial Skeleton** contains all of the bones that do not correspond to any appendages: the **skull**, **vertebral column**, and **thoracic cage**. These bones make up the trunk.

The **Appendicular Skeleton** contains all of the bones that correspond to the appendages: the **humerus**, **radius**, **ulna**, **carpals**, **metacarpals**, **phalanges**, **femur**, **tibia**, **fibula**, **tarsals**, **metatarsals**, **phalanges**, the **pectoral girdle**(clavicles and scapulae) and **pelvic girdle**(ilium, ischium, pubis, and sacrum).

Bones of the Axial Skeleton

Skull

The skull's primary function is to **protect the brain**. The bones that create the skull are:

Parietal
Frontal
Temporal
Occipital
Zygomatic
Maxilla
Mandible
Vomer
Ethmoid
Lacrimal
Sphenoid
Nasal

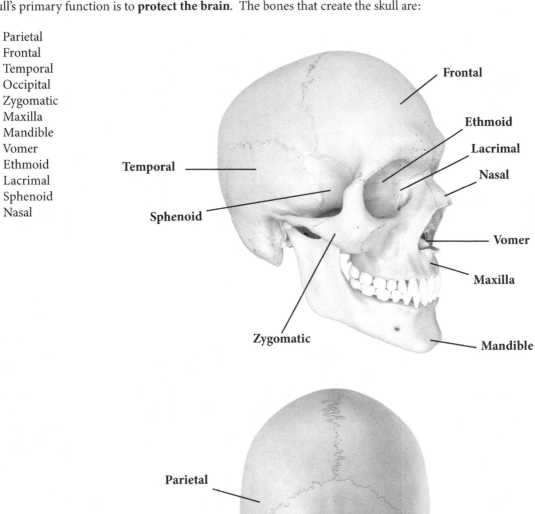

Vertebral Column

The vertebral column consists of **26 individual bones**. Its primary function is to **protect the spinal cord**, which runs through it. There are five regions of the vertebral column. They are:

Cervical(7 vertebrae)
Thoracic(12 vertebrae)
Lumbar(5 vertebrae)
Sacral(1 vertebrae*)
Coccygeal(1 vertebrae*)

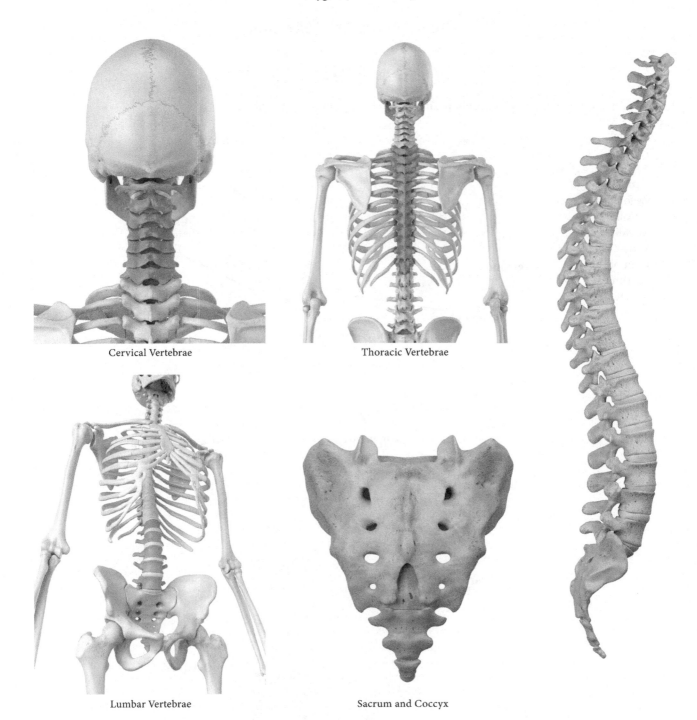

Cervical Vertebrae

Thoracic Vertebrae

Lumbar Vertebrae

Sacrum and Coccyx

 Easy to Remember: To remember how many vertebrae are in the cervical, thoracic, and lumbar regions, just think of breakfast, lunch, and dinner! Breakfast at 7(cervical), lunch at 12(thoracic), dinner at 5(lumbar)!

* The sacrum starts as five bones that fuse together to create one bone, and the coccyx starts as 3-5 bones that fuse together to create one bone.

Chest

The chest consists of the rib cage, and it contains **12 pairs** of bones. The primary function of the rib cage is to **protect vital organs** inside the thorax, and assist in breathing by giving the diaphragm a place to attach. The rib cage consists of:

True ribs(superior seven ribs, connect directly to the sternum via costal cartilage)
False ribs(inferior five pairs, do not directly connect to the sternum)
Floating ribs(ribs 11 and 12, protect the kidneys)

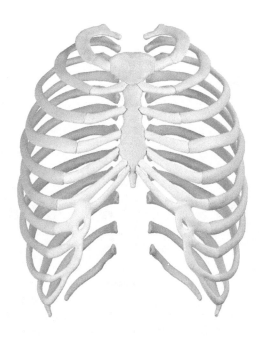

Bones of the Appendicular Skeleton

Pectoral Girdle

The pectoral girdle is responsible for holding the upper limbs to the body. The pectoral girdle consists of four bones:

Scapulae(2 bones)
Clavicles(2 bones)

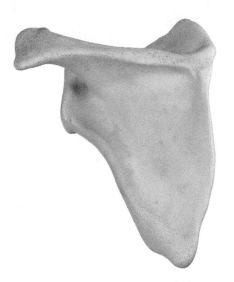 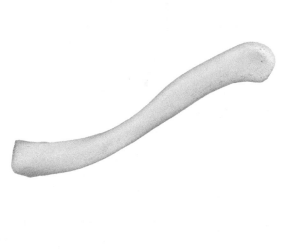

Pelvic Girdle

The pelvic girdle is primarily responsible for holding the lower limbs to the body. The pelvic girdle contains:

Ilium (2 bones)
Ischium (2 bones)
Pubis (2 bones)
Sacrum (1 bone)

The iliofemoral ligament, which holds the head of the femur to the acetabulum, is the strongest ligament in the body!

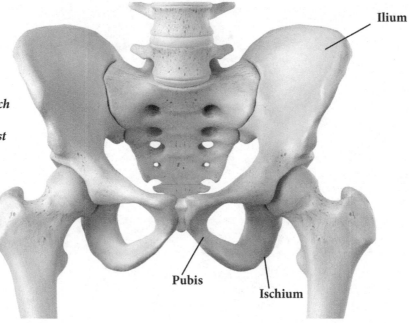

Ilium

Pubis

Ischium

Arm

The arm contains one bone:

Humerus

Forearm

The forearm contains two bones:

Radius   **Ulna**

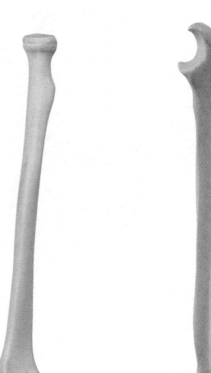

Wrist

The wrist is located distally to the forearm, and it contains the **carpal bones**. The carpal bones are divided into two separate lines, each containing four bones. The order begins on the lateral side and moves medially, then after the proximal line is finished, the order resumes on the lateral side of the distal line. The proximal line is listed first, then the distal line:

Proximal Line:
Scaphoid
Lunate
Triquetrum
Pisiform

Distal Line:
Trapezium
Trapezoid
Capitate
Hamate

The carpometacarpal joint of the thumb, made by the trapezium and first metacarpal, is the only place in the body you find a saddle joint!

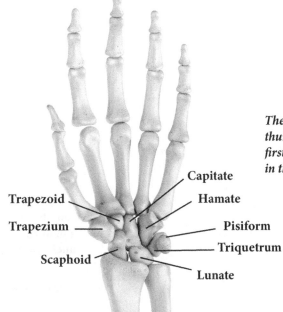

 Easy to Remember: To remember the order of the carpals, think of this old saying: Some Lovers Try Positions That They Can't Handle(Scaphoid, Lunate, Triquetrum, Pisiform, Trapezium, Trapezoid, Capitate, Hamate)!

Hand

There are **19 bones** in each hand:

Metacarpals: 5 bones
Phalanges: 14 bones

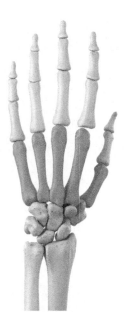

Metacarpals

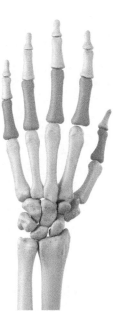

Proximal Phalanges

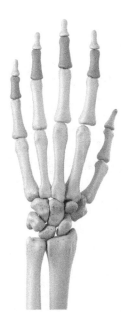

Intermediate Phalanges

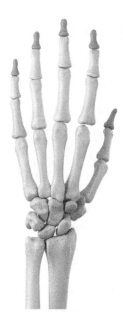

Distal Phalanges

Thigh

The thigh contains one bone:

Femur

Leg

The leg contains two bones:

Fibula   **Tibia**

Ankle

The ankle is located distally to the leg, and contains the bones of the **tarsals**:

Calcaneus   Cuneiform I
Cuboid   Cuneiform II
Talus   Cuneiform III
Navicular

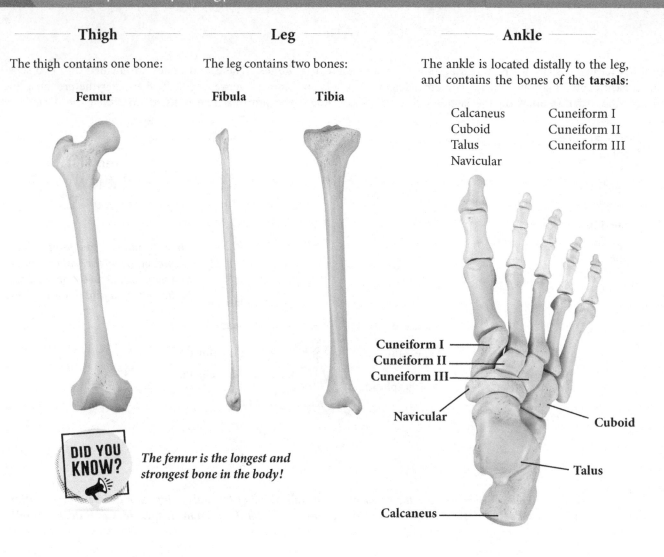

Cuneiform I
Cuneiform II
Cuneiform III

Navicular

Cuboid

Talus

Calcaneus

DID YOU KNOW? *The femur is the longest and strongest bone in the body!*

Foot

There are **19 bones** in each foot:

Metatarsals: 5 bones
Phalanges: 14 bones

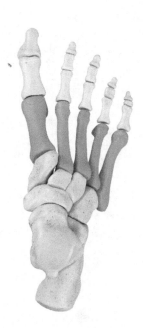

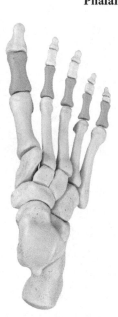

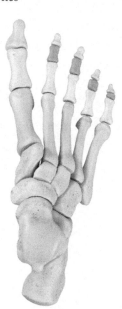

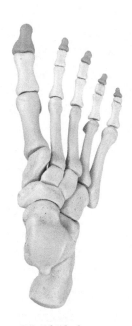

Metatarsals   **Proximal Phalanges**   **Intermediate Phalanges**   **Distal Phalanges**

Urinary System

The Urinary System is primarily responsible for **elimination of waste** from the body. It also assists in regulating the **pH level** of the body, and may also assist in reabsorption of substances back into the body. The four main structures of the Urinary System are(in descending order) the **kidneys, ureters, urinary bladder, and urethra**.

pH Scale

A **pH scale** is used to determine the **acidity or alkalinity** of a substance. If a substance reads between **7-14** on a pH scale, it is base, or **alkaline**. The higher the number, the more alkaline a substance is. An example, bleach is highly basic, and comes in at 12.6. Blood is slightly basic, and comes in at 7.4. On the other hand, if a substance comes in between **0-7** on a pH scale, it is **acidic**. The lower the number, the more acidic a substance is. An example, hydrochloric acid(the kind of acid in the stomach that helps digest food) comes in at 2.0, so it is highly acidic. Black coffee registers at about 5.0, so it is slightly acidic. The kidneys help regulate substances in the body that make the body's fluids either too acidic or too basic by filtration.

The pH Scale

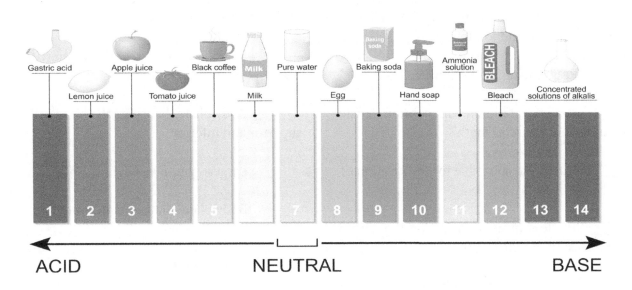

Flow of Urine

Blood enters the kidneys through the renal arteries. Inside the kidneys, blood is **filtered through the nephrons**, which extract waste products such as urea out of the blood. Inside each kidney, there are over one million nephrons. The waste products filtered out of the blood by the nephrons become **urine**. The nephrons also allow nutrients and water to be reabsorbed back into the blood stream.

Once urine has been created, it is sent from the kidneys to the urinary bladder through two small tubes known as ureters. The ureters only function as a **passageway for urine**.

Urine **collects in the urinary bladder**, until it is ready to be eliminated from the body. The urinary bladder expands as more urine is added to it. The urinary bladder can typically hold between 300-500 ml of fluid. Once urine is released from the urinary bladder, it passes through the urethra.

The urethra, much like the ureters, is a small tube that has one function: **transporting urine** from the urinary bladder **out of the body**.

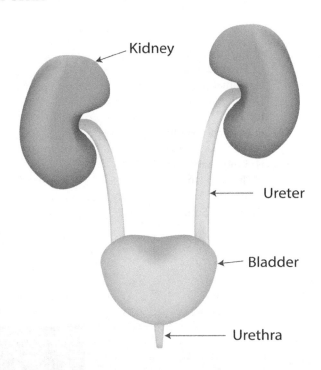

Anatomy and Physiology Matching

_____: Constant internal environment

_____: Suture connecting the two parietal bones

_____: Organ that creates bile and detoxifies blood

_____: Tissue responsible for separating structures

_____: Anatomical law stating bone density and strength will increase when under load

_____: Anatomical law stating a nerve that innervates a muscle that crosses a joint will also innervate the skin and joint itself

_____: "Rest-and-digest" response

_____: Muscle contraction with constant tension and decreasing muscle length

_____: Structure responsible for the creation of T-cells

_____: Muscle contraction with constant tension and increasing muscle length

_____: Region of vertebral column with five bones

_____: Suture connecting the occipital bone and parietal bones

_____: Sensory receptor that detects pain

_____: Cell responsible for transporting oxygen and carbon dioxide

_____: Tissue responsible for protection, secretion, and absorption

_____: "Fight-or-flight" response

_____: Glands responsible for production of estrogen and progesterone

_____: Region of the vertebral column with seven bones

_____: Body plane that splits the body into superior and inferior

_____: Largest lymph vessel in the body

_____: Body plane that splits the body into anterior and posterior

_____: Organ that filters blood and creates urine

A: Erythrocytes
B: Thymus
C: Homeostasis
D: Hilton's Law
E: Liver
F: Cervical Vertebrae
G: Transverse Plane
H: Epithelial Tissue
I: Thoracic Duct
J: Ovaries
K: Sagittal Suture

L: Concentric Contraction
M: Parasympathetic Response
N: Lambdoid Suture
O: Nociceptor
P: Lumbar Vertebrae
Q: Eccentric Contraction
R: Frontal Plane
S: Sympathetic Response
T: Connective Tissue
U: Wolff's Law
V: Kidneys

Answer Key on Page 308

Anatomy and Physiology Crossword

Across

3. Organ responsible for filtering old red blood cells from the blood stream
5. Existence and maintenance of a constant internal environment
6. Tissue responsible for protection, secretion, and absorption
8. Type of muscle responsible for performing peristalsis
9. Blood vessel responsible for bringing blood towards the heart
10. Gland responsible for producing and secreting melatonin, regulating the body's wake/sleep cycle
12. The largest lymph vessel in the body
15. Body cavity created by the cranium and vertebral column responsible for protecting the brain and spinal cord
17. Tissue covering the entrance to the larynx that functions to prevent choking
18. Substance created by the liver that helps emulsify fats
19. Organelles responsible for breaking down protein and waste products inside the cell

Down

1. Region of the vertebral column that contains twelve bones
2. Strongest ligament in the body
4. Type of joint located at the shoulder and hip
7. Organ located in the right hypochondriac region of the abdomen
10. Organ responsible for the production of insulin and glucagon
11. Bone that articulates with the metacarpal of the thumb to create the saddle joint
13. First segment of the small intestine
14. Body plane that splits the body into left and right sides
16. Nerve that controls and regulates the parasympathetic response

Answer Key on Page 310

Anatomy and Physiology Practice Test

1. Increased epinephrine, blood sugar, and heart rate are all key markers of
A. Parasympathetic response
B. Homeostatic mechanisms
C. Sympathetic response
D. Skeletal muscle heat production

2. The largest veins in the body, responsible for returning deoxygenated blood to the heart
A. Aorta
B. Pulmonary arteries
C. Pulmonary veins
D. Vena cavae

3. Which of the following describes the process of mitosis
A. The division of one mother cell into two daughter cells
B. The destruction of a pathogen or foreign agent performed by leukocytes
C. Production of adenosine triphosphate to provide energy to the body
D. Introduction of electrolytes into muscle tissue to produce contraction

4. Upon reaching tissue, oxygen attached to hemoglobin is exchanged with which other substance, a waste product
A. Ammonia
B. Carbon monoxide
C. Urea
D. Carbon dioxide

5. The spleen is located in which abdominal region
A. Left hypochondriac
B. Right lumbar
C. Left iliac
D. Epigastric

6. Organ that stores bile and empties bile into the duodenum
A. Gallbladder
B. Pancreas
C. Liver
D. Stomach

7. The inferior five pairs of ribs are also called
A. True ribs
B. False ribs
C. Inferior ribs
D. Superior ribs

8. Receptor that detects potential over-stretching of a muscle by sending an impulse to the spinal cord, which responds by returning a motor impulse to the muscle to force an involuntary increase in tension in the muscle to prevent injury
A. Pacinian corpuscle
B. Golgi tendon organ
C. Nociceptor
D. Muscle spindle

9. Site of communication between nerve cells via neurotransmitters
A. Axon
B. Synapse
C. Dendrite
D. Nucleus

10. The saddle joint is created by which two bones
A. Scaphoid and radius
B. Lunate and ulna
C. Trapezium and metacarpal of the thumb
D. Medial cuneiform and metatarsal of the great toe

11. To observe all four chambers of the heart simultaneously during an MRI, which body plane would the image need to be positioned in
A. Frontal
B. Midsagittal
C. Sagittal
D. Transverse

12. Afferent impulses are carried along which type of axon
A. Motor
B. Efferent
C. Sensory
D. Ocular

13. The liver is located in which abdominal quadrant
A. Upper left
B. Upper right
C. Lower right
D. Lower left

14. Stimulation of the parasympathetic nervous response has what action on the digestive tract
A. Decreases absorption
B. Shuts down peristalsis
C. Increases lymph circulation
D. Increases peristalsis

15. Saliva has a pH of around 6. What would saliva be considered as a result
A. Highly acidic
B. Slightly alkaline
C. Slightly acidic
D. Highly alkaline

16. The hip joint is considered which type of synovial joint
A. Ellipsoid
B. Hinge
C. Ball-and-socket
D. Pivot

17. The circadian rhythm is regulated by
A. Melatonin
B. Prolactin
C. Estrogen
D. Testosterone

18. The dorsal body cavity
A. Surrounds the heart and lungs
B. Houses internal reproductive organs
C. Protects the digestive organs in the abdomen
D. Protects the brain and spinal cord

19. Which of the following is the order of the structures from superficial to deep
A. Bone > Muscle > Skin > Periosteum
B. Muscle > Periosteum > Bone > Skin
C. Skin > Muscle > Periosteum > Bone
D. Periosteum > Skin > Bone > Muscle

20. Adipose is considered which type of connective tissue
A. Cartilage
B. Loose connective tissue
C. Dense connective tissue
D. Bone

21. Substance released by sarcoplasmic reticulum upon contact with sodium ions, which binds to tropomyosin and reveals attachment sites on actin for myosin, allowing a muscle to contract
A. Calcium
B. Magnesium
C. Potassium
D. Vitamin A

22. The lumbar region contains how many vertebrae
A. Seven
B. Twelve
C. One
D. Five

23. Contraction of cardiac muscle in the right ventricle sends blood
A. To the aorta
B. To the body
C. To the lungs
D. To the right atrium

24. Which of the following is the strongest ligament in the body
A. Iliofemoral ligament
B. Glenohumeral ligament
C. Atlantoaxial ligament
D. Sacroiliac ligament

25. Anatomical law stating a nerve that innervates a muscle will also innervate tissues around the muscle as well
A. Harrah's Law
B. Hilton's Law
C. Davis's Law
D. Wolff's Law

Answer Key on Page 322

Greatness is setting ambitious goals that your former self would have thought impossible, and trying to get a little better every day.

- Tim Ferriss

Pathology

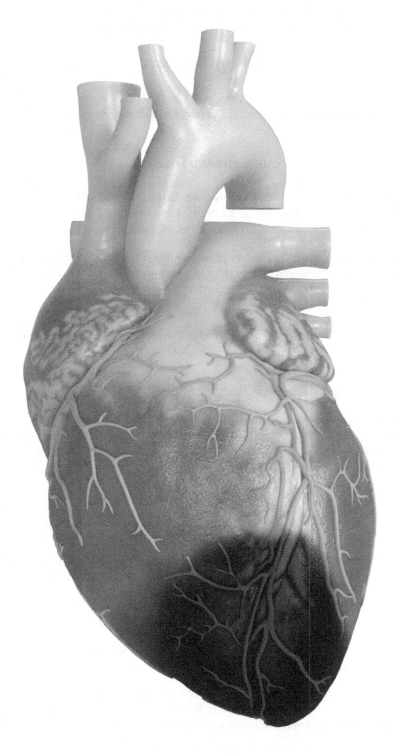

Disease

A disease is a condition affecting certain functions or structures in the human body, which can usually be associated with **signs or symptoms**. Diseases most commonly affect a specific location in the body, and aren't the result of physical trauma. Diseases range in severity from mild to severe, and in length from acute to chronic. These factors are determined by the type of disease, and the ability to treat the disease.

An **acute** disease or disorder has a **sudden onset**, which lasts for a **short period of time**. Acute conditions can be seen often with infections or trauma, and as the body's immune system fights off the infection, the acute condition dissipates. However, if the condition is severe enough, it may result in death. It is in this way that acute conditions are typically more dangerous in the short term than chronic conditions.

Chronic diseases or disorders are present for **long periods**, usually over three months. Examples of chronic diseases include asthma and hepatitis C. Chronic diseases may have periods of exacerbation and remission. The period where the disease is not actively showing signs or symptoms is the remission period, while the period where the disease is affecting a person's health is the exacerbation period. Other forms of chronic diseases, such as cancer or diabetes, are always present, and can make a person continuously ill.

Acquired Diseases

An acquired disease is a disease a person has obtained at some point **after birth.** Commonly thought of as some sort of infection, it actually just means the disease has appeared after birth. If a person has a disease that was not congenital, then it is referred to as an acquired disease.

Autoimmune Diseases

Autoimmune diseases are the result of the body's **immune system attacking cells and structures in the body that it cannot differentiate** from pathogens that have entered the body. Autoimmune diseases can attack different parts of the body with differing levels of severity.

In a person with an autoimmune disease, the body releases proteins known as **autoantibodies**. Autoantibodies are the cells that cannot tell the difference between normal tissue and foreign substances. Autoantibodies may attack only one specific structure, such as Graves' disease where the thyroid is the only structure attacked, or they may attack structures throughout the entire body, such as in lupus.

Autoimmune diseases may be hereditary, such as multiple sclerosis. If one person in a family has an autoimmune disorder, it may increase the likelihood of another family member having it as well.

Congenital Diseases

A congenital disease is a disease that is **present at birth**. These diseases may be inherited, or may be the result of certain environmental factors. Common examples of congenital diseases include heart defects, cleft lip, Down syndrome, HIV infection, and spina bifida. Causes for these diseases vary, but many are likely due to lack of maternal nutrition intake, alcohol use, drug use, and the fetus not receiving adequate nutrients.

Deficiency Diseases

Deficiency diseases are the result of the body **not receiving adequate nutrients**, vitamins, and/or minerals in the diet. Examples of nutrients include iron, vitamin C, zinc, calcium, and iodine. When a person does not receive these nutrients in adequate amounts, it can cause organs and structures in the body to function improperly, or not at all. For example, if a person lacks sufficient vitamin C in the diet, they may develop scurvy. If a person does not consume enough calcium, they may develop osteoporosis. Other examples of diseases caused by a nutrient deficiency include anemia, goiter, and rickets.

Hereditary Diseases

A hereditary disease, also known as a genetic disease, is the result of some sort of **abnormality in a person's genome**. These abnormalities vary in severity, and in turn, may cause differing levels of difficulty in normal function.

Genetic disorders are commonly passed down from the parents, but some genetic disorders may be the result of mutations in the genes due to environmental factors. Other times, the mutation in the gene may be completely random. There are differing types of gene inheritance that contribute to the development of hereditary diseases.

Single gene inheritances are the result of mutations occurring in **one single gene**. This leaves the majority of the body operating normally, but can change one specific aspect of the body. An example is cystic fibrosis, where the mutated gene causes the respiratory passages to produce an extremely excessive amount of mucous.

Multifactoral gene inheritances are the result of a **mutation in multiple genes,** in association with environmental factors. The gene may be present that can cause the disease, but it may lie dormant unless it is activated by environmental factors. Examples include cancers, hypertension, and cardiovascular disease. If the person avoids the environmental factors, they see less of a chance of developing the disease associated with the mutated gene.

Abnormal chromosomes are often caused by problems during cell division, known as **nondisjunction**, which can damage the chromosomes in the cell's DNA. An example of an abnormal chromosome disease is Down syndrome. This is caused by having an extra copy of chromosome 21. This gives the person 47 total chromosomes, instead of the standard 46.

Idiopathic Diseases

An idiopathic disease is a disease that has an **unknown origin or cause**. These diseases show no obvious sign of origin, and spontaneously appear. There may be theories about why a disease occurs, but the exact reason is unknown. Examples of idiopathic diseases include ankylosing spondylitis, chronic fatigue syndrome, and fibromyalgia.

Infectious Diseases

An infection is an **invasion of a microorganism** inside the body in some way, which can range from localized and less serious, to systemic and life-threatening. These microorganisms are usually not inside the body, and therefore, the body does not have a knowledge of how to exactly combat the infection when first exposed. When there is an infection, the body develops antibodies, and these are used to destroy the invading microorganism.

There are four primary types of infections: bacterial, viral, parasitic, and fungal.

Bacterial Infections

Bacteria are **single-celled organisms** that can only be seen under a microscope. They have a membrane surrounding the cell, and are able to freely reproduce via cell mitosis.

Bacterial infections are caused by an invasion of certain types of bacteria, such as H. pylori, staphylococcus, streptococcus, and salmonella. Bacteria come different shapes and sizes, some looking like rods(bacillus), and others looking like balls(borrelia) or spirals(spirilla). Bacterial infections make a person sick by **releasing toxic substances in their waste**. An overabundance of these toxins cause a person to become ill, depending on the severity. Bacteria are known to reproduce quickly, and treatment should be sought for serious bacterial infections such as pneumonia and strep throat. Treatment for bacterial infections involves taking a course of antibiotics, such as penicillin, which destroy the bacteria. Any course of antibiotics should be completed fully, as ceasing taking the prescribed dosage could result in any remaining bacteria becoming resistant to the antibiotics. It's in these cases where infections such as MRSA(methicillin-resistant staphylococcus aureus) may appear and become extremely difficult to treat, which may be life-threatening.

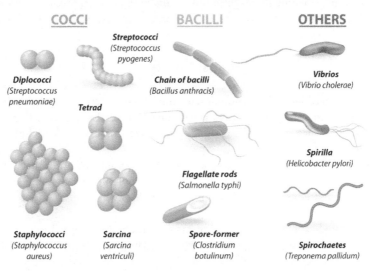

Viral Infections

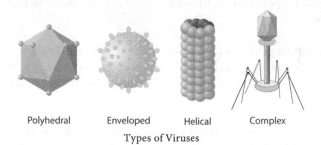

Polyhedral Enveloped Helical Complex

Types of Viruses

Viral infections are caused by viruses, structures smaller than bacteria, that contain RNA or DNA in their core. They attach to healthy cells and **insert code into the cell** that changes the behavior in the cell and **causes the infected cell to create more virus particles**. These particles come together in the cell, creating new viruses. When too many of these viruses have formed, they break through the host cell and enter the body, infecting more healthy cells. This process is known as the **lytic cycle**.

When the body detects a viral infection, it releases chemicals known as **pyrogens** into the body, which elevate body temperature. This increased body temperature, known as a fever, does not give the viruses an environment to thrive in, and ultimately the viruses die or fail to reproduce due to the extreme temperature change. Treatments for viral infections typically are used to treat the symptoms, as there is no way to destroy the virus itself. Vaccines can be used to introduce dead or weakened viruses into the body, which allow the body's immune system to develop antibodies for them, preventing future infections. Antiviral medications can be used to prevent a virus from reproducing, but cannot kill the virus.

Some viruses never leave a person's body and become dormant, not always causing problems. Others never leave the body and actively affect the body, such as HIV. Most of the time, in instances such as influenza, the body's immune system naturally fights off the virus over the course of a week or two.

Parasitic Infections

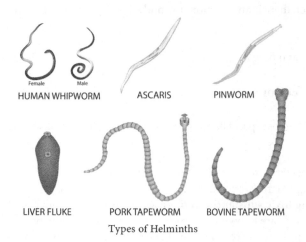

HUMAN WHIPWORM ASCARIS PINWORM

LIVER FLUKE PORK TAPEWORM BOVINE TAPEWORM

Types of Helminths

Parasitic infections are caused by small organisms that **use a host** in order to survive. These parasites may affect their host in some way, or they may not, depending on the type of parasite. The three types of parasites are protozoa, helminths, and ectoparasites.

Protozoa are single-celled organisms, and they live inside the host's body, multiplying beyond safe levels. A protozoa infection is considered serious, most commonly the result of drinking water that may contain the parasite.

Helminths are also known as **worms**, such as tapeworms, flukes, and roundworms. Worms most commonly enter the host's body through consuming a food or drink that contains the worm or worm larvae.

Ectoparasites are parasites that attach to the surface of the host, often feeding off the blood of the host to survive. Examples include mosquitoes, leeches, and ticks.

Some parasitic infections do not require treatment. If symptoms or infection appears, treatment should be sought. Common parasitic infection treatments include anti-parasitic medications used to destroy any parasites, and removal of the parasite if medication does not work.

Fungal Infections

Fungal infections are caused by a fungus **coming into contact with the skin** or entering into the body via means such as **inhalation**. Certain fungi thrive in specific environments that are **dark, warm, and humid**. Examples of these include athlete's foot and jock itch. Other fungi may attach to dead tissues, such as the nails or skin. An example of these include ringworm and onychomycosis.

Common forms of fungi that result in infection include candidiasis, aspergillosis, sporothrix, talaromyces, and histoplasma. These fungi can be found in various parts of the world, and can affect people differently depending on the strength of their immune system. Some fungi thrive in extremely moist environments, while other fungi may not need as much moisture to grow.

Fungal infections are treated with medications known as antifungals, which are designed to destroy fungus. These can be used directly on the skin as ointments or shampoos, orally in gel or liquid form, or inserted into a part of the body such as the vagina in cases such as yeast infections. Serious fungal infections may need to be treated with antifungals injected into the body.

Psychological Diseases

Psychological diseases, often referred to as **mental disorders**, are often associated with problems a person may experience with their mood or thoughts. Causes are hard to pin-point, and may vary from person to person. These mental disorders can have an extremely adverse affect on the overall well-being of the person. Treatment via medications and psychotherapy may be available.

Mental disorders commonly seen in children include autism, ADHD(Attention Deficit/Hyperactivity Disorder), attachment disorder, and stuttering. Disorders commonly seen in adults may include addiction, depression, bipolar disorder, eating disorders, PTSD, and panic disorder.

Personality disorders are disorders that may influence how a person acts or responds to certain situations. Examples of personality disorders include Antisocial Personality Disorder, Dissociative Identity Disorder, and Obsessive-Compulsive Personality Disorder.

Immunity

Immunity refers to the ability of the body to **protect itself from disease and pathogens**. Immunity is the responsibility of the **immune system**, which destroys foreign objects that enter the body that may produce infection or disease. The process through which these substances are destroyed is known as the **immune response**.

The **humoral immune system** is the part of the immune system that takes place in the body's **fluids**, known as the **humors**. This results in the production of **antibodies** when a foreign substance is observed in the body. Antibodies react by neutralizing the pathogen, or allowing the pathogen to be destroyed easier by other cells.

The **cell-mediated immune system** involves **T-lymphocytes**, also known as **T-cells**. These cells vary in type, depending on the kind of pathogen involved. The T-lymphocytes are responsible for destroying the pathogen, and do not utilize antibodies. Types of T-cells include effector, helper, cytotoxic, natural killer, memory, and regulatory, each responsible for a different aspect of immune support.

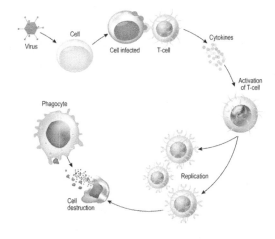

When a pathogen is detected in the body, a **B-cell** or **T-cell** will bind to the pathogen, and release **cytokines**. Cytokines are proteins responsible for allowing communication between cells. Cytokines will send a message to the immune system, which will then bring more B-cells or T-cells into the area to combat the pathogen.

Phagocytes

Phagocytes, which are certain types of **white blood cells**, are responsible for "**eating**" pathogens or debris in a process known as **phagocytosis**. Debris can include foreign objects or substances that have entered the body, or dead or dying cells that need to be removed from the body. An example is the fading of tattoos. Over time, tattoo ink is broken down by the body's phagocytes, because the body senses it is a foreign substance that should not be present. When enough ink is broken down by phagocytes, the tattoo fades. Laser tattoo removal works by breaking the ink into smaller pieces, which the phagocytes can then absorb and eliminate from the body easier.

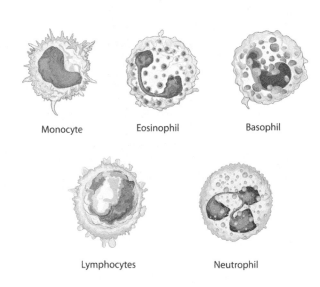

Monocyte   Eosinophil   Basophil

Lymphocytes   Neutrophil

Examples of phagocytes include neutrophils, monocytes, macrophages, and dendritic cells. **Neutrophils** are typically the first phagocyte into the area. Neutrophils release enzymes that **destroy bacteria**, and perform phagocytosis. **Monocytes** move from the blood into the area, where they are then known as **macrophages**. Much like neutrophils, they perform phagocytosis to eliminate the debris or infection. **Dendritic cells** are located on **surfaces** of the body such as the skin and gastrointestinal tract. Dendritic cells act by performing phagocytosis on a pathogen to retrieve its specific **antigen**. Once this information has been obtained, it is **passed on to T-cells** via cytokines produced by the dendritic cells.

Phagocytosis

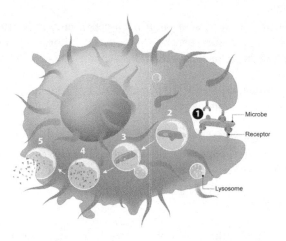

Phagocytosis is the process of a cell "**eating**" an object or substance, a process known as **endocytosis**. The phagocyte envelops the debris or pathogen in a vesicle known as a **phagosome**. A phagosome is produced when the cell wraps the cell membrane around the structure and the cell membrane fuses together. The phagosome is introduced into the cell, holding the substance, where the substance is broken down by granules that produce toxic or acidic matter to dissolve the substances. Once the substance has been destroyed, the waste is removed from the cell in a process that is essentially the opposite of bringing the substance into the cell. The phagosome fuses back with the cell membrane, and the waste product is expelled into the extracellular fluid. This process is known as **exocytosis**.

| 1. Binding and absorption | 2. Phagosome formation | 3. Phagosome and lysosome to form a phagolysosome | 4. Digestion | 5. Release of microbial products |

Antibodies

Antibodies mark antigens for elimination

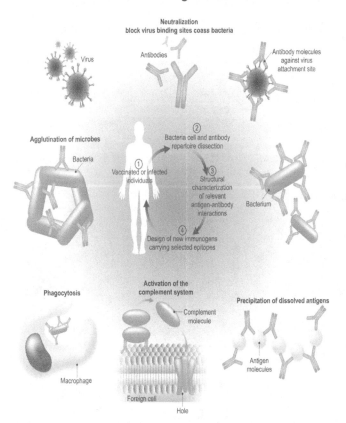

An **antibody**, also known as **immunoglobulin**, is a protein produced by **plasma cells** to neutralize pathogens in the body such as viruses and certain bacteria. Antibodies are **Y shaped**. The tips of the antibodies that produce the Y shape contain what's known as a **paratope**, which binds together with the **epitope**, the substance found in antigens that the body's immune system recognizes. **Antigens** are molecules the pathogen contains that the antibodies recognize and attach to, similar to a key fitting into a lock.

Antibodies are **produced and secreted by B-cells**, in two different forms. The first form is **soluble** and moves freely throughout the body. These types of B-cells are known as **plasma cells**. The second is a **membrane-bound form**, and it attaches to the surface of B-cells. These types are known as **B-cell receptors**. B-cell receptors bind to the surface of B-cells and are able to quickly identify pathogens seen before in the body. This allows the B-cells to produce sufficient antibodies to attack the pathogen with a faster response time.

Antibodies vary depending on the type of pathogen detected. For each different pathogen, a different type of antibody is produced. The amount of pathogens exposed to the body determines the amount of different antibodies being produced. If a person has been exposed to the pathogen before, **memory cells** may be produced, which **store information** on how the immune system is to destroy the pathogen. It is when this happens that a person is considered **immune** to a certain disease.

Tissue Repair

When a part of the body is injured or damaged, the damaged tissue must go through repair to allow proper functioning of the structure once again. The amount of repair correlates to the amount of tissue damage that has occurred. Some tissue may not be able to be repaired effectively, and may require scar tissue to complete the repair.

Inflammation

Upon damage to tissue, the tissue will experience **inflammation**. Inflammation starts with **dilation of capillaries** in the area of the trauma. Damaged tissues **release histamines** into the area, which stimulates the capillaries to dilate. When the capillaries dilate, the walls of the capillaries become thinner and **more permeable**. This allows **leukocytes and plasma** from the blood to enter the extracellular fluid in the damaged area, which is what produces inflammation. Because there is an increase in blood in the area, the inflamed area will feel **warmer** to the touch, and have a **reddish appearance**. The leukocytes release chemicals into the area, such as bradykinin, which causes **pain** by stimulating the nerve endings in the area. The four markers of inflammation are **pain**, **swelling**, **redness**, and **heat**.

As more leukocytes enter the area, they destroy any tissue that is damaged and any foreign objects or organisms that are present. Once the area is clear of damaged tissue and other organisms, the inflammation resolves. The capillary walls constrict, and the excess fluid in the area is removed through **lymphatic ducts**. As the blood and fluid is removed from the area, the swelling, redness, and heat subside.

Healing

Most tissue in the body can regenerate and create more tissue to replace any damaged tissue. Some tissue, such as nerve tissue and brain tissue, usually cannot. If a large portion of the body has experienced damage, the tissue may need to be removed to prevent the area from becoming gangrenous.

If a person has suffered a wound, and the **damaged areas are close together**, the body will heal itself through a process known as **primary intention**. Examples of wounds that are healed via primary intention are small cuts, scratches, and surgical incisions. These wounds allow for **blood clots** to form that hold the tissues together and stop bleeding. Beneath the clot, which is known as a **scab**, new tissue is formed, and the two sides of the wound join together. Once the new tissue is formed, the scab sloughs off, revealing the new tissue.

If a person suffers a wound that requires healing via **secondary intention**, the edges of the wound **cannot be approximated**. The edges are uneven, do not properly align, and may be far apart. This type of healing requires **granulated tissue** to form at the base and sides of the wound. As the healing progresses, the granulated tissue fills in the area missing tissue. This type of healing often takes far longer than primary intention healing, and will leave the area with scar tissue to help fill the damaged area. An example of secondary intention healing is seen with decubitus ulcers.

When a person experiences a wound that requires medical intervention, **delayed primary closure** may be utilized. With delayed primary closure, the **wound is left open** to ensure it is properly cleaned and free of bacteria or other pathogens before being closed. This is also known as **tertiary intention healing**. Once it is determined that there is no infection present, the wound is then surgically closed. An example of wounds that often require tertiary intention healing is animal bites.

Bone Healing

Damage to bones, such as fractures, requires the use of **osteoclasts and osteoblasts** to help repair the structure. These cells continuously maintain the bone matrix, but if the bone is injured, they are the primary cells responsible for healing. After a bone is fractured, **osteoclasts** will begin **breaking down** the damaged bone tissue. This leaves the bone with a clean surface in which to build new bone tissue. It is similar to demolishing a building and erecting another building in its place. The rubble from the demolished building needs to be removed before another building can be constructed.

After the damaged surface has been cleared by the osteoclasts, **osteoblasts begin forming new bone matrix** to replace the matrix that has been lost. The material produced by osteoblasts is known as **callus**, and it binds the two sides of the fracture together, similar to scar tissue in the skin. The bone will absorb the callus, and the callus is then replaced by bone tissue. These cells are known as **osteocytes**. The bone is then remodeled into essentially its original shape, and osteoblasts stop producing osteocytes to replace the damaged bone.

Scar

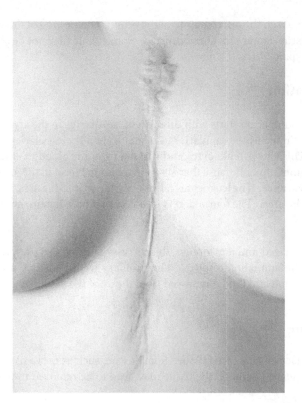

A scar, also known as **cicatrix**, is a fibrous tissue formed to help a wound heal. Scar tissue acts as a bandage, holding the damaged tissue together when it cannot be effectively replaced on its own. Scarring depends on the size, location, and depth of the wound suffered. Other factors that may play a role in scar development is a person's age, genes, and overall health of the person and the part of the body involved.

Different types of scars include acne scars, keloid scars, contracture scars, and hypertrophic scars.

Acne Scars

Acne scars may occur in a person with severe acne. These scars can leave **deep pits** in the skin, usually the result of a follicle wall being broken by an excessive accumulation of oil, bacteria, or fluid.

Keloid Scars

Keloid scars are more commonly seen in people with darker skin tone. These scars are the result of over-healing in the area. Keloid scars are often **raised off the skin**, extending beyond the area of damage. If large enough, these may be uncomfortable, cause pain, or reduce movement.

Contracture Scars

Contracture scars are usually seen in people who have suffered **burns**. These scars are spread out, and may extend deeper into the skin and affect muscles and nerves. The larger the burn, the more likely it is contracture scars may affect the ability to move certain parts of the body, depending on the location. If a person develops a contracture scar early in life, the scar may become mixed with healthy tissue.

Hypertrophic Scars

Hypertrophic scars are similar to keloid scars, but they do not extend past the area of damage. These scars often **appear red**, and may be **tender or painful**. Hypertrophic scars are the result of a **collagen imbalance** at the site of injury, which does not allow the scar to form properly. **Excessive tension** on the area may also lead to the development of hypertrophic scars.

Striae

Striae, also known as **stretch marks**, are scars that form in the skin when the body experiences a **rapid growth**, such as during pregnancy, puberty, or during activities such as weight lifting. These scars generally have a different color than the surrounding skin. As the area grows, the skin is stretched and pulled apart. In response, the skin develops fibrous tissue to hold the expanding area together, which produces scarring.

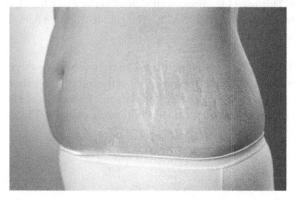

Sutures

Sutures are used to **close wounds** produced through damage to tissues or surgery. Suturing a wound closed allows the damaged tissue to join together and produce a scar. There are many types of sutures, but all are either absorbable or non-absorbable. Absorbable sutures will be absorbed by the body and will not require surgical removal, while non-absorbable sutures require a doctor to surgically remove them.

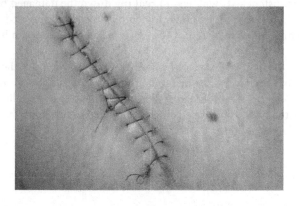

Medications

There are many different types of medications used to treat many types of illnesses, diseases, and infections. Among the most common are:

Analgesics, which help to **relieve pain**. Examples include acetaminophen and non-steroidal anti-inflammatory drugs. These help treat symptoms of conditions that cause pain, such as cancer.

Antacids, which **reduce the activity of acids** in the stomach. These help treat conditions such as Gastroesophageal Reflux Disease.

Antibiotics, which are used to **combat bacterial growth**. Examples include penicillin, amoxicillin, and erythromycin. These are used to treat infections in the body, such as cellulitis, impetigo, and strep throat.

Anticoagulants, which are used to **reduce the formation of blood clots**. Examples include aspirin, heparin, and warfarin. These are used to treat conditions such as deep vein thrombosis and phlebitis.

Antidepressants, which are used to **combat depression**. Common forms include selective serotonin reuptake inhibitors(SSRIs), serotonin and norepinephrine reuptake inhibitors(SNRIs), and tricyclic antidepressants.

Antidotes, which are used to **counteract the effects of poison** on the body. These are used when too much of a substance has entered the body that can result in harmful, or even fatal effects.

Antifungals, which aid in **destroying fungus**. Examples include terbinafine and fluconazole. These are used to treat any type of fungal infection, such as Tinea Pedis(Athlete's Foot) or Tinea Capitis.

Antihistamines, which **reduce the effects of histamines** on the body, including runny nose and itching. These are used to treat allergic reactions.

Anti-inflammatory agents, which help to **reduce inflammation**. Examples include non-steroidal anti-inflammatory drugs such as ibuprofen. These are used to help treat inflammation in conditions such as bronchitis, and potentially Alzheimer's Disease.

Antipyretics, which help to **reduce fever**. Examples include ibuprofen and aspirin. These are used to treat symptoms of fever and other systemic infections.

Antivirals, which aid in **preventing virus reproduction**. Examples include amantadine and rimantadine. These are used to combat virus reproduction in conditions such as encephalitis.

Beta blockers, which help to **reduce blood pressure**. Examples include acebutolol, nadolol, and nebivolol. These are used to treat conditions such as hypertension, arrhythmia, and myocardial infarction.

Bronchodilators, which aid in **dilation of the bronchial tubes**. Examples include albuterol and salmeterol. These are used to treat conditions such as asthma and bronchitis.

Decongestants, which **reduce inflammation in the nasal cavity**. Examples include pseudoephedrine and phenylephrine. These are used to treat congestion caused by allergies.

Expectorants, which are used to help a person **expectorate**, or cough/spit mucous from the lungs. Common forms include over-the-counter brand names such as Mucinex and Robitussin. These are commonly used to treat chest congestion.

General anesthetics, which are used to **numb the entire body**. Examples include propofol, ketamine, and etomidate. General anesthetics are primarily used when a person is having surgery performed that requires them to be in an unconscious state. These can be administered via needle injection or may be inhaled.

Insulin, which **lowers the amount of sugar in the blood stream**. Insulin is primarily used to treat diabetes.

Laxatives, also known as stool softeners, which are used to help **loosen and eliminate feces from the digestive tract**. Common forms include mineral oil and milk of magnesia. These are used to treat constipation.

Local anesthetics, which are used to **numb an area**. They are most commonly administered via needle injection. Examples include lidocaine and nitracaine. These are typically used before performing a surgical procedure around the area of incision.

Sedatives, which are used to **calm and relax the body**. Examples include diazepam and clonazepam. These are typically used to calm a person before a painful or uncomfortable procedure is performed, such as a colonoscopy.

Statins, which aid in **lowering cholesterol levels in the blood stream**. Examples include atorvastatin, rosuvastatin, and lovastatin. These are used to treat and/or prevent heart disease and its various symptoms, including hypertension and stroke.

Steroids, which are primarily used to **combat inflammation in specific areas**. Common forms include corticosteroids and anabolic steroids. Corticosteroids are useful in treating conditions such as asthma, arthritis, and lupus.

Thrombolytics are used to **dissolve a blood clot** that is already present in the body, which can prevent major complications in conditions such as stroke, myocardial infarction, and pulmonary embolism. Common forms include anistreplase, reteplase, and streptokinase.

Vaccines, which are used to **prevent a contagious disease from developing** in a person. Common vaccines include MMR(Measles-Mumps-Rubella), DTaP(Diphtheria, Tetanus, and Pertussis), influenza, and human papilloma virus. Vaccines are commonly administered via intramuscular needle injection.

Medical Tests

Computerized Axial Tomography

Computerized Axial Tomography, also known as CT or CAT Scan, is an imaging technique in which a **snapshot** is taken of a part of the body on a **given body plane**. This allows viewing of structures in the body from differing points of view. CT is extremely similar to MRI, but uses **X-ray** to produce images instead of magnetic fields.

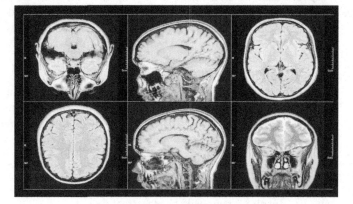

Echocardiogram

An echocardiogram is a type of **ultrasound** performed on the **heart** in order to view all the **structures and chambers of the heart**. This can be used to determine if there are any issues with the heart, such as valve defects, how strong the heart muscle is, or if there are any abnormal holes in the heart.

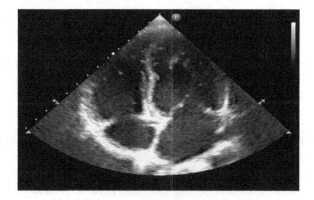

Electroencephalogram

An electroencephalogram is a test used to detect the **electrical activity of the brain**. It uses electrodes placed around the head that attach directly to the scalp to detect electric activity. Electroencephalograms are performed to help diagnose **brain disorders**, such as encephalitis, tumors, epilepsy, and damage to the brain from concussions.

Electrocardiogram

If a doctor feels as if a patient needs to have their heart rhythm monitored, they may administer an ECG/EKG. During this procedure, **ten pads attached to electrodes** are attached to the patient's bare skin on specific points around the trunk. The ECG/EKG picks up the electrical activity of the heart, and produces a visualization that shows **each wave of electrical activity**. The first wave seen is known as the **P wave**, and shows the contraction of the atria. Next is the **QRS wave**, which shows the depolarization and contraction of the ventricles. Following that is the **T wave**, which represents re-polarization of the ventricles.

In some cases, a person may need to have heart activity recorded over 24-48 hours. In these cases, a **Holter Monitor** is used. These are **portable machines** that remain attached to a patient, continuously recording heart activity. These can be used if a person has irregular heart rhythms that come and go, and aren't present during an initial ECG/EKG reading.

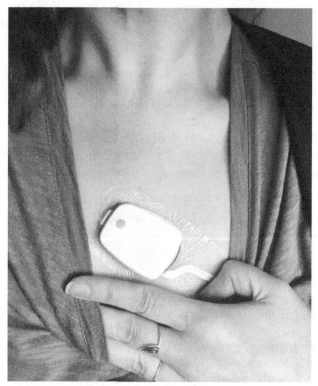

Holter Monitor

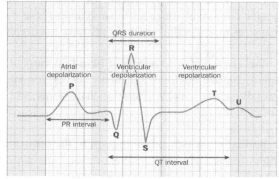

ECG/EKG

Electromyography

Electromyography is a test used to detect the proper functioning of **muscles and the nerves that innervate the muscles**. This is done to assess any **nerve or muscle damage** that may be present, or if communication between the nerve and muscle has been impaired. Electromyography is performed by several different means. A needle may be placed directly into the muscle to read electrical activity. Adhesive pads may be placed on the skin above the muscle to detect nervous conduction as well.

Magnetic Resonance Imaging

Magnetic Resonance Imaging is the use of **high powered magnetic fields** to help **produce images of structures and organs** inside the body. These images are typically much more detailed than X-rays, especially when viewing organs. MRI is used to help diagnose conditions such as tumors, issues with the Digestive System, and issues with the heart and blood vessels. The MRI machine is a large tube in which a person lies for an extended period of time, which allows a thorough image to be produced.

Myelogram

A myelogram is an imaging procedure used to view problems that may be occurring in the **spinal canal**. Special dyes are injected into the spinal column, and the patient is given X-rays, which allow the structures inside the spinal canal to be properly viewed. Myelograms are used to examine conditions such as herniated discs, infections such as meningitis, and tumors in the brain or spinal cord.

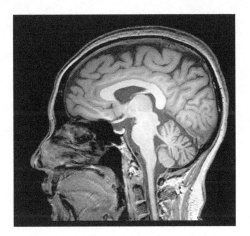

Mammogram

A mammogram is a procedure used to detect **breast cancer** in patients who are **not showing any symptoms**. It uses an X-ray to view the internal breast tissue. A mammogram is typically performed by placing the breast between two glass plates that compress the tissue. Compressing the tissue allows the X-ray to view all of the breast without missing anything.

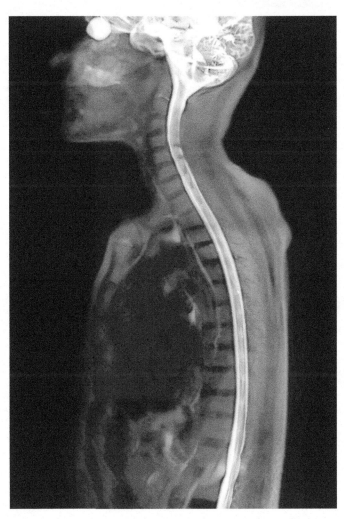

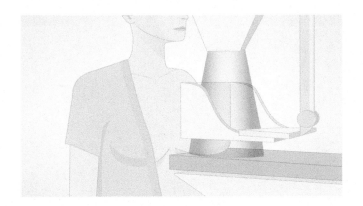

Ultrasound

An ultrasound, also known as **sonography**, is an imaging technique utilizing **sound waves** to produce pictures of structures inside the body. Commonly, ultrasound is used to view the development of a fetus during pregnancy, but may also be used to examine infections inside the body, liver and gallbladder function, and heart conditions. The part of the machine that is used to perform the scanning is known as the transducer.

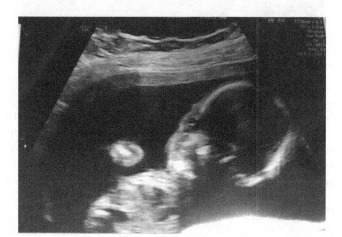

X-Ray

An X-ray is an imaging technique using radiation to view structures that light typically does not pass through. Structures most commonly seen using X-rays are **bones and metals**. X-rays allow visual examination of structures that may be broken, damaged, or infected.

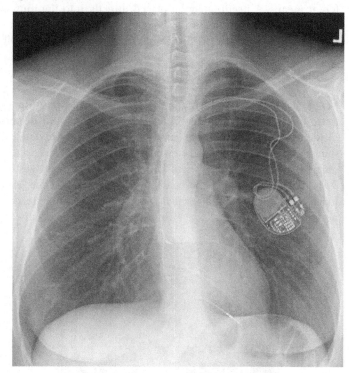

Medical Equipment

Automated External Defibrillator

An Automated External Defibrillator, or **AED**, is a **portable defibrillator** used to send electric shocks to the heart in a person who is suffering from **sudden cardiac arrest**. The person will have two sticky pads attached to their skin that connect to the AED, one pad placed on the chest and one on the left side of the trunk. The AED sends a shock to the person through the pads, directly into the heart, which can help return the heart to its normal rhythm.

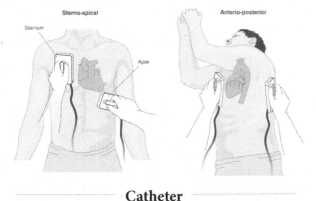

Catheter

A catheter is a **small tube** inserted in to a part of the body to **help fluid drain**. The most common form is a **urinary catheter**. These are inserted into the urethra and into the urinary bladder. From there, fluid is able to drain freely from the bladder.

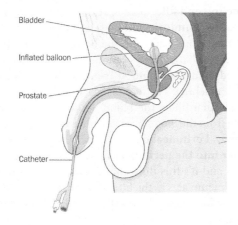

Centrifuge

A centrifuge is a medical device used to **separate solids from liquids**. This is especially useful in separating **plasma from the blood cells** in blood. Centrifuges accomplish this by spinning in circles extremely fast, forcing the solids in a substance to move to the bottom of the vial, and the liquids move to the top.

Compression Devices

Compression devices are used to **mimic the Lymphatic System** by **rhythmically compressing the legs** to increase the flow of lymph. This can decrease lymphedema. Typical compression devices may also include compression socks, and cuffs that wrap around the legs.

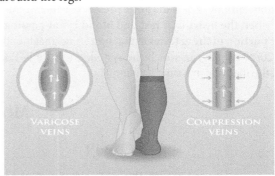

Endoscope

An endoscope is a **tube** inserted into a part of the digestive tract with a **camera and light attached**, allowing a doctor to see inside the organs. Commonly, this is performed to view the esophagus, stomach, and small intestine. An endoscopy performed to view the large intestine is known as a colonoscopy.

Pacemaker

If a patient suffers from severe arrhythmia, a pacemaker may be implanted into the body to help **regulate heart rhythm**. The pacemaker is usually placed under the skin on the upper left side of the chest, just inferior to the clavicle. A pacemaker is a small metal device with a battery inside that sends **electric shocks to the heart** when it detects the heart rhythm is not functioning properly. It accomplishes this with the use of leads that travel through the superior vena cava directly into the heart. The leads go into the atrium, ventricle, or both, depending on the type of arrhythmia a person has. The battery in a pacemaker typically lasts between five and ten years, and can be replaced.

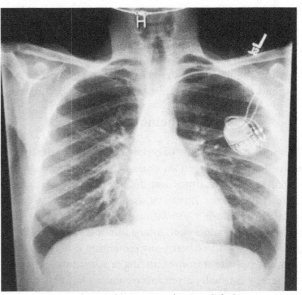

Pacemaker visible in patient's upper left chest

Sphygmomanometer

When measuring blood pressure, a sphygmomanometer is wrapped around a person's arm. The **cuff around the arm inflates**, and the **pressure of the blood passing through the arteries** can be felt. The sphygmomanometer produces two numbers: the systolic number and diastolic number. The systolic number reads **systolic pressure**, which is the pressure felt as **blood is pumped from the heart and passes through the arteries**. The diastolic number reads **diastolic pressure**, which is the **pressure felt when the heart is at rest and blood is not passing through that portion of the arteries** at that time. A normal blood pressure is 120/80 mmHg, in which the systolic pressure is 120 mmHg, and the diastolic pressure is 80 mmHg.

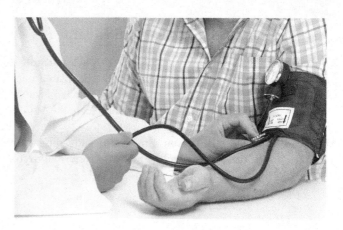

Medical Procedures

Arthroscopy

Arthroscopy is used to **view the inner structures of a joint**. It is performed by making a small incision, and inserting a **tube with a camera attached** directly into the joint. This allows a view of any structural damage that may occur, such as torn ligaments. If surgery is being performed, it may be performed arthroscopically, where all the instruments being used are inserted into the joint through small holes, without making a large incision.

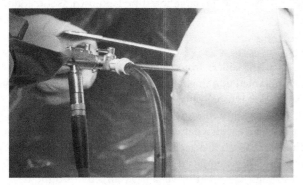

Bone Graft

A bone graft, similar to a skin graft, is the **removal of a small amount of bone tissue** from one part of the body, **placing the removed tissue on another bone** that may be lacking in sufficient tissue. This can be done if part of a bone is removed during surgery, or in cases such as joint replacements to help the new structures anchor in to the bone more securely. The new bone sets, and the area where the graft is located becomes stronger.

Chemotherapy

Chemotherapy is the use of certain **chemicals to destroy cancerous cells and tumors** in the body. Chemotherapy may be administered at different times and different ways, depending on the cause of the cancer. It may be used to destroy some cancer cells and shrink a tumor to aid with pain relief, or to make surgery on the tumor more successful. After a tumor is removed, chemotherapy may be used to destroy any remaining cancerous cells in the body and prevent it from recurring or spreading elsewhere. Chemotherapy is usually given intravenously, but may also be given orally or topically.

Cryotherapy

Cryotherapy is the use of **cold or ice** in a treatment. Cryotherapy can be used to reduce inflammation, increase circulation after a short period of application, destroy tissues such as warts, or even destroy nerves that may be causing pain. Cryotherapy can be applied many different ways, from the use of cold packs, to ice baths.

Dialysis

Dialysis is used when the **kidneys are no longer able to properly function and filter waste products** from the blood. Dialysis is meant to **mimic the kidneys**, pulling waste from the blood and filtering blood back into the body. There are two types of dialysis: hemodialysis and peritoneal dialysis. **Hemodialysis** is performed by **drawing blood from the body**, which is cycled through a machine. The dialysis machine contains a permeable membrane that filters the blood, known as a **dialyzer**. When the waste from the blood has been filtered, the blood is returned to the body. **Peritoneal dialysis** is performed by administering a **catheter into the peritoneum**. Dialysate, a fluid, is placed in the body, and it's this **fluid that draws waste from the blood**. The peritoneum acts as the filter. The waste is removed from the body, and blood never leaves the body like it does with hemodialysis.

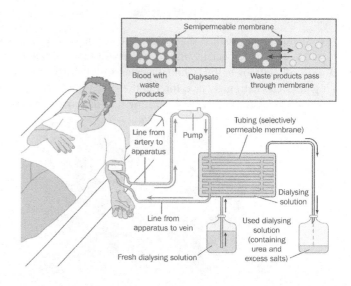

Epidural

An epidural is a medical procedure used to **block pain and sensation in the lower body**. It is performed by injecting analgesics and anesthetics around the **spinal cord in the lumbar region**. The medications are delivered via a catheter inserted into the site of injection. Epidurals are commonly used during labor to eliminate pain associated with child birth.

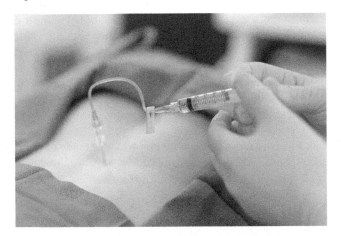

Lithotripsy

Lithotripsy is the use of **sound waves** administered via ultrasound to **break up or destroy deposits** building up in the body, such as **kidney stones and gallstones**. Lithotripsy is typically only performed if one of these deposits is too large to pass from the body on its own. The sound waves produced break up the deposit, and allow it to be passed normally. These sound waves are produced by a machine known as a lithotripter.

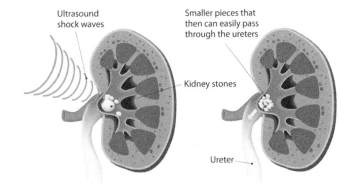

Radiation Therapy

Radiation therapy is a type of treatment used to **destroy cancerous tissue**. It is performed by exposing the affected portion of the body to a **highly concentrated beam of radiation**. The machine responsible for administering the radiation is pointed directly at the spot to be treated, and uses X-rays to destroy cancerous cells. It may also destroy healthy tissue, however. Radiation therapy may also be used to make tumors smaller and prevent a tumor from growing or spreading before surgery may be performed.

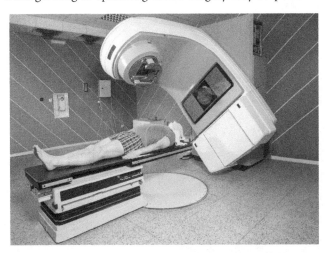

Skin Graft

A skin graft is **transplanting skin from one location on the body to another** where skin has been lost, commonly from burns or injuries. A thin layer of epidermis is removed using a shaver(similar to a potato peeler), then placed on the area where skin is needed. The area is covered in bandages to allow healing. Over time, the skin adheres to the injured area and becomes new skin for the area.

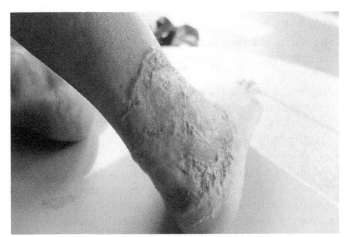

Area of skin where skin graft has been placed and healed

Cardiovascular Pathologies

Anemia
(an-: without; -emia: blood)

Sickle Cell Anemia

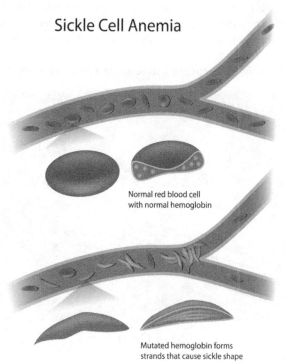

Normal red blood cell
with normal hemoglobin

Mutated hemoglobin forms
strands that cause sickle shape

Anemia is a disease of the blood, resulting in a **lack of oxygen** and an **over-abundance of carbon dioxide** in the blood. There are many different types of anemia, ranging from **iron-deficient anemia** to **sickle cell anemia**. Anemia is the most common blood condition in the United States, with an estimated 3.5-4 million people afflicted with it.

Iron-deficient anemia is the most common form of anemia. The cells in the blood that are responsible for carrying oxygen and carbon dioxide throughout the body are the erythrocytes, or red blood cells. In the cytoplasm of erythrocytes, there is a protein present known as hemoglobin, which is made of iron. The hemoglobin attracts oxygen and carbon dioxide, allowing these molecules to attach to the erythrocytes.

Causes

In iron-deficient anemia, the primary cause is a lack of iron being consumed. Less iron being consumed results in **less hemoglobin** in the erythrocytes, which in turn causes a lack of oxygen and carbon dioxide attaching to the red blood cells.

Sickle cell anemia is an inherited form of anemia, in which the erythrocytes have a sickle shape, as opposed to a normal erythrocyte, which is circular. This shape can cause the erythrocytes to become stuck in blood vessels, and reduce adequate blood flow to tissues.

Symptoms

People with anemia may feel sluggish, tired, have an increased heart rate, may show paleness in the skin, shortness of breath, and experience dizziness, all due to a lack of sufficient oxygen reaching tissues.

Sickle cell anemia may also result in the further development of infections due to damage caused to the spleen, pain in the thorax and abdomen(known as crises) due to blockage of blood vessels in these locations, and a lack of nutrients to the body, which can stunt growth.

People whose diet lacks proper amounts of iron or vitamin B-12 may develop anemia. Pregnancy, and a lack of folic acid, may result in anemia in pregnant women. Sickle cell anemia is primarily seen in African-Americans, resulting from a genetic defect.

Treatments

Treatments for anemia vary depending on the type, but may include increasing iron intake, bone marrow transplants, or blood transfusions. Pregnant women may require an increased intake of folic acid. People with sickle cell anemia face less treatment options. The only potential cure is through a bone marrow transplant. Often times, the only treatment is trying to minimize the number of crises a person may experience. Antibiotics and pain relievers may help in preventing infections in younger patients and reducing pain experienced during crises.

Contraindications

Massage is indicated for a client with anemia. Massage helps increase circulation and oxygen intake, which provides the body with needed nutrients.

Aneurysm
(Greek "aneurysma": a widening)

An aneurysm is a condition of the arteries, resulting in a **bulge in the wall of an artery**. There are several different forms and causes of aneurysms. Different types of aneurysms include Aortic(bulge in the wall of the aorta), Cerebral(bulge in an artery supplying blood to the brain), and Ventricular(bulge in the wall of the heart).

Causes

Aneurysms are the result of a **part of an arterial wall becoming weakened**, which forces the wall out, creating a pouch or bubble. Most commonly, aneurysms are the result of hypertension putting too much pressure or strain on the artery. Ventricular aneurysms are most commonly caused by myocardial infarction, which can weaken the heart muscle.

When the arterial wall stretches due to weakness, it makes it much easier for the artery to rupture. Because the artery carries oxygen-rich blood, this makes aneurysms very dangerous, as any rupture will severely cut off blood flow to the structure supplied with blood by the artery.

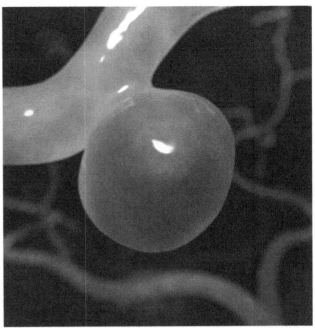

Berry Aneurysm

Symptoms

Unfortunately, aneurysms that have not ruptured are asymptomatic. In fact, aneurysms themselves, unless very large, cause no symptoms at all. When an aneurysm ruptures, however, a person may experience severe chest or back pain, low blood pressure, severe headache, tachycardia, and lightheadedness.

People may develop aneurysms for many different reasons, including obesity, hypertension, diabetes, advanced age, and alcoholism. Some people develop aneurysms for no apparent reason at all.

Treatments

Common locations for aneurysms include the abdominal aorta and the brain. Aneurysms may be treated surgically before rupture to prevent major medical emergencies in the future. Beta blockers are commonly used as medications before surgery is required.

Contraindications

Massage is indicated with a doctor's note. Any massage that increases blood pressure should be avoided, such as deep tissue, because it can put pressure on arteries, which may lead to bursting of an aneurysm.

Arrhythmia
(a-: without; rhythm: rhythm)

Arrhythmia is a condition of the heart, which results in the **heart's natural rhythm being altered**. There are several different forms of arrhythmia. Some of the most common forms of arrhythmia are Atrial Fibrillation, Bradycardia, and Tachycardia.

Causes

Atrial fibrillation, the most common form of arrhythmia, results when the atria, the heart's upper chambers, contract irregularly, which sends blood into the ventricles at uncoordinated times. This is caused by an electrical signal from the SA Node not firing correctly, which disrupts the timing of the atria contracting. This can affect the ability of the heart to consistently deliver oxygenated blood to the body.

Bradycardia(*brady-: slow; -cardia: heart*) results in the heart rate being reduced to a rate of contraction that is considered too slow to deliver substantial oxygen to the body.

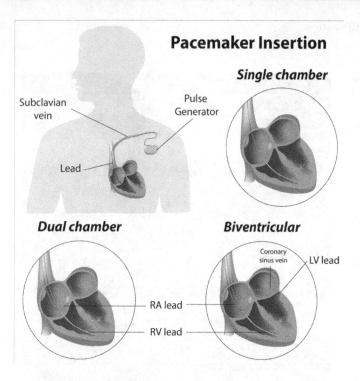

Pacemaker Insertion

Single chamber

Subclavian vein
Pulse Generator
Lead

Dual chamber

Biventricular

Coronary sinus vein
LV lead
RA lead
RV lead

Tachycardia*(tachy-: rapid; -cardia: heart)* results in the heart rate being increased to a rate of contraction that is considered too rapid. In tachycardia, the ventricles of the heart are contracting too rapidly, which may cause a lack of oxygen-rich blood from reaching the body, as the quick contractions do not allow the ventricles to properly fill with blood before being pumped out to the rest of the body. Older adults, those over age 60, are more likely to develop arrhythmia than younger adults and children. Heart diseases are a main contributing factor towards older adults developing arrhythmia. Other diseases may also play a role in the development of arrhythmia, so people who have had myocardial infarction may be more prone to developing the disease. Diabetes, sleep apnea, and hypertension all have contributed to the development of arrhythmia.

Symptoms

There are many different symptoms seen with arrhythmia. Symptoms include dizziness, fatigue, shortness of breath, pain in the chest, lightheadedness, and fainting. In severe cases, arrhythmia may result in cardiac arrest.

Treatments

Treatments vary, depending on the type of arrhythmia a person suffers from. Medical devices such as pacemakers may be implanted into the body to help regulate and control heart rhythm(IE, if a person's heart rate drops too low, the pacemaker will stimulate the heart muscle and cause it to contract, increasing heart rate back to safe levels). Alternative methods to controlling arrhythmia, such as massage therapy and yoga, may be applied in some cases.

Contraindications

Untreated arrhythmia is an absolute contraindication for massage therapy. If a client has a pacemaker, massage may be performed. A client may have discomfort while lying prone due to pressure on the pacemaker, which may call for side-lying massage to be performed, or pillows to be used to take pressure off the area. Avoid massaging the site of the pacemaker(upper left chest just below clavicle).

Arteriosclerosis/Atherosclerosis
(arterio: artery; scler-: hard; -osis: condition);
(athero: fatty plaque; scler-: hard; -osis: condition)

Arteriosclerosis is a **hardening of the walls of arteries**, a condition that progresses slowly over time. Atherosclerosis is a **build-up of fatty plaque** inside the arteries. These two conditions are commonly caused by one another, and are often interchangeable.

STAGES OF ATHEROSCLEROSIS

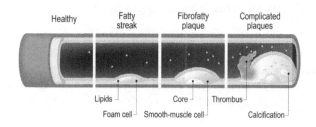

Healthy | Fatty streak | Fibrofatty plaque | Complicated plaques

Lipids
Foam cell | Core
Smooth-muscle cell | Thrombus
Calcification

Causes

Arteriosclerosis has many different contributing factors, including hypertension, high cholesterol, and smoking. Each of these can damage an artery. The body's response to this damage is to increase the thickness of the artery to prevent further damage. When this occurs, the artery becomes much harder and unable to move and stretch normally. This may also lead to increased deposits of plaque in the arteries, a condition known as atherosclerosis. This increased plaque, along with the hardening of the artery, may restrict blood flow and lead to conditions such as angina pectoris and myocardial infarction.

Symptoms

Symptoms include angina pectoris, shortness of breath, fatigue, and pain in any area of the body that may have any sort of restriction in the arteries.

Treatments

Medications are effective treatments for arteriosclerosis/atherosclerosis, including beta-blockers, statins, calcium channel blockers, and diuretics. If an increased plaque buildup is severe, an angioplasty may be performed, or a stent may be placed inside the artery to increase blood flow. Plaque may be surgically removed, or a bypass surgery may be performed to increase circulation into areas that may be experiencing ischemia.

Contraindications

Massage for atherosclerosis/arteriosclerosis may be performed. Certain medications may require a lighter massage to be performed, because they may thin the blood and damage to a blood vessel can lead to increased bleeding internally.

Deep Vein Thrombosis
(thromb/o: clot; -osis; condition)

Deep Vein Thrombosis(DVT) is a condition in which **blood clots(thrombi) form in the veins** deep in the body, typically the **legs**. These blood clots can **block blood flow** in the veins, which can lead to several serious issues.

Causes

There are various causes for DVT. Primary causes are injury to a vein, surgery, impaired or limited mobility, and certain medications. An injury to a vein can result in blood clots, especially if there is significant damage to the vein. Surgery, which can result in cutting through veins, can also lead to blood clots. Post-surgery, if a patient is immobilized for extended periods, circulation starts to decrease in efficiency, which can lead to blood pooling in the veins of the legs. This pooling of blood can result in clots. It is this same reason people who have paralysis may develop blood clots as well.

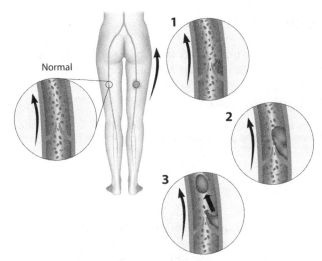

1. Clot formation, 2. Clot growth,
3. Clot dislodging and becoming an embolus

Symptoms

Although symptoms may not be present in someone with DVT, others do show symptoms, which include a warm sensation in the affected area, pain in the affected area that can increase in intensity, and discoloration in the affected area. Most commonly, DVT affects the lower limb, so this is where a person will most likely experience these symptoms.

Treatments

The primary treatment for DVT is medication. Certain medications can help reduce the chance of developing DVT in the future, or even remove the blood clot from the body. Intravenous anticoagulants such as heparin help to thin the blood. Other anticoagulants, such as warfarin, work extremely well in conjunction with injectable anticoagulants.

If the blood clot is severe, the patient might be given a thrombolytic, a type of medication that destroys blood clots. These are typically only given in serious cases of blood clots, such as those that result in pulmonary embolism. Compression socks, which compress the leg up to the knee, can help reduce the amount of swelling a patient might experience with DVT.

Contraindications

Deep vein thrombosis is typically a local contraindication. Avoid the site of the thrombus, as dislodging the clot may lead to circulation being cut off in organs such as the lungs, brain, or heart. Massage that increases blood pressure may be contraindicated, and deeper massages may be contraindicated due to the use of anticoagulants and thrombolytics.

Heart Murmur
(murmur: to mutter)

A heart murmur is a condition of the heart, which results in blood **flowing backwards in the heart**. A "murmur" refers to the sound of blood flowing through the heart. There are two types of heart murmurs: Innocent and Abnormal. Innocent heart murmurs are seen in children and infants, usually the result of congenital heart disease. Abnormal heart murmurs are much more serious, most likely due to the development of heart disease or valve malfunction.

Causes

Heart murmurs may not require any medical attention, depending on the cause. Other times, medical attention may be needed. Most commonly, heart murmurs are the result of a **bicuspid/mitral valve prolapse**, where the valve is pulled backwards into the left atrium. This allows blood to flow backwards in the heart, which may reduce the ability of the heart to pump enough oxygen-rich blood to the body.

People who have developed endocarditis or Rheumatic fever often develop heart murmurs due to damage to the valves in the heart.

Symptoms

While most heart murmurs aren't serious, abnormal heart murmurs may present with symptoms such as cyanosis on the fingers, chest pain, dizziness, shortness of breath, and fainting.

Treatments

Heart murmurs may require the person to take anticoagulants to prevent the formation of blood clots, may be treated for hypertension if it is resulting in heart murmurs, or may need surgery to repair or replace the malfunctioning valve.

Contraindications

Massage may be performed on a client with a heart murmur.

Hypertension
(hyper-: above; -tension: tension)

Hypertension is a condition of the Cardiovascular System, resulting in **elevated blood pressure**. There are numerous factors that may contribute to the development of hypertension. For an average healthy adult, systolic blood pressure(pressure felt in arteries when the heart beats) is around 120 mmHg, and diastolic pressure(pressure felt in arteries when the heart is at rest) is around 80 mmHg. To be diagnosed with hypertension, a person's systolic pressure would be 140 mmHg and diastolic pressure would be 90 mmHg.

Causes

Hypertension may have no underlying cause, or may be the result of factors such as dysfunction of the adrenal glands or thyroid, dietary issues such as obesity or high sodium intake, kidney disease, and alcohol consumption. Hypertension is most commonly associated with people who smoke, drink excessive amounts of alcohol, are overweight, are older in age, consume excessive salt, and more.

Symptoms

Unfortunately, hypertension is largely asymptomatic. Only in extreme cases, where the heart's blood pressure spikes extremely high, will someone experience symptoms, such as dizziness and headaches. Most symptoms people associate with hypertension are actually side effects of medications.

Treatments

Untreated, hypertension may lead to numerous serious medical conditions, such as myocardial infarction, stroke, atherosclerosis, and aneurysm. Luckily, hypertension is very easy to detect, and very treatable. Often times, treatment is as simple as making lifestyle or dietary changes, such as consuming less sodium and increasing exercise. Other times, hypertension may require the use of medications such as beta blockers, statins, and diuretics.

Contraindications

Hypertension is generally not contraindicated for massage. Massage that increases blood pressure, such as deep tissue or hot stone, may be contraindicated if the client is not taking medication to control hypertension. Light massage, which promotes lowering blood pressure, should be performed.

Migraine Headaches

Migraine Headaches are a type of headache that affect the brain, which results in most side effects experienced.

Migraines have been referred to as "**vascular headaches**", due to the involvement of **blood vessels**. In migraines, when the brain is stimulated by a trigger, neurons rapidly send impulses which affects the blood vessels surrounding the meninges, three layers of connective tissue that surround and protect the brain. At first, the blood vessels constrict, which does not result in pain. A short time after constricting, the blood vessels will dilate, which places immense pressure on the meninges, which results in severe pain.

Causes

Migraines have numerous causes, which may be from exposure to substances like tyramine(a naturally occurring chemical found in foods such as aged cheese, alcoholic beverages, and cured meats), caffeine, stress, or even hormonal imbalance during stages such as menstruation. Migraines may even be considered hereditary.

Symptoms

Symptoms include nausea, fatigue, extreme pain, loss of sight, blurred vision, sensitivity to sound, and pain on one side of the head. Not everyone that experiences a migraine experiences all of the symptoms detailed, as each migraine is different.

Treatments

If a migraine is in the beginning stages, taking pain medication such as aspirin or ibuprofen can help reduce the symptoms of mild migraines. Other medications, called triptans, can help to constrict blood vessels, which can help reduce the effects of migraines.

Preventative drugs may be taken to reduce the chances of developing a migraine in the future. These medications include beta blockers, non-steroidal anti-inflammatory drugs, and even antidepressants.

Contraindications

Migraine headaches are generally not contraindicated for massage.

Myocardial Infarction
(myo-: muscle; -cardia: heart; infarct: obstruction of blood flow)

A Myocardial Infarction, or **heart attack**, is a condition that affects the heart muscle, reducing blood flow throughout the body.

An infarction is an **obstruction of blood flow** to a specific part of the body. In this case, blood flow to the heart is obstructed. The two arteries that supply blood to the heart muscle are known as the **coronary arteries**. When an abundance of substances such as **plaque build up** inside these arteries, it restricts blood flow to the heart muscle. When blood flow is restricted, the tissue does not receive adequate oxygen, which results in **necrosis of the affected tissue**. When too much cardiac muscle dies, the body experiences a myocardial infarction, or heart attack.

Causes

Myocardial infarctions may be the result of atherosclerosis, a condition which causes the artery walls to harden and thicken due to a build-up of plaque in the arteries. Hypertension, smoking, and obesity may also contribute to the development of atherosclerosis.

Symptoms

Symptoms of myocardial infarction may be acute, or build up over a period of days leading up to the myocardial infarction. In the preceding days, a person may experience malaise, fatigue, and discomfort in the chest. Acute stages of myocardial infarction include

Anatomy of a heart attack

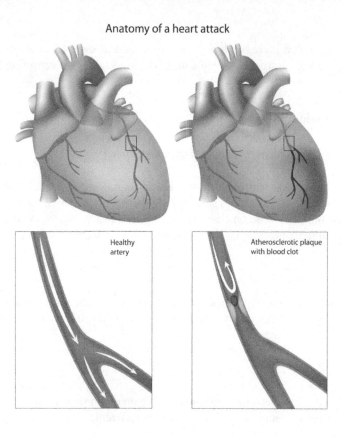

Healthy artery

Atherosclerotic plaque with blood clot

intense chest pain, pain in the neck and left arm, and increased heart rate.

Treatments

A person who has suffered from a myocardial infarction may have a coronary bypass surgery performed, an angioplasty or stent placed in the affected artery, or may not need any surgery and only require medications such as aspirin, beta blockers, and statins.

Contraindications

Massage is an absolute contraindication during a myocardial infarction. After a myocardial infarction has occurred and a client has been treated, it is a good idea to get a note from a doctor before proceeding. Depending on the severity of the infarct and treatment, certain massages should not be performed due to strain they may place on the heart when increasing blood pressure.

Phlebitis

(phleb-: vein; -itis: inflammation)

Phlebitis is a condition of the Cardiovascular System, affecting the **veins**, causing them to become **inflamed**. **Blood clots** may form in these veins.

Causes

Phlebitis may have numerous causes, including **trauma to a vein**, and **immobility**. Trauma to a vein results in what is known as superficial phlebitis, usually the result of IV catheters being placed into a vein via needles.

Deep vein thrombosis is another type of phlebitis, taking place deeper in the body. Deep vein thrombosis(DVT) is most commonly caused by immobility of a limb. The body's veins move and stretch with the rest of the body during movement. If the veins are immobilized, they will become irritated, due to blood pooling in the veins. The blood pooling may result in blood clot formation. If a blood clot dislodges from its location and flows freely in the blood stream, it is known as an embolus, which could become lodged in other blood vessels throughout the body, cutting off blood flow and resulting in ischemia. Depending on the part of the body this takes place, it could even lead to possible death.

Symptoms

Symptoms of superficial phlebitis include tenderness and swelling around the injured vein, often with the affected vein presenting with a red line in the skin following the vein. The vein may feel hard to the touch due to inflammation.

Deep vein thrombosis may present with pain in the entire affected limb(usually the leg), along with swelling. If infection results, people may have fever.

Treatments

Treatments of phlebitis include anticoagulants for deep vein thrombosis such as heparin, ibuprofen, and antibiotics for superficial phlebitis.

Deep vein thrombosis requires immediate medical attention, as it may result in embolism, which could potentially be fatal.

Contraindications

Phlebitis should be treated as a local contraindication. Because medications may be prescribed that thin the blood, lighter massage should be performed to prevent internal bleeding from damaged blood vessels. Massaging the site of phlebitis may dislodge a clot, which can result in an embolism.

Raynaud's Syndrome

Raynaud's Syndrome is a condition that results in **constriction of the blood vessels in the fingers and toes**, **reducing circulation** to these areas. This constriction is known as "vasospasm". Primary Raynaud's Syndrome occurs independently, while Secondary Raynaud's Syndrome is typically associated with other conditions.

Causes

The primary contributors to Raynaud's Syndrome are **cold temperatures**, **stress**, and **cigarette smoking**. Raynaud's Syndrome is typically not a debilitating disease. During a flare-up, the skin typically turns pale, the person may experience numbness or pain, and the affected areas become very cold.

Secondary Raynaud's Syndrome may be associated with conditions such as lupus or scleroderma, and develops later in life than Primary Raynaud's Syndrome.

Symptoms

Symptoms of Raynaud's Syndrome include discoloration of the skin in affected areas, cold fingers and/or toes, numbness, and stinging pain upon warming of the area.

Treatments

Treatments for Raynaud's Syndrome include exercise, reducing stress, not smoking, and avoiding cold temperatures whenever possible. Secondary Raynaud's Syndrome may require medications such as statins to help regulate blood pressure and cholesterol.

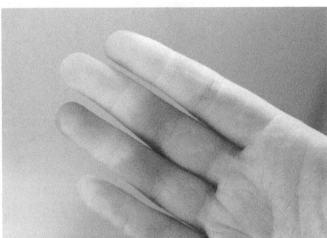
Discoloration of fingers typical of Raynaud's Syndrome

Contraindications

Raynaud's Syndrome is indicated for massage. Using heat should be avoided, as sensation in the affected area may be decreased and tissue damage may result. Massaging the area can help dilate blood vessels and bring blood back into the fingers and toes. Increasing the temperature of the massage room may also help dilate blood vessels.

Varicose Veins
(varicose: abnormally swollen)

Varicose veins are the **abnormal swelling of veins** in the body, most commonly seen in the **legs**, but may be present in any vein. There are many different types, ranging from regular varicose veins, to spider veins, and even hemorrhoids.

Causes

Inside the veins, there are valves that push deoxygenated blood back up to the heart. Typically, as a person ages, the valves stop working as efficiently, which allows **blood to pool backwards** in the veins. This added pressure causes irritation and swelling of the veins. Blood pooling in the veins may also lead to complications such as the development of blood clots.

Because veins are much more superficial than arteries, when a vein becomes swollen, it is often visible. Varicose veins often present with a purple color, may look cord-like, and may even cause pain and discomfort. Causes of varicose veins include sitting or standing for prolonged periods, age, and even pregnancy.

Symptoms

Often times, varicose veins occur with no symptoms other than visual symptoms, such as discoloration of veins. If a varicose vein becomes painful, a person may experience burning, itching, edema, and cramping in the legs around the site of the varicose vein.

Treatments

Treatment is often unnecessary, outside of self-care. Self-care may include wearing compression socks, exercise, diet, and elevating the legs to help circulation. If treatment is required, there are a number of different things that can be done, such as sclerotherapy, laser therapy, and removing the varicose vein from the body.

Contraindications

Varicose veins are a type of phlebitis, and are considered a local contraindication. Massaging a swollen vein may dislodge a clot, which could become an embolism.

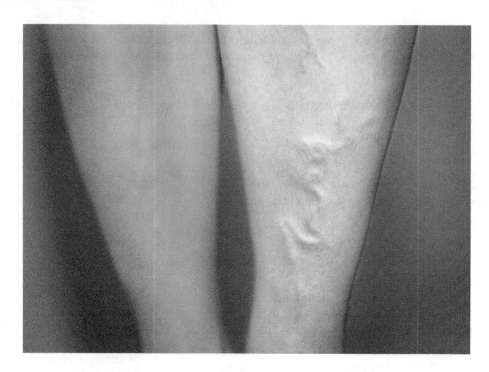

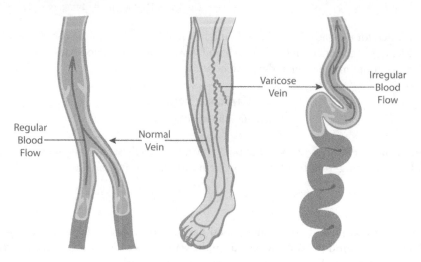

Digestive Pathologies

Cholecystitis
(chole-: bile; cyst-: bladder; -itis: inflammation)

Cholecystitis is **inflammation of the gallbladder**. If untreated, cholecystitis may lead to extremely serious conditions such as rupture of the gallbladder.

Causes

Most commonly, cholecystitis is the result of **formation of gallstones**. Gallstones can block the cystic duct, which connects the gallbladder to the bile duct on its way to the duodenum, causing inflammation of the gallbladder as bile backs up in the organ.

There is no consensus on what causes gallstones to form. Some theories state gallstones form because the bile contains too much cholesterol, too much bilirubin, or the gallbladder doesn't properly empty bile into the duodenum.

Symptoms

Symptoms of cholecystitis include severe abdominal pain in the upper right quadrant near the liver, nausea, vomiting, fever, and pain in the right shoulder/back. These symptoms often occur after ingesting large meals.

Gallbladder removal with presence of gallstones

Treatments

A diagnosis of cholecystitis almost always results in a hospital stay. Treatments may include antibiotics to fight off any associated infection, pain medication to reduce discomfort, and fasting to let the gallbladder rest and reduce inflammation.

Cholecystitis often recurs, and therefore most people who are diagnosed with cholecystitis require surgery to completely remove the gallbladder. The liver is then connected directly to the duodenum, allowing bile to enter into the small intestine.

Contraindications

Cholecystitis is considered an absolute contraindication in the acute stage. After the underlying cause has been determined, medications may be prescribed to help deal with the formation of gallstones and infection, or the gallbladder may be removed completely. This will require a hospital stay, in which massage will not be performed.

Crohn's Disease

Crohn's Disease is an **inflammatory bowel disease**, which causes **inflammation of the digestive tract**. Crohn's has periods of exacerbation and remission, where the disease is actively causing inflammation, then periods where it is not. Crohn's disease typically appears in younger people, people who are of East European Jewish descent, people who have relatives with the disease, and people who smoke cigarettes.

Damage to the digestive tract, including ulcerations and scarring, may result. Depending on the location of ulceration and scarring, abscesses and constipation may result.

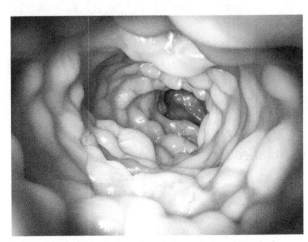

Causes

The leading theories are heredity and an immune system that does not function properly are the main causes of Crohn's.

Symptoms

In acute stages of Crohn's, symptoms may include diarrhea, abdominal pain, cramping, fatigue, fever, and bloody stool. Depending on the severity of these symptoms, a person may need to visit a doctor.

Treatments

A variety of medications may be prescribed for a patient with Crohn's, including anti-inflammatory drugs such as corticosteroids to reduce inflammation in the digestive tract, immunosuppresors to help regulate the effects of the immune system on the digestive tract, and antibiotics to reduce any abscesses that may result. Pain relievers may also be prescribed.

In serious cases, surgery may be required. During Crohn's, scarring in the ileum or large intestine may result. In this surgery, the damaged portion of the digestive tract may be removed. This does not cure Crohn's, but can make it easier to manage.

Changes in diet, especially in acute stages, may be beneficial.

Contraindications

Massage in the acute stage of Crohn's disease should be avoided, as the client may be in pain and experience symptoms such as diarrhea. In the post-acute stage, massage is indicated for Crohn's disease.

Diverticulitis
(diverticula: tubular sac branching off a cavity; -itis: inflammation)

Diverticulitis is a condition affecting the large intestine, but may also affect other structures such as the abdomen, or the entire Cardiovascular System. If a person is affected by diverticulosis, they have **small pouches** that develop in the large intestine. In certain cases, these pouches may become **inflamed and/or infected**, which then becomes diverticulitis.

Causes

Because diverticulitis puts strain on sections of the large intestine that are already weakened, ulcerations or open sores may result. These open sores may lead to infection, and leaking of feces into the abdomen, which results in peritonitis(inflammation of the peritoneum, a very serious condition that requires medical attention).

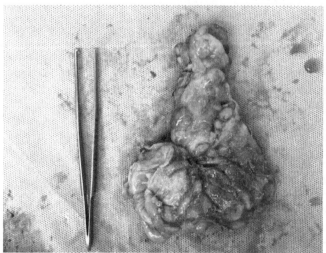

Removal of a segment of the large intestine affected by diverticulitis

Symptoms

Symptoms of diverticulitis include fever, nausea, vomiting, pain in the lower left abdomen, and constipation. Tenderness in the abdomen may also be present.

Treatments

Diverticulitis may be treated in several different ways, depending on the severity. Pain medication may help with discomfort in less severe cases. In recurring diverticulitis, scarring may be present, which could lead to backing up of fecal content in the large intestine. Infections will require antibiotics.

If scarring is severe due to ulceration, surgery to remove the damaged part of the large intestine may be required.

Contraindications

Diverticulitis is considered an absolute contraindication to massage.

Diverticulosis
(diverticula: tubular sac branching off a cavity; -osis: condition)

Diverticulosis is a condition affecting the large intestine, which presents with **pouches forming in the walls of the large intestine**, typically in the descending and/or sigmoid colons. It is a common condition seen in roughly half of people over the age of 65.

Causes

During peristalsis, the smooth muscle located in the walls of the large intestine contract, forcing food to move further through the organ and eventually out of the body. If the large intestine does not contain enough fecal matter, as in the case of a **low-fiber diet**, the contractions may result in weakening of the wall of the large intestine. As a result, small pouches may develop.

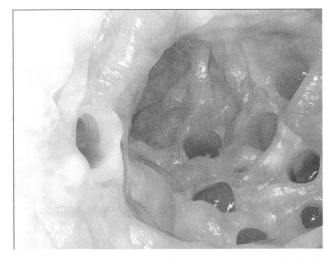

If a person develops diverticulosis, small pieces of feces, nuts, seeds, etc, may become stuck inside the pouches. If feces becomes trapped in a pouch, the large intestine will absorb all of the water from it, and it will become very solid and extremely hard to remove. This may result in pain in the abdomen.

Symptoms

Typically, people with diverticulosis don't exhibit symptoms. When they do, however, symptoms may include diarrhea, abdominal cramping, or fever. These are typically the result of infection, which may lead to diverticulitis.

Treatments

Treatment primarily includes increasing intake of fiber via fruits and vegetables, and increasing fluid intake to make passing of stool easier to manage.

Contraindications

Diverticulosis is not contraindicated for massage. If pain is present, massage of the lower back and abdomen should be avoided, but may be performed elsewhere.

Gastritis
(gastr/o: stomach; -itis: inflammation)

Gastritis is **inflammation of the stomach**, specifically the **lining of the stomach**. Gastritis may occur suddenly or slowly over time.

Causes

Some primary causes of gastritis include **infection by H. pylori bacterium**, excessive use of **alcohol**, use of **anti-inflammatory drugs**, **vomiting**, and **stress**. Gastritis should be treated, as it may lead to more serious conditions such as stomach cancer.

Symptoms

Some people with gastritis actually don't exhibit any symptoms. Those that do, however, may present with nausea, vomiting, loss of appetite, pain in the abdomen, and bloating in the abdomen.

Treatments

Treatment often consists of dietary changes, such as avoiding spicy food and dairy, taking antacids to reduce the amount of stomach acid present, and possibly even a round of antibiotics to combat infection by the H. pylori bacterium.

Contraindications

Massage on a client with gastritis is dependent on the cause and severity. If gastritis is causing nausea and vomiting, massage should not be performed.

Gastroenteritis

(gastr/o: stomach; enter/o: small intestine; -itis: inflammation)

Gastroenteritis is **inflammation of the stomach and small intestine**, commonly known as the "**stomach flu**".

Causes

The primary cause of gastroenteritis is a **viral or bacterial infection**. These infections can be spread by coming into contact with someone who has it, or consuming contaminated food or water that contains the virus or bacterium. The main types of virus that cause gastroenteritis are **rotavirus and norovirus**. The main types of bacterium that cause gastroenteritis are **E. coli and salmonella**.

Symptoms

Symptoms of gastroenteritis include diarrhea, vomiting, fever, abdominal pain, and body chills.

Treatments

Most people recover from gastroenteritis without requiring any treatment. The primary goal of treatment for gastroenteritis is to prevent dehydration. Therefore, drinking plenty of fluids is advised. Over-the-counter medications that help with nausea and vomiting may also help.

Contraindications

Gastroenteritis is often caused by a viral infection, and is contagious. Therefore, gastroenteritis is an absolute contraindication to massage.

Gastroesophageal Reflux Disease

(gastr/o: stomach; esophag/o: esophagus; reflux: flowing back)

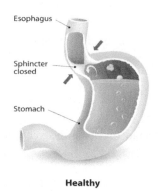

Healthy

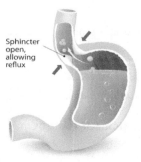

GERD

Gastroesophageal Reflux Disease(GERD) is a condition in which **stomach acid**, or food from the stomach, comes **back up into the esophagus**, causing **irritation and burning** in the lining of the esophagus.

Causes

GERD is the result of acid flowing backwards into the esophagus. This is primarily caused by the lower gastroesophageal sphincter(also known as the cardiac sphincter) relaxing when it normally is contracted and tightened. This can happen abnormally, or be caused by the sphincter weakening over time.

Symptoms

Symptoms include burning in the chest, pain in the chest, a dry cough, a sour taste in the mouth, and a sore throat. It is advisable to seek medical attention if chest pain is present, because symptoms are very similar to those seen in myocardial infarction.

Treatments

Over-the-counter medications, such as antacids, are the primary treatment for GERD. Other medications may be prescribed by a doctor if the GERD is not helped by antacids, such as H-2-receptor blockers, which reduce stomach acid production, and proton pump inhibitors, which completely block the production of stomach acid and give the lining of the esophagus time to heal.

Contraindications

Unless chest pain is present, massage is indicated for Gastroesophageal Reflux Disease. Semi-reclined position may help reduce acid from moving into the esophagus.

Hepatitis

(hepat-: liver; -itis: inflammation)

Hepatitis is a condition that results in **inflammation of the liver**.

Causes

There are numerous causes of hepatitis, which affect numerous different organ systems. Most commonly, hepatitis is the result of a **viral infection**, but may also result from **toxic substances** entering into the body, such as **alcohol**. Short-term symptoms of hepatitis include jaundice(yellowing of the skin due to increased bilirubin in the blood stream), fever, and nausea. Long-term symptoms include cirrhosis(destruction of healthy liver cells), scarring of the liver, liver cancer, and liver failure.

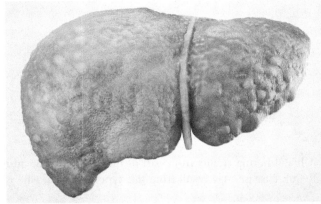

Liver with cobblestone appearance consistent with cirrhosis

There are five known hepatitis viruses: Hepatitis A, B, C, D, and E. Each varies in mode of contraction, and severity of symptoms.

Hepatitis A is the most common form, and is typically transmitted through ingestion of fecal matter(most commonly seen in parts of the world with low sanitation standards). People infected with Hepatitis A most frequently make a full recovery, and develop an immunity to the virus.

Hepatitis B is typically transmitted through exposure to body fluids such as blood. The virus produces symptoms for a period greater than Hepatitis A, but most people will develop an immunity to it after about four weeks. A small percentage of people who contract Hepatitis B will become chronically affected by it. Vaccines for Hepatitis B are available.

Hepatitis C, much like Hepatitis B, is contracted through exposure to body fluids such as blood. Hepatitis C is a chronic condition which damages the liver even further each time the person's symptoms are in the acute stage. Hepatitis C is one of the leading causes of liver failure.

Hepatitis D is an infection that only results in symptoms if the person is also infected with the Hepatitis B virus. When this occurs, major complications may arise. Because Hepatitis D is only activated by the Hepatitis B virus, the Hepatitis B vaccine may contribute to the prevention of Hepatitis D.

Hepatitis E, like Hepatitis A, is contracted through exposure to fecal matter. It is most commonly seen in developing countries, where sanitation standards may not be high. Hepatitis E, if severe, may lead to liver failure, despite being an acute infection.

Symptoms

Hepatitis often results in no symptoms. More severe cases of hepatitis may result in a person presenting with nausea, fatigue, mild fever, loss of appetite, abdominal tenderness, and jaundice, among others.

Treatments

Treatments vary, depending on severity. Immunizations are available for Hepatitis B, and medications may help reduce the symptoms.

Contraindications

In the acute stage, massage is an absolute contraindication for hepatitis. In the post-acute stage, massage is indicated.

Hernia
(hernia: a rupture)

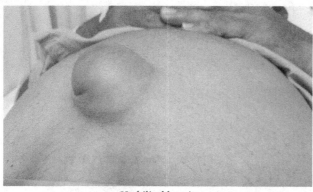

Umbilical hernia

A hernia is a rupture in a muscle or connective tissue, allowing an organ or other tissue to **protrude** through its normal location. There are many different types of herniae in the Digestive System, including **hiatal**, **umbilical**, and **inguinal**.

Causes

A hernia is caused by a weakness in the affected tissue, and/or straining of the tissue. When the tissue tears, the organ, usually the small intestine, protrudes through it. This can lead to many complications, such as organ strangulation, constipation, pain, or even trauma to other structures, such as the testes.

A hiatal hernia results from part of the stomach protruding upwards through the diaphragm, into the chest. Gastroesophageal Reflux Disease may result from this type of hernia, where stomach acids leak from the stomach backwards into the esophagus.

An umbilical hernia, most commonly seen in infants, is caused by the small intestine protruding through the abdominal wall and into the umbilicus. This condition usually resolves on its own.

An inguinal hernia, most commonly seen in men, is caused by the small intestine protruding through the wall of the abdomen, which typically descends into the scrotum. This may cause trauma to the testes. Sometimes, the small intestine may even drop farther down the body, into the thigh.

Symptoms

Symptoms vary depending on the type of hernia suffered. Examples include swelling beneath the skin in the abdomen or groin in an inguinal or umbilical hernia, and heart burn and pain in the upper abdomen in hiatal herniae.

Treatments

Treatments may include dietary changes in cases such as a hiatal hernia, weight loss, medication such as antacids, or even surgery to repair the hernia.

Contraindications

Massage of a hernia is locally contraindicated.

Pancreatitis
(pancreat/o: pancreas; -itis: inflammation)

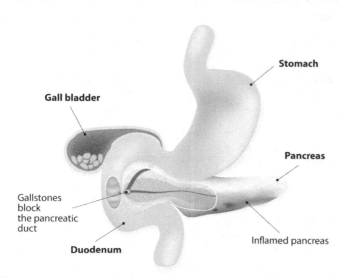

Stomach

Gall bladder

Pancreas

Gallstones block the pancreatic duct

Duodenum

Inflamed pancreas

Pancreatitis is **inflammation of the pancreas**. Pancreatitis may be either acute or chronic, each presenting with differing levels of severity.

Causes

Pancreatitis results when **enzymes** produced by the pancreas, **insulin and glucagon, become active in the pancreas** before entering into the digestive tract or blood stream. This causes the pancreas to become irritated and inflamed. Things that may contribute to pancreatitis include blockage of the bile duct by gallstones, alcoholism, pancreatic cancer, infection, and cystic fibrosis.

Symptoms

Acute pancreatitis presents with fever, nausea, vomiting, pain in the upper abdomen, abdominal tenderness, and pain radiating to the back. Chronic pancreatitis may also present with the same symptoms in the acute stage, but weight loss may also occur.

Pancreatitis may lead to the development of other serious conditions such as diabetes, pancreatic cancer, and kidney failure.

Treatments

Upon admission to a hospital, a patient with pancreatitis will be prescribed pain medication. Fasting reduces the production of insulin and glucagon, and is therefore beneficial to decrease irritation. Other treatments that treat the underlying causes of pancreatitis can include removal of the gallbladder or gallstones, and treatment for alcohol dependency.

Contraindications

In the acute stage, pancreatitis is considered an absolute contraindication. In a client with chronic pancreatitis, massage may be performed in the post-acute stage.

Pharyngitis
(pharyng/o: pharynx; -itis: inflammation)

Pharyngitis is **inflammation of the pharynx**, or the throat. A **sore throat** is considered pharyngitis.

Causes

Pharyngitis is usually the result of a **viral infection** from the **common cold or the flu**. **Bacterial infections** may also result in pharyngitis, such as **strep throat**. Non-exudative pharyngitis, the kind usually caused by a virus, does not produce increased mucous, while exudative pharyngitis, the kind usually caused by bacteria, does produce mucous. Both types of pharyngitis are contagious.

Symptoms

Pain in the throat is one of the main symptoms of pharyngitis. Speaking and swallowing food may be painful. A person may develop a fever, and the tonsils and lymph nodes in the neck may enlarge. Excessive mucous may be produced if it is caused by bacterial infection.

Treatments

Antiviral medications may prevent the condition from worsening. If the condition is caused by bacterial infection, antibiotics can help combat the infection and improve the condition.

Contraindications

Pharyngitis is commonly considered an absolute contraindication to massage during the acute stage. After the infection has cleared, massage may be performed.

Strep Throat

Strep throat is a **bacterial infection**, resulting in **sore throat**. Typically, a throat culture is performed in order to diagnose strep throat.

Causes

Strep throat is caused by an infection of the **streptococcal bacteria**, which is contagious. Children are most at risk of contracting strep throat, but it can occur in people of all ages.

Symptoms

In addition to sore throat, a person with strep throat may exhibit red spots on the roof of the mouth, white patches on the tonsils, swollen lymph nodes in the neck, pain upon swallowing, and fever, amongst others. If left untreated, strep throat may contribute to the development of rheumatic fever, which can cause damage to heart valves.

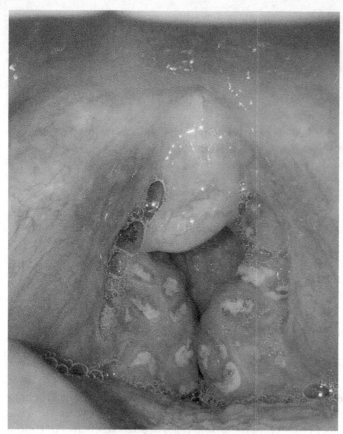

Inflamed tonsils presenting with white spots
consistent with streptococcal infection

Treatments

Because strep throat is caused by bacteria, antibiotics are the primary treatment. Acetaminophen is useful in treating any pain that may be present due to the infection. After starting a course of antibiotics, a person should begin feeling better within a couple days. Taking all the medication prescribed is required to prevent the infection from returning and becoming resistant to the antibiotics.

Contraindications

Because strep throat is highly contagious, it is considered an absolute contraindication until the condition has completely cleared.

Endocrine Pathologies

Acromegaly

(acro-: extremity; -megaly: irregular enlargement)

Acromegaly is **abnormal growth during adulthood**, resulting from the release of **excessive amounts of growth hormone** by the **pituitary gland**. This can cause bones to keep growing, increasing a person's size and changing their appearance.

Acromegaly can result in numerous severe complications, such as cardiovascular issues, hypertension, sleep apnea, and arthritis.

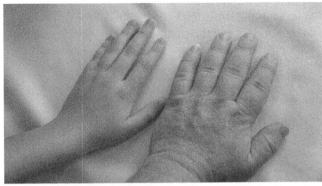

Enlarged features pictured on the right

Causes

Acromegaly is caused by increased amounts of growth hormone being produced by the pituitary gland. The most common reason for this to occur is a tumor growing on the pituitary gland. The tumor produces growth hormone and secretes it into the blood stream, increasing the growth hormone levels in the body. Rarely, a tumor elsewhere in the body, such as the adrenal glands, may produce growth hormone. This can also increase growth hormone levels in the body.

Symptoms

Symptoms of acromegaly generally take some time to appear as the disease slowly progresses. Enlarged hands and feet are an extremely common symptom. Enlargement of facial features, including the jaw and brow lines, can typically be seen in advanced stages. Skin can become thickened and the voice can deepen.

Treatments

If acromegaly is the result of a tumor, surgery may be performed to remove the tumor. Removing the tumor should stabilize the growth hormone levels in the body. After surgery, radiation therapy may be performed to destroy any remaining tumor cells in the body. This can help ensure the tumor does not return. Medications may help reduce the effects of growth hormone in the body.

Contraindications

Massage is indicated for acromegaly.

Addison's Disease

Addison's Disease is an **autoimmune disorder affecting the adrenal glands**, which results in a lack of cortisol and/or aldosterone production.

Causes

Addison's Disease is caused by **damage to the adrenal cortex** by the body's **immune system**. Damage to these glands results in an inability to produce cortisol, which regulates stress levels in the body by helping control blood sugar, blood pressure, and metabolism, and aldosterone, which aids in reabsorption of water and sodium back into the blood stream.

Symptoms

Addison's Disease may result in fatigue, weight loss, low blood pressure, hair loss, hyperpigmentation of the skin, and nausea. It may become life-threatening if not treated.

Acute adrenal failure, also known as Addisonian Crisis, may result in severe vomiting and diarrhea, dehydration, low blood pressure, and pain in the low back, abdomen, and/or legs.

Treatments

Treatment primarily consists of hormone replacements, which may be taken orally or injected.

Contraindications

Massage is indicated for a client with Addison's Disease. However, the type and length of massage varies depending on how a client is feeling and their stamina. Clients with low stamina should receive shorter, lighter massages, while clients with increased stamina may receive longer and stimulating massages.

Cushing's Disease

Cushing's Disease is a disease of the pituitary gland, which results in **hyper-production of adrenocorticotropic hormone(ACTH)**.

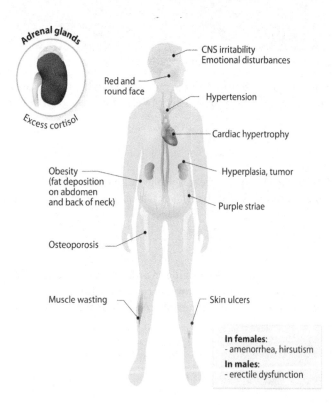

Causes

Cushing's Disease is the result of hyperplasia(excessive growth) of the pituitary gland, or development of a tumor. This causes too much ACTH to be released in the body, which stimulates **hyper-production of cortisol.**

Symptoms

Cushing's Disease may result in weight gain around the face and torso, weakening of bone, thinning of skin, fatigue, and acne, amongst other complications.

Treatments

Treatments for Cushing's Disease include surgery to remove a tumor, and hormone therapy to reduce the amount of cortisol being produced.

Contraindications

Massage is indicated for Cushing's Disease, but precautions may be taken in clients with weakened bones. Lighter massage is recommended for these clients to prevent damaging bone.

Diabetes Mellitus
(diabetes: to pass through; mellitus: sweet)

Diabetes Mellitus is a condition of the Endocrine System that affects **insulin function in the body**. There are three types of diabetes: Diabetes Type I, Diabetes Type II, and Gestational Diabetes.

Causes

Diabetes Type I is often known as **juvenile diabetes**, as it begins in childhood. In Type I, the body's immune system attacks the pancreas, the organ that produces insulin. This results in the body not producing enough insulin, which the body needs in order to convert glucose to energy.

Diabetes Type II, the most common form of diabetes, is caused by the body having an **insulin resistance**. The insulin in the body is unable to break down glucose, which causes high levels of sugar in the blood stream. Obesity is a common cause of Diabetes Type II.

Gestational Diabetes is only present **during pregnancy**. Gestational Diabetes affects less than 10% of all pregnant women, and typically resolves after pregnancy ends.

Symptoms

Symptoms of diabetes include frequent urination, fatigue, weight loss, pain and/or numbness in the hands or feet, extreme thirst, and extreme hunger.

Treatments

Treatment for Diabetes Type I is primarily insulin injections. Treatment for Diabetes Type II includes medications, but exercise and dietary changes are most common. Treatment for Gestational Diabetes includes exercise, regulating weight gain during pregnancy, and insulin medication depending on the severity.

Contraindications

Massage is indicated for a client with diabetes. If neuropathy is present, lighter massage in the affected area should be performed. If ulcers are present in areas afflicted with neuropathy, ulcers should be treated as local contraindications. If a client injects insulin, the injection site should also be avoided.

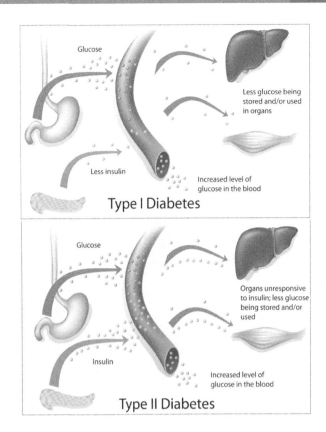

Goiter

(Latin "guttur": throat)

A goiter is an **enlargement of the thyroid gland**, located at the base of the neck.

Causes

The primary cause of a goiter is a **lack of iodine in the diet**. If a person does not consume enough iodine, the body is unable to produce sufficient thyroid hormones. Other conditions such as Graves' disease or Hashimoto's disease can affect the levels of thyroid hormone being produced. Too much thyroid hormone or too little thyroid hormone being produced can have negative effects on the thyroid and could produce a goiter.

Symptoms

Goiters produce a bulge in the throat, which may place pressure on other structures such as the esophagus or trachea, making it difficult to eat or breathe.

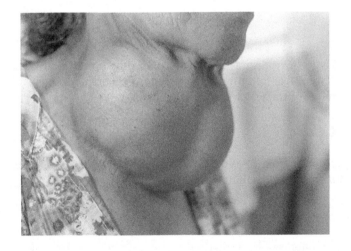

Treatments

Treatment of a goiter typically depends on the cause. If it is caused by low levels of thyroid hormones, thyroid hormone replacement medications may be prescribed. If the thyroid is producing too much thyroid hormone, medications may be prescribed to stabilize the levels of thyroid hormone in the body. Surgery to remove the thyroid may be an option if the goiter causes any difficulty in breathing or swallowing, or causes discomfort.

Increasing iodine consumption may be all it takes to reduce the goiter. Iodized salt may be added to the diet, along with other foods high in iodine such as seafood.

Contraindications

A goiter is considered a local contraindication.

Graves' Disease

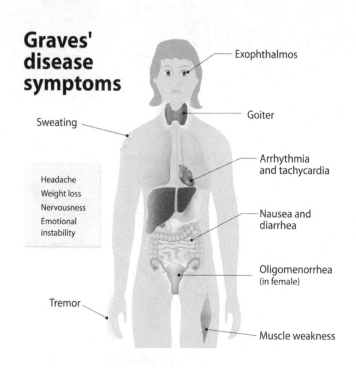

Graves' disease symptoms

- Exophthalmos
- Sweating
- Goiter
- Arrhythmia and tachycardia
- Nausea and diarrhea
- Oligomenorrhea (in female)
- Tremor
- Muscle weakness

Headache
Weight loss
Nervousness
Emotional instability

Graves' Disease is an **autoimmune disorder** in which the body's **immune system attacks the thyroid gland**, causing an **increase in thyroid hormone production(hyperthyroidism)**.

Causes

The exact cause of Graves' disease is unknown.

Symptoms

Graves' disease can affect numerous parts of the body, resulting in sensitivity to heat, weight loss, the development of a goiter(enlargement of the thyroid), bulging of the eyes, and irregular heart rhythm. Women are more likely to develop Graves' disease, as well as people under the age of 40.

Treatments

Treatment for Graves' disease include medications such as beta blockers and anti-thyroid medications. If medication isn't helpful, surgical removal of the thyroid may be an option.

Contraindications

Graves' disease is generally considered not contraindicated. However, a client with Graves' disease may be sensitive to heat, so anything that uses heat in the massage treatment should be avoided. A goiter may also be present, which would be considered a local contraindication.

Hyperthyroidism

(hyper-: excessive; thyroid: thyroid gland; -ism: condition)

Hyperthyroidism is an **increase in production of thyroxine**, a hormone secreted by the thyroid gland. Thyroxine is primarily responsible for **stimulating tissues to consume oxygen**. Excessive amounts of thyroxine can significantly increase the body's metabolism, which can have numerous effects.

Causes

Hyperthyroidism is often caused by other conditions such as Graves' disease. Tumors may grow in or on the thyroid, which can increase production of thyroxine.

Symptoms

Symptoms of hyperthyroidism are vast, and may be confused with other medical conditions. The main symptom of hyperthyroidism is sudden, rapid weight loss due to an increased metabolism. This may even cause an increase in appetite, despite the lost weight. Arrhythmia, specifically tachycardia, may also result. Heat sensitivity and sweating are other symptoms to be aware of.

Treatments

Treatments are often the same as those seen with Graves' disease, including a prescription of oral radioactive iodine. Other medications may help lower the amount of hormone being produced by the thyroid. If a person has tachycardia as a result of hyperthyroidism, beta blockers may also be prescribed. In cases where these treatments aren't helpful, surgical removal of the thyroid may be performed.

Contraindications

Generally, hyperthyroidism is not contraindicated. However, conditions such as arrhythmia that can be caused by hyperthyroidism may be contraindicated if uncontrolled.

Integumentary Pathologies

Acne

Acne is an infection of the skin, resulting from numerous factors. Acne may result in whiteheads, blackheads, or even cysts if left untreated.

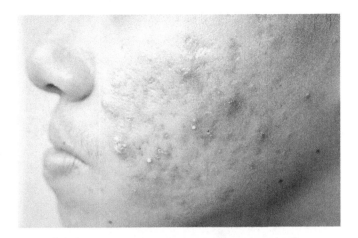

Causes

Acne is caused by an increased production of sebum on the skin, which results in blocked pores. These **blocked pores may become infected**, which may develop into pustules. There are several contributing factors that lead to the development of acne, including **testosterone production**, stress, hormonal imbalances, and poor personal hygiene.

Symptoms

Acne may result in the development of whiteheads, blackheads, pimples, or even cystic lesions beneath the skin. These are often painful to the touch and may present with infection and inflammation.

Treatments

Treatment includes over-the-counter skin care products for mild acne, or in the case of severe acne, medications such as birth control pills to regulate hormone levels in women, and antibiotics to eliminate bacterial growth. Other treatments include light therapy and chemical peels.

Contraindications

Whiteheads are considered local contraindications. Any part of the body experiencing inflammation from acne should also be considered a local contraindication.

Athlete's Foot
(tinea: fungus; pedis: foot)

Athlete's Foot(also known as Tinea Pedis) is a **fungal infection of the foot**. Despite the name, anyone may develop athlete's foot, not just athletes. Athlete's foot, like other fungal infections such as ringworm and jock itch, is highly contagious.

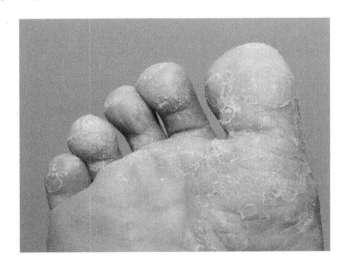

Causes

Athlete's foot is caused by exposure to fungus on the foot. When a person wears tight-fitting shoes, it provides an environment for the fungus to thrive: a warm, humid, dark space. The fungus spreads, growing between the toes, then expanding across the foot. The infection causes the skin to become dry and scaly, which may result in breaking of the skin and bacterial infection.

Symptoms

Symptoms of athlete's foot are typically the development of a red, scaly rash between the toes, which may spread proximally. Blisters and ulcers may be present in the area. Itching of the affected area is common.

Treatments

Treatment of athlete's foot primarily consists of over-the-counter medications, in addition to self-care, such as ensuring the foot and footwear are dry as much as possible, wearing shower shoes in public bathing areas, etc.

Contraindications

Because athlete's foot is contagious, it is considered a local contraindication. The feet should be avoided, and any linens the feet have come in contact with should be treated as contaminated.

Boil

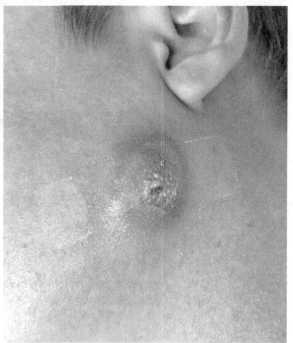

A boil is a **bacterial infection of a hair follicle**, also known as a **furuncle**. A group of these infections together in one localized area is known as a carbuncle.

Causes

A boil typically results from small cuts in the skin(caused by things like shaving), allowing staphylococci bacterium to enter the body and reproduce. Boils can be red, inflamed, and painful to the touch. The lump initially produced by the infection begins to soften over a few days, and becomes much more painful. Pus develops on the affected area.

Symptoms

A boil may result in pain around the boil, the development of a fever, and swelling of lymph nodes. More boils may develop around the site of the original boil.

Treatments

Boils are treated by lancing(draining) the area with application of antibacterial soap and water, or in more severe cases, prescription of antibiotics to combat the bacterial infection.

Contraindications

A boil is considered a local contraindication for massage.

Burns

Burns are a skin condition in which the skin is damaged due to exposure to **heat**, **chemicals**, or other means. This may result in inflammation, blister formation, or necrosis, depending on the severity of the burn.

Burns of the skin can be categorized as first, second, third, or fourth degree, with first being the least severe.

A **first degree burn** only affects the **epidermis**. It may lead to pain and inflammation of the skin, but nothing more. A common first degree burn is a sun burn. The pain and inflammation subsides in a day or two, and the skin returns to normal.

A **second degree burn** is more severe. In a second degree burn, the burn moves through the epidermis and **into the dermis**. Because the burn goes deeper into the skin, it causes more damage, which can be seen by **blistering**. Blisters form to help repair the damage done by the burn. Second degree burns may result in scarring if they are too severe.

Third degree burns move even deeper into the skin, reaching the **subcutaneous layer of the skin**. Third degree burns often cause **severe tissue damage and necrosis**. Skin grafts may be needed to help repair an area damaged by a third degree burn.

While first, second, and third degree burns are most common, a **fourth degree burn** moves completely **through all layers of the skin**, and goes deeper into tissues beneath the skin such as tendons, ligaments, muscles, and bones.

Causes

Burns may be caused by many different factors, including heat(thermal burns), chemicals, electricity, radiation(such as sunburns), friction(rug burns), and even extreme cold temperatures.

Symptoms

Burn symptoms vary based on severity. First degree burns often present with inflammation and pain. Second degree burns present with pain, blistering, and discoloration of the skin as the body repairs the damaged tissue. Third degree burns may present with blackened, charred tissue, with the skin having a waxy appearance. Because tissue is destroyed in third and fourth degree burns, loss of sensation may occur resulting from nerves being destroyed.

Treatments

Treatment for burns often depends on the severity of the burn. Application of aloe vera may help reduce the pain in first degree burns. Second degree burns may require bandages with topical antibiotic cream to prevent infection. Third degree burns may require surgery and skin grafts to repair the affected areas.

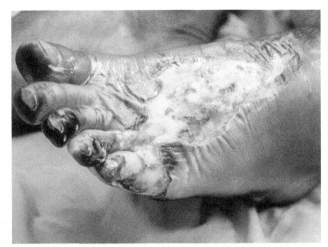

Tissue damage resulting from third degree burn

Contraindications

Burns are considered local contraindications for massage. Avoid any area experiencing inflammation, blistering, or has suffered necrosis.

Cellulitis
(cell: cell; -itis: inflammation)

Cellulitis is a **bacterial infection of the skin**, causing symptoms such as inflammation of the infected area, fever, pain, and blisters.

Causes

Cellulitis is caused by **staphylococci bacterium** entering the body through **exposure to wounds**, most commonly on the legs. The infection typically stays localized, but continues to spread to surrounding tissues as the bacteria grows. The infection can present with well-defined borders of infection. If the infection enters the blood stream, it may result in septicemia, a potentially life-threatening condition.

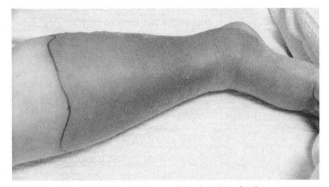

Cellulitis presenting with defined border of infection

Spider or insect bites may also introduce the bacterium into the body. Any insect bite should be cleaned thoroughly to prevent infection.

Symptoms

Cellulitis may present with many symptoms, including a red area of skin that spreads and increases in size over time, swelling, pain, fever, and blisters on the infected area.

Treatments

Treatment for cellulitis includes antibiotic medication, taken orally. Cellulitis is not typically contagious.

Contraindications

Cellulitis is considered a local contraindication. Any open wounds should be avoided.

Contusion

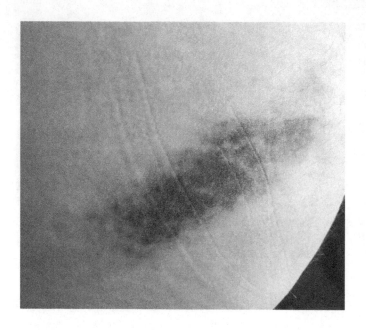

A contusion, also known as a **bruise**, is **damage to blood vessels in the skin**, resulting in **bleeding**. The bleeding usually stops quickly due to thrombocytes clotting the blood, but blood remains in a localized area until it can be slowly removed by the body over time.

Causes

Contusions are caused by trauma to an area damaging and breaking open capillaries in the skin. The trauma is usually caused by a direct blow to the skin.

Symptoms

In the acute stage, pain may be present in the area, as there is trauma. Inflammation may occur as a result to tissue damage. After the contusion has stopped bleeding, the inflammation usually subsides. There may be a dull ache in the contusion as the tissue is being repaired internally.

Contusions leave discoloration in the skin until they are healed and the blood has been removed from the area. The closer to the time trauma occurs, the darker the bruise is. The contusion lightens over time as the blood is removed from the area.

Treatments

PRICE is the best method of treating a bruise: protect the area from further damage, rest the area, ice the area to reduce pain and inflammation, compress the area to further decrease inflammation, and elevate the area to promote effective blood flow and limit inflammation. Over-the-counter pain medication may be used if the area is painful.

Contraindications

A contusion is considered a local contraindication to massage, due to the potential presence of blood clots in the contusion.

Decubitus Ulcer

(decubitus: the act of lying down; ulcer: open sore)

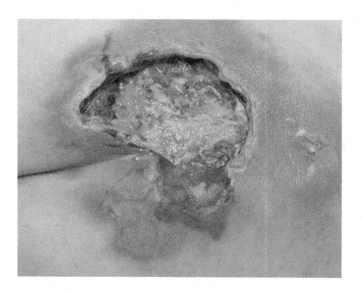

A decubitus ulcer is a condition affecting the skin, resulting in the development of open sores.

Causes

Decubitus ulcers are also known as **bed sores or pressure ulcers**. When the body is in a static position for an extended period of time, such as when lying down, the parts of the body coming in contact with the bed, floor, or chair experience **ischemia**, a reduction of blood flow to the tissues due to pressure. When ischemia is present for too long, the tissue experiences **necrosis** due to a lack of oxygen. The dead tissue becomes ulcerated, and bacterial infection may occur.

People who are prone to decubitus ulcers are the elderly, disabled people, and people confined to a bed or wheelchair.

Symptoms

Symptoms of decubitus ulcers include discoloration of the skin, tenderness in the affected area, temperature variation in the affected area, and swelling. In severe cases, infection may result after ulceration has occurred.

Treatments

Treatments for decubitus ulcers vary, depending on the severity of the ulceration. If an infection is present, antibiotics may be prescribed. If there is an abundance of necrotic tissue, cleaning of the area(debridement) may be performed. If there is ischemia, but no ulcer, massage and application of heat may help bring blood back into the area.

Contraindications

A decubitus ulcer is considered a local contraindication if the skin has developed into an ulcer. If the skin has not opened, massage in the area is indicated to increase blood flow into the affected tissue. If the sore is present, massage up to two inches around the area is indicated to increase circulation and prevent further necrosis.

Dermatitis
(dermat/o: skin; -itis: inflammation)

Dermatitis is **inflammation of the skin.** There are several types of dermatitis, including **contact dermatitis**, **atopic dermatitis**, and **seborrheic dermatitis**. Each has different causes, but each presents with some sort of inflammation of the skin.

Causes

Contact dermatitis results when the skin comes in to contact with some sort of irritant or allergen, causing the skin to become inflamed. Atopic dermatitis, also known as **eczema**, can be caused by numerous factors, including an improperly functioning immune system, bacteria, dry skin, and the environment. Eczema usually begins in infancy. Seborrheic dermatitis is typically the result of a fungus growing on the skin, usually in regions that are more oily than others such as the scalp.

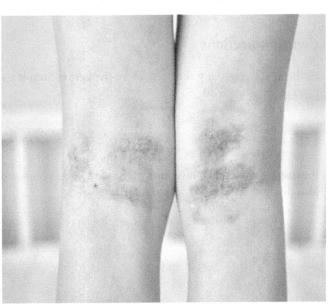

Atopic dermatitis, also known as eczema

Symptoms

Contact dermatitis presents with inflammation and possible blistering where the skin has come into contact with an irritant. This is usually an acute condition, and will improve after the irritant has been cleaned or removed from the body. Atopic dermatitis presents with red, itchy patches on the body, usually near joints that flex and extend. This can be a chronic condition, and the patches may go away and come back later depending on factors such as the weather. Seborrheic dermatitis can cause itchy patches around the face, cheeks, nose, back, and chest.

Treatments

Often times, application of an over-the-counter corticosteroid cream is all that's needed to alleviate dermatitis symptoms. If over-the-counter creams are ineffective, prescription strength corticosteroid creams may be administered, which usually take care of the dermatitis. Other treatments can even include exposure to sunlight.

Contraindications

Dermatitis is considered a local contraindication, as massage to the affected area will increase inflammation.

Herpes Simplex
(herpein: to creep; simplex: simple)

Herpes Simplex is a **viral infection of the skin**. There are two types of herpes simplex: **Herpes Simplex I**, which causes sores around the mouth, and **Herpes Simplex II**, which causes sores around the genitals.

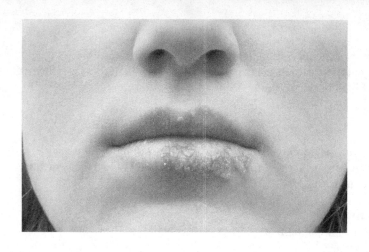

Causes

Herpes simplex is highly contagious, passing between people via direct contact. During an acute outbreak, a sore may appear on the skin, most commonly the mouth, face, or genitals. This sore disappears after a short time. Despite not having any sores present, a person may still be able to transmit the virus to another asymptomatically.

Symptoms

Symptoms vary depending on the type of herpes simplex a person has. Herpes simplex I primarily presents with sores around the mouth, while herpes simplex II may cause painful urination. Both forms, however, may result in fever, headache, and swollen lymph nodes.

Treatments

While there is no cure for herpes simplex, medications may be prescribed to reduce the chance of spreading the infection to others.

Contraindications

In the acute stage, any sore caused by the herpes simplex virus is considered a local contraindication. In the post-acute stage, massage is indicated.

Impetigo
(impetere: to attack)

Impetigo is a **bacterial infection of the skin**, most commonly seen in **children**. Impetigo is often confused with Hand, Foot, and Mouth Disease, which is a viral infection.

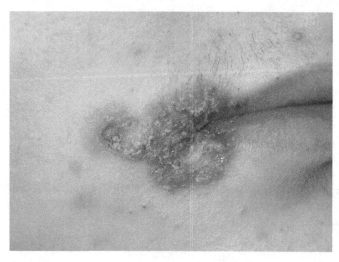

Causes

Impetigo is a highly contagious infection, caused by staphylococci or streptococci, which most commonly enter the body through already damaged skin, but may affect healthy skin as well. When the bacteria enters the skin, it produces sores that blister and leak a yellow, crust-like fluid. These sores typically develop around the mouth, nose, and ears.

Symptoms

Symptoms of impetigo include red sores that may pop and leave a yellowish crust, swollen lymph nodes, and fluid-filled blisters. The affected areas may also itch.

Treatments

Depending on the severity of the infection, impetigo may be treated with topical antibiotic cream for less severe cases, or with oral antibiotics for more severe cases. Recovery time is typically around one week with the use of medication.

Contraindications

Impetigo is a highly contagious bacterial infection, and therefore, is an absolute contraindication.

Lice

Lice, plural for a head louse, are small **parasites** that live on the **head** that **feed on human blood**. They primarily live on the scalp. Children are most likely to contract a lice infestation, also known as **pediculosis capitis**.

Causes

Lice are spread via direct contact. Lice do not jump or fly, and therefore must physically come into contact with a person to transfer to them. After lice have attached to a new host, they lay eggs on hair shafts. Once the eggs hatch, more lice are present.

Symptoms

The main symptom of lice is itching, caused by an allergy to the saliva of the lice.

Treatments

Over-the-counter or prescription medications may be prescribed to help kill the lice. Shampoos specifically designed to eliminate lice are often used.

Contraindications

Lice is a highly contagious parasitic infection, and is therefore an absolute contraindication.

Onychomycosis
(onycho-: nails; myc-: fungus; -osis: condition)

Onychomycosis is a **fungal infection of the nails**, most commonly the result of an infection by the **dermatophyte fungi**.

Causes

Onychomycosis is caused by fungi entering a nail, typically more common in older people due to the natural drying and cracking of nails that happens with age. The fungus enters into these cracks and begins growing, infecting the nail. Athlete's foot may also spread in to the area and infect the nail.

Symptoms

Symptoms of onychomycosis include thickening of the infected nail, change in the nail shape, discoloration of the nail turning it yellow or brown, and the nail becoming brittle.

Treatments

If symptoms are mild, treatment may not be necessary. When treatment is required, however, antifungal medications are the main form of treatment. Oral antifungals are used more often than topical creams, as they can work quicker. If the infection is severe, the nail may need to be surgically removed to allow antifungal cream to be applied directly to the nail bed.

Contraindications

Onychomycosis is a contagious fungal infection, and is considered a local contraindication.

Psoriasis
(psora-: to itch; -iasis: condition)

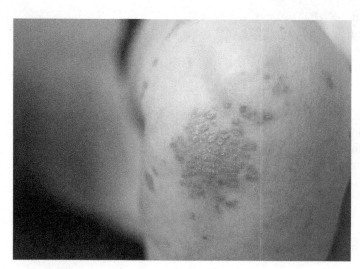

Psoriasis is an **autoimmune disorder of the skin**, resulting in the **production of thick, dry, scaly patches.** Psoriasis has periods of exacerbation and remission, where the patches appear and then may resolve themselves.

Causes

The exact cause of psoriasis is unknown. Certain triggers, such as stress, may cause the body's immune system to attack the skin. Normally, skin cells have a life span of 3-4 weeks, and ultimately flake off the body. When the immune system attacks the skin, the body responds by increasing production of epithelial cells at an extremely rapid pace, which is much faster than the cells are being destroyed. This rapid pace of cell production is what produces the patches on the skin.

Symptoms

Symptoms of psoriasis differ based on each person, but may include red, patchy skin covered in thick, silvery scales, dry skin that may crack and bleed, thickened finger and toe nails, and itchy skin.

Treatments

There is no cure for psoriasis, but treatments are available to help manage the condition. Treatments include topical creams(which may contain steroids), exposure to sunlight, and application of aloe vera.

Contraindications

Psoriasis is not contraindicated for massage. Massage may be altered if the patches are painful or are scabbing, but otherwise, the patches may be massaged.

Ringworm
(dermato-: skin; phyt-: plant; -osis: condition)

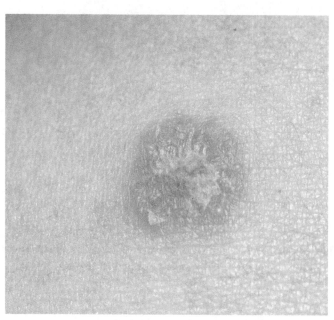

Ring of infection typical of ringworm

Ringworm. also known as dermatophytosis, is a **fungal infection of the skin** similar to athlete's foot. Despite the name, it is not a parasitic infection. It results in a **ring-like area of infection**.

Causes

Fungus, like the kind found in ringworm, live on the dead cells of the body, such as the epidermis. When ringworm is contracted, it forms red blisters and a ring of infection begins to show, which then spreads as the infection grows through the skin.

Ringworm is contagious, and may be spread from person to person. It is especially common in athletes, whose bodies come in close contact with one another, such as wrestlers.

Symptoms

Ringworm typically presents with well-defined circular patches of infection on the skin, usually more red on the outer edges than inside. These patches can be itchy and develop blisters.

Treatments

Treatment includes good personal hygiene, and most commonly application of antifungal ointment to the affected area. More severe cases may require oral antifungal medication.

Contraindications

Ringworm is a highly contagious fungal infection, and is considered a local contraindication. Linens should be treated as contaminated.

Scabies

Scabies is a **parasitic infection caused by a mite**, known as **Sacroptes scabiei**. This mite **burrows under the skin and lays eggs**, causing **intense itching**. The tunnels the mite creates are visible in the skin. Scratching due to a scabies infection may lead to an infection, and is not recommended.

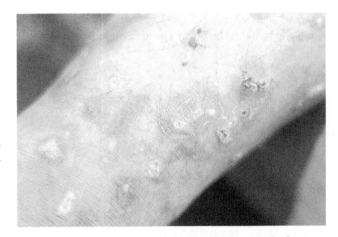

Causes

Scabies are extremely contagious, transmitting easily from one person to the next via physical contact, or sharing clothing or other linens.

Symptoms

The main symptoms of a scabies infection are severe itching and visible burrows in the skin where the mite has worked its way in to the body.

Treatments

Topical creams that are specifically designed to kill mites are prescribed to treat scabies. They kill the mites quickly, but itching may persist for some time after treatment begins.

Contraindications

Scabies is a contagious parasitic infection, and is considered an absolute contraindication.

Sebaceous Cyst

A sebaceous cyst is a condition affecting the skin, but may affect other tissues as well. These are typically the result of a **blockage in a sebaceous gland** that causes a backup of sebum, which is then **surrounded by a membrane** to keep it or an infection from harming the rest of the body.

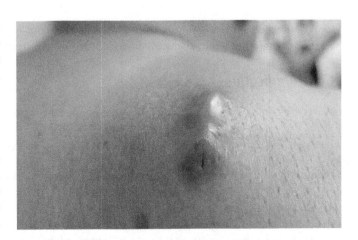

Causes

A sebaceous gland produces oil, and secretes oil onto the surface of the skin. If a blockage of a sebaceous gland occurs, oil cannot escape the gland, and bacteria may infect the area. If too much bacteria is present, the body may develop connective tissue that surrounds the infected sebaceous gland, trapping it inside.

Sebaceous cysts may be large or small. They may be painful to the touch, or may lead to localized infections known as abscesses. Cysts may need to be removed surgically. If the entire cyst membrane is not removed, there may be a chance of the cyst returning in the future.

Symptoms

Some cysts show no symptoms, but symptoms are more likely to appear the larger the cyst is. Small cysts usually do not cause pain, but large cysts may cause pain and discomfort in the surrounding area.

Treatments

Treatment, if necessary, includes moist compresses on the area to help drain the cyst, or possible surgery if there is a risk of infection. Surgical removal may be required if the cyst is large, causes pain, or may be cancerous.

Contraindications

Sebaceous cysts are considered local contraindications, and should be avoided to prevent damaging the cyst and allowing the fluid inside to harm the body. The area may also be painful.

Wart

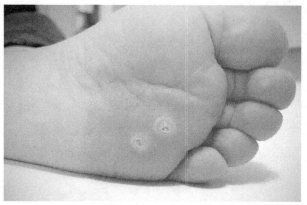

Plantar warts

Warts, also known as verrucae, are small **benign growths on the skin** caused by the **human papilloma virus(HPV)**.

Causes

Warts are contagious, and may be spread by direct skin contact. The human papilloma virus stimulates the skin to produce more keratin, which causes a hard, thick overgrowth on a small localized area.

Warts may be located in numerous locations on the body, including the hands, feet(plantar warts), and genitals(genital warts).

Symptoms

Warts are typically rough, grainy bumps, which may be a range of colors, from the color of the person's skin to white, tan, or even pink. Often, warts may have black spots in them, which is nothing more than blood clots.

Depending on the location of the wart, such as plantar warts, the wart may be painful due to calluses forming over them, pushing them deeper into the skin.

Treatments

Warts often go into remission on their own, and treatment is not necessary. Treatment options include cryotherapy to freeze the wart, excising(cutting out) the wart, or electrosurgery to burn the wart.

Contraindications

Warts are contagious, and should be treated as a local contraindication.

Wounds

Wounds are the result of a **breakage in the skin**, which exposes underlying tissues. There are several different types of open wounds.

An **abrasion** is a **scraping off of layers of the skin**, such as a skinned knee from falling. An **avulsion** is when the skin or another structure, such as a finger or toe nail, is **pulled and ripped**. An **incision**, such as produced during surgery, is a **clean cut through tissue**. A **laceration** is a cut that produces **jagged edges**. A **puncture** is caused by an object **piercing the skin**, producing a hole.

Causes

Wounds can be caused by many different factors. Ischemia may cause wounds in cases such as decubitus ulcers. Infections may cause wounds to appear in the skin as well. Damage to blood vessels, like those seen in diabetes mellitus can result in wounds. Trauma is usually the main cause of wounds, however. These include abrasions, lacerations, incisions, and punctures.

Symptoms

Wounds in the acute stage often present with bleeding, pain, and redness in the area. These symptoms usually resolve with the healing process. If a wound is not properly treated, infection may occur, along with fever if the infection becomes systemic. A wound that becomes infected and results in necrosis is known as gangrene, caused by a severe lack of blood flow in the area.

Treatments

Wounds should be cleansed with soap and water, and a sterile bandage should be applied to stop bleeding. If a wound is caused by a bite from an animal or insect, medical attention may(and probably should) be recommended.

Contraindications

Wounds should be treated as local contraindications until healed.

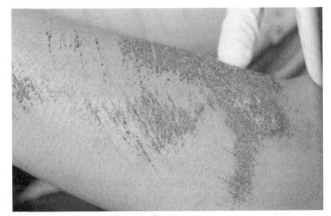

Abrasion

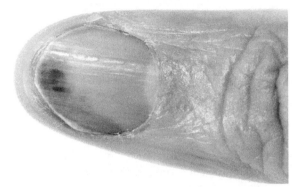

Avulsion

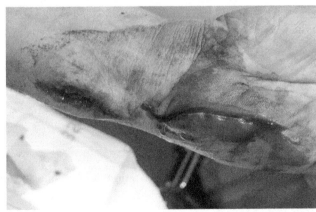

Laceration

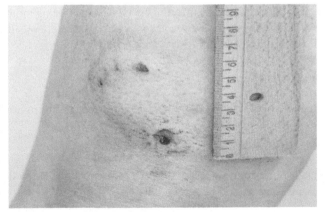

Puncture

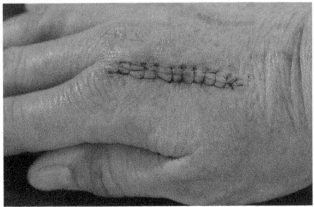

Suture

Lymphatic Pathologies

Acquired Immunodeficiency Syndrome

HIV Entry to T Cell

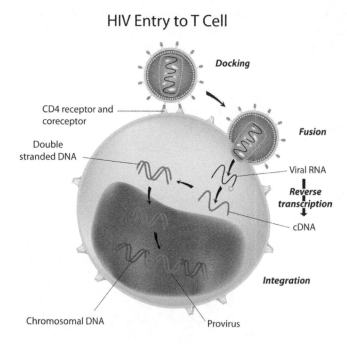

Acquired Immunodeficiency Syndrome, also known as **AIDS**, is a chronic condition caused by HIV, the human immunodeficiency virus. Once in the body, **HIV destroys the body's T-cells**, which function to regulate the response of the body's immune system to antigens. When HIV destroys too many of the body's T-cells, the immune system is considered compromised, and a person is then diagnosed with AIDS. While most people who are infected with HIV in the United States are properly treated and don't develop AIDS, a small portion of people do gets AIDS after HIV infection, typically around ten years after initial infection.

Causes

HIV is spread though unprotected sex, through needles that have been shared by an infected person, as a result of a mother passing HIV on to their unborn child, or even through blood transfusions if the blood has not been properly screened beforehand. HIV cannot be spread through skin contact, water contact, through the bites of insects such as mosquitoes, or breathing in the air of an infected person.

Symptoms

Close after the initial infection has occurred, a person may experience fever, fatigue, body aches, headache, and swollen lymph nodes. As the infection spreads, symptoms emerge such as diarrhea and weight loss in conjunction with previously mentioned symptoms.

Complications caused by infection by HIV include being more prone to infection of other conditions such as pneumonia. A type of cancer known as Kaposi's Sarcoma may develop. Severe wasting of the body may occur, in which a person loses at least ten percent of their total body weight.

Treatments

A person infected with HIV should be prescribed antiretroviral therapy to help prevent the virus from further replicating.

Contraindications

AIDS is not a contraindication to massage. Any open sores should be treated as a local contraindication. If the client isn't feeling well, massage should be rescheduled.

Allergy

An allergy is a reaction of the body's immune system in response to substances that **normally do not affect people**. Common substances people may be allergic to include dust, pollen, mold, certain foods, pet dander, and medication.

Causes

Allergies occur when a substance enters the body that the body's immune system thinks is dangerous. The body produces **antibodies** for that specific substance. When the substance enters the body, the body releases the antibodies and other substances such as **histamines** to attack the substance. The release of histamines is what gives people allergy symptoms.

Symptoms

Allergies may be mild, or may be severe and result in serious conditions such as anaphylactic shock. Anaphylactic shock requires the use of an epinephrine shot to reverse the effects of the allergen. Less severe allergies may result in a runny nose, itchy eyes or skin, and hives.

Treatments

Typical treatments of allergens include the use of antihistamines, decongestants, and steroid nasal sprays. Avoiding the allergen is advised.

Contraindications

Allergies should be determined prior to massage to avoid using any allergens in massage lubricant. If a client develops any signs of contact with an allergen during the massage, massage should be stopped. If essential oils are the cause of the allergic reaction, effects can be managed with the application of vegetable oil.

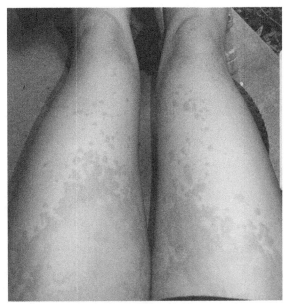

Hives occuring due to exposure to an allergen

Lupus Erythematosus

(lupus: wolf; erythemat-: red skin; -osus: pertaining to)

Lupus Erythematosus is an **autoimmune disorder affecting the connective tissues of the entire body**, but can be physically seen in the skin by the formation of a **butterfly rash** that appears on the face during flare-ups. This rash is similar in shape to the markings found on the face of a wolf, which is where lupus gets its name.

Causes

The exact cause of lupus is unknown. Some experts believe it is a genetic disorder that influences the immune system's function. Lupus may also be triggered by smoking, sunlight, infections, and medications.

Symptoms

Symptoms of lupus erythematosus include fever, the formation of a butterfly rash, joint pain, discomfort, fatigue, and sensitivity to sunlight. It may also contribute to the development of other medical conditions, such as Raynaud's Syndrome.

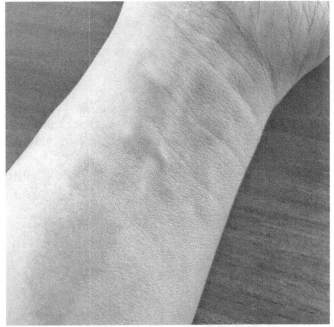

Rash consistent with exacerbation of lupus

Treatments

There is no cure for lupus erythematosus, but treatment is available to help manage the condition. Non-steroidal anti-inflammatory drugs may help with systemic inflammation in non-severe cases. Topical corticosteroid creams may help alleviate rashes. Blood thinners may also be used in more severe cases.

Contraindications

During flare-ups, lupus may cause extensive pain over the body, and massage would likely be postponed until the condition has gone into remission. If there are no symptoms, lupus is not contraindicated.

Lymphedema
(lymph: lymph; -edema: swelling)

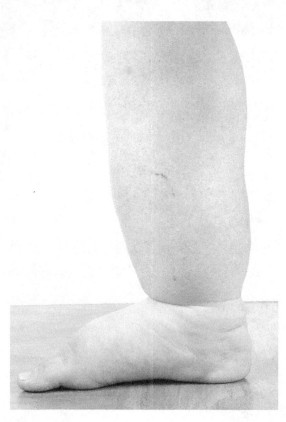

Lymphedema is a condition of the Lymphatic System that results in **increased interstitial fluid in a limb**, which causes **swelling**.

Causes

Causes of lymphedema vary. Most commonly, it results from damage to the lymph nodes and vessels during treatment for cancer(such as a mastectomy, where breast tissue and lymph channels may be completely removed). This results in lymph not draining properly. Other causes include obesity and advanced age.

Symptoms

Symptoms of lymphedema include swelling in the limbs, restricted range-of-motion, discomfort in the affected area, and thickening of the skin.

Treatments

While there is no cure for lymphedema, treatments may help reduce the amount of fluid in the area by stimulating lymph circulation. Massage therapy is highly effective at increasing lymph circulation. Compression clothing may help move lymph. Exercise is also extremely helpful in increasing lymph flow.

Contraindications

Lymphedema is not contraindicated for massage. Lymphatic drainage may help move lymph out of the area. When performing lymphatic drainage, light strokes moving towards the trunk should be performed on the proximal end of the affected limb, then distal areas may be worked on, again with strokes moving towards the trunk.

Pitting Edema
(edema: swelling)

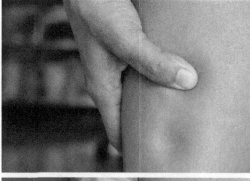

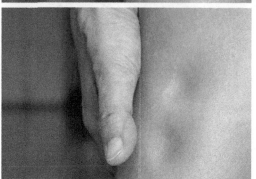

Pitting edema is a form of lymphedema that produces **pits in the skin after pressure is applied and released**. Lymphedema does not leave pits, and the skin rebounds immediately due to the amount of fluid in the area.

Causes

Pitting edema may be non-serious, or may have severe underlying causes. A common cause of pitting edema is pregnancy, due to the body creating much more fluid than it normally has. This increases fluid retention. Other more serious causes include heart failure, liver failure, or most commonly amongst these, **renal failure**. If these organs are not functioning properly, fluid is not effectively drained from the body, which increases swelling.

Symptoms

Pitting edema results in pits left in the skin after applying pressure. Other symptoms may include swelling, pain, numbness, and cramping in the area. If the swelling is near a joint, movement of the joint may become difficult.

Treatments

For serious cases of pitting edema, it is recommended to visit a doctor to find the underlying cause. Once the cause is determined, a proper treatment plan may be developed. Typically, if a person is suffering from organ failure, diuretics may be prescribed to help drain excess fluid from the body. Keeping limbs such as the legs elevated may also help reduce swelling.

Contraindications

Massage on a client with pitting edema should not be performed until the cause of pitting edema is established. If the cause is something such as pregnancy and not organ failure, massage of the limb may be performed as it would be done with lymphedema.

Muscular Pathologies

Adhesive Capsulitis
(capsul-: capsule; -itis: inflammation)

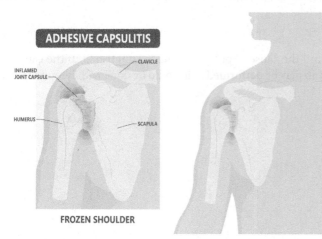

Adhesive capsulitis is a condition resulting in **restricted range-of-motion at the shoulder joint**. Another name for adhesive capsulitis is "**Frozen Shoulder**".

Causes

Surrounding the glenohumeral joint is connective tissue known as the joint capsule. This joint capsule holds everything in the joint in place, such as the bones themselves, synovial membrane, synovial fluid, etc. If there is irritation or over-use of the shoulder joint, **adhesions may form between the joint capsule and the head of the humerus**. These adhesions can decrease range-of-motion in the joint, and make movement in the joint uncomfortable.

The **subscapularis** muscle is often called the "Frozen Shoulder Muscle", due to its possible role in adhesive capsulitis. If the subscapularis is hypertonic, it may pull back on the humerus, which can restrict range-of-motion.

Symptoms

As adhesive capsulitis progresses, symptoms vary. In beginning stages, pain may be present, with a gradual decrease in the range-of-motion. As the condition advances, pain may subside, with a severely reduced range-of-motion.

Treatments

Treatments include stretching exercises and massage therapy to help break up the adhesions restricting range-of-motion, or to relax the subscapularis.

Contraindications

Adhesive capsulitis is not a contraindication. Massage may help loosen adhesions and increase range-of-motion. Stretching should be performed, as well as compression in the joint.

De Quervain's Tenosynovitis
(teno-: tendon; synov-: synovial; -itis: inflammation)

De Quervain's Tenosynovitis is a form of tenosynovitis that specifically **affects the thumb**.

Causes

De Quervain's Tenosynovitis is caused by **over-use of the thumb**, which contributes to straining of the tendons around the thumb and their protective sheaths. This may cause pain around the thumb, inflammation, and difficulty in moving the area.

Symptoms

Symptoms include pain and inflammation at the base of the thumb, loss of sensation in the posterior thumb, and difficulty moving the thumb and/or wrist while performing certain actions. Pain may gradually increase and radiate to other areas, such as the posterior forearm.

Treatments

Treatments primarily consist of rest and ice to reduce pain and inflammation in the area. Any repetitive actions that are causing the inflammation should be stopped to allow irritation to subside.

Contraindications

Massage is a local contraindication for De Quervain's Tenosynovitis, as it may increase inflammation and pain. Application of cold may be performed to decrease inflammation around the thumb.

Dupuytren's Contracture

Dupuytren's Contracture is a condition that results in **deformation of the hand**, due to tissues under the skin **hardening, thickening, and shortening**. These tissues pull the fingers into flexion, and don't allow the fingers to completely straighten.

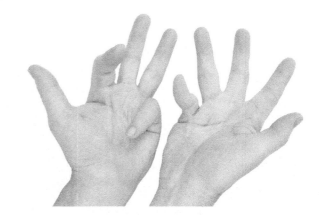

Causes

There are no known causes of Dupuytren's contracture. Men over the age of 50 are more likely to develop the condition, but exact reasons why are still not understood.

Symptoms

Deformity of the hand, specifically in the pinky finger, can occur. The skin on the palm of the hand can thicken, and the fascia under the skin thickens, pulling the pinky and ring finger towards the palm. This causes the affected fingers to lose the ability to fully extend, impairing function of the hand.

Treatments

Treatments include injecting enzymes into the cords to help soften them, a technique called needling in which needles are inserted in to the cords that help to break them, or surgery to partially or completely remove the cords from the hand. Each treatment has varying degrees of success, and the contracture may return.

Contraindications

Dupuytren's contracture is indicated for massage, although massage is unlikely to help loosen the tendon and help the finger return to its normal position.

Fibromyalgia
(fibro-: fibrous; my-: muscle; -algia: pain)

Fibromyalgia is a condition causing **pain throughout the body**, in conjunction with **fatigue**. Trouble with memory may also be present. Fibromyalgia may occur suddenly, or may worsen over time. Fibromyalgia typically affects women much more often than men. Diagnosis involves first ruling out other conditions that may be causing symptoms. If these other conditions are ruled out, then the duration of pain(over three months) and location of pain(using the **Widespread Pain Index**) are taken into account.

Causes

The exact cause of fibromyalgia is unknown. Many theories state the cause could range from hereditary to environmental factors, such as stress or trauma.

Symptoms

Symptoms of fibromyalgia primarily include widespread pain, usually a dull ache, in specific regions of the body for longer than three months, general fatigue, and issues with memory.

Treatments

Medications are important in the treatment of fibromyalgia. Pain relievers help to reduce the pain a person may be experiencing, while antidepressants can help treat depression that may result due to the fatigue a person can experience.

Contraindications

Fibromyalgia is indicated for massage, working within the client's pain tolerance.

Golfer's Elbow

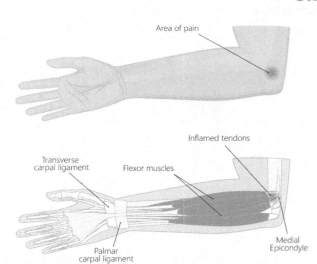

Golfer's Elbow is a form of **tendonitis** that affects and weakens the **flexors of the wrist**. Golfer's Elbow is also known as Medial Epicondylitis, **inflammation of the medial epicondyle**.

Causes

Golfer's Elbow is caused by repetitive motions such as elbow flexion, which put strain on the tendons connecting the flexors of the wrist to the humerus, at the medial epicondyle.

Symptoms

Golfer's Elbow may present with pain and inflammation at the medial epicondyle of the humerus, weakness in the elbow joint, and numbness in digits four and five.

Treatments

Treatment typically involves rest, and ice on the medial epicondyle to reduce inflammation. Any repetitive actions that are causing the inflammation should be stopped to allow irritation to subside.

Contraindications

Golfer's Elbow should be treated as a local contraindication. Application of cold may help reduce pain and inflammation at the medial epicondyle of the humerus.

Muscle Cramps

Muscle cramps are **involuntary contractions of a muscle**, and are usually **painful**.

Causes

Dehydration and overuse of a muscle are prime causes of muscle cramps. However, a cramp may develop due to other factors, including a low supply of blood which reduces oxygen intake in the muscle, or compression of nerves. Loss of electrolytes, such as sodium or potassium, may also lead the muscle cramping.

Symptoms

Pain in the location of the cramp is the prime symptom of muscle cramps. A person may also be able to visibly see the muscle cramping under the skin.

Treatments

Cramps are typically not serious, and only require minimal treatment to fix. Stretching and utilizing **reciprocal inhibition**(contracting the opposing muscle of the muscle cramping) can help calm the cramping in the acute stage. Keeping hydrated and providing the body with nutrients such as potassium may help prevent muscle cramping.

Contraindications

Muscle cramps in the acute stage should be considered a local contraindication. Reciprocal inhibition should be performed to stop the cramp. After a cramp has subsided, massage may be performed on the area, bringing fresh blood and nutrients into the area. The client should increase water intake after the massage as a preventative measure.

Strain

A strain is an **injury to a tendon or muscle**, usually caused by over-exertion or over-use.

Causes

Activities such as exercise are a common cause of strains. Much like burns, there are three grades of strains: grade 1, grade 2, and grade 3. The less severe the strain, the lower the grade.

A **grade 1 strain** results in **slight tearing** of a tendon or muscle. An example could be a person's muscles being sore after exercise. The muscles have experienced slight tears during exercise, but will heal after a day or two.

A **grade 2 strain** results in more tearing of a muscle or tendon. Grade 2 strains may require surgery to repair, or may heal on their own with rest. There may be accompanying **bruising and inflammation** around the strain.

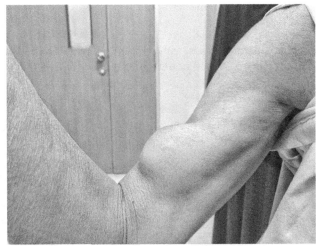

Grade 3 strain of the tendon of the long head of biceps brachii

A **grade 3 strain** results in **complete tearing of a muscle**, or more commonly, **a tendon**. Surgery is required to repair a grade 3 strain. The quadriceps and biceps brachii are two muscles prone to grade 3 strains more than others. Grade 3 strains will inhibit movement involved with the muscle involved, due to its inability to pull on the bone.

Symptoms

Strains may result in pain, inflammation, and an inability to move the injured muscle or tendon.

Treatments

Treatment varies depending on the severity of the strain. Grade 1 strains should be able to receive massage and heat therapy after 24-48 hours to increase circulation and promote healing. Grade 2 strains may need to rest longer before treatment. Grade 3 strains would require surgery to repair.

Contraindications

Acute strains are considered a local contraindication, and should be avoided to prevent increasing pain and inflammation in the area. Contrast therapy, utilizing alternating cold and heat, ending with cold, may be performed to decrease inflammation and bring fresh blood to the area.

 Easy to Remember: To remember the difference between a strain and sprain, look for the "t" in "strain"! "T" for "tendon"!

Tendonitis
(tendon-: tendon; -itis: inflammation)

Tendonitis is an injury that results in **inflammation of a tendon.**

Causes

Tendonitis is a mostly repetitive strain injury, caused by repeated use of one specific muscle, which can over-exert the tendon. When the tendon is over-exerted, it may tear slightly, which causes pain and inflammation.

There are several different types of tendonitis, including Golfer's Elbow(inflammation of the tendon at the medial epicondyle of the humerus), Tennis Elbow(inflammation of the tendon at the lateral epicondyle of the humerus), and Jumper's Knee(inflammation of the patellar tendon). All these conditions are caused by repetitive movements.

Symptoms

Symptoms may include pain upon moving a muscle connected to an affected tendon, and inflammation.

Treatments

Treatment for tendonitis is primarily rest and application of ice to reduce any inflammation. Repetitive actions causing the inflammation should be stopped until the irritation subsides.

Contraindications

Tendonitis should be treated as a local contraindication. Alternating application of cold and heat, ending with cold, can assist in decreasing inflammation and associated pain.

Tennis Elbow

Tennis Elbow is a form of tendonitis that **affects and weakens the extensors of the wrist**. Tennis Elbow is also known as Lateral Epicondylitis, **inflammation of the lateral epicondyle**.

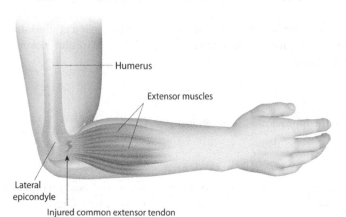

Humerus

Extensor muscles

Lateral epicondyle

Injured common extensor tendon

Causes

Tennis Elbow is caused by repetitive motions such as elbow extension, which put strain on the tendons connecting the extensors of the wrist to the humerus, at the lateral epicondyle.

Symptoms

Tennis Elbow commonly presents with pain that radiates distally to the posterior forearm. Weakness may result, especially when performing actions that require grasping.

Treatments

Treatment typically involves rest, and ice on the lateral epicondyle to reduce inflammation. Any repetitive actions that are causing the inflammation should be stopped to allow irritation to subside.

Contraindications

Tennis Elbow should be treated as a local contraindication. Alternating application of cold and heat, ending with cold, can assist in decreasing inflammation and associated pain at the lateral epicondyle of the humerus.

Tenosynovitis
(teno-: tendon; synov-: synovial; -itis: inflammation)

Tenosynovitis is a **repetitive strain injury** that results in **inflammation of a tendon and its protective sheath**.

Causes

Tenosynovitis primarily affects the hands, wrists, and feet due to the length of the tendons in these areas. The longer the tendon is, the easier it becomes to strain. Because there may be inflammation, pain may be present, and it may be difficult to move the affected area.

A common type of tenosynovitis is known as De Quervain's Tenosynovitis, which causes inflammation around the thumb due to over-use.

Symptoms

Tenosynovitis may produce pain and inflammation in affected joints, making it painful to move these joints. The area of the inflamed tendon may also be red.

Treatments

Tenosynovitis is typically treated the same as any strain, with rest and ice to reduce pain. Less commonly, tenosynovitis may be the result of bacterial infection, which may produce a fever. If a fever is present, medications such as antibiotics and antipyretics may be prescribed to combat bacterial growth and fever.

Contraindications

Massage is a local contraindication for tenosynovitis, as it may increase inflammation and pain. Application of cold may be performed to decrease inflammation in the tendon and reduce pain.

Torticollis
(torti-: twisted; collis: neck)

Torticollis, also known as **wry neck**, is a condition causing the **neck to twist to one side**, which tilts the head.

Causes

Trauma to the cervical region may cause torticollis. An injury to the **sternocleidomastoid** is often the prime cause. Spasms of the sternocleidomastoid may cause a type of torticollis known as spasmodic torticollis, and is usually a chronic condition. An injury to the trochlear nerve may cause a separate type of torticollis known as trochlear torticollis, in which a person must adjust the position of their head to see properly due to the trochlear nerve, which provides stimulation to muscles controlling the eye, no longer functioning as effectively.

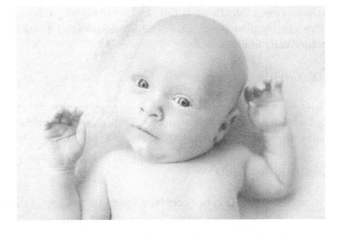

Symptoms

A person affected by torticollis will have their head tilted to one side. This can be uncomfortable or painful, especially when trying to move the neck or head back to a normal position. This can also lead to pain in the back and shoulders, and headaches.

Treatments

Because torticollis is the result of a spasm or contraction of neck muscles, treatments aim to relax the affected muscles. These treatments may include physical therapy, prescribing muscle relaxants, or possible surgery to correct any structural issues that may arise. Torticollis usually resolves itself within a few days, unless there is a more severe cause.

Contraindications

Torticollis is generally not considered a contraindication, but precautions should be taken if damage to a muscle or nerve is the cause.

Nervous Pathologies

Alzheimer's Disease

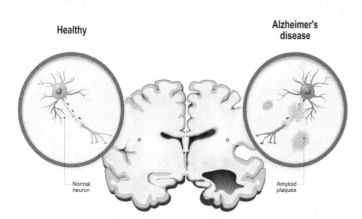

Healthy

Alzheimer's disease

Normal neuron

Amyloid plaques

Alzheimer's Disease, the most common form of **dementia**, is an over-arching term for **memory loss, confusion**, and a **general loss of intellectual abilities**. Alzheimer's is a result of brain tissue gradually dying over time. Increased age is a risk factor of developing Alzheimer's, and becomes much more common after the age of 65 in those affected.

Causes

While the exact cause of Alzheimer's is unknown, environmental factors are the most likely culprit. Few people with Alzheimer's disease develop the disease due to genetic factors.

Two factors strongly contribute to the death of nervous tissue: plaque and tangles. Plaque is the formation of deposits of a protein known as beta-amyloid, which develops in the space between nerves, restricting communication between nerve cells. Tangles are the development of another protein known as tau inside the nerve cells, which can cut off the natural flow of nutrients through cells.

Symptoms

Symptoms begin with difficulty remembering information, such as locations of items or things just learned. As the condition progresses, more brain tissue is lost, and a person may have difficulty making decisions, identifying people or places, and become more irritable or aggressive. Later stages of Alzheimer's may see the loss of the ability to read, write, dance, sing, and other activities learned early in life.

Treatments

There is no cure for Alzheimer's, but there are treatments available that can help manage the condition. Medications may be prescribed that can help with memory loss and other cognitive symptoms. In later stages, other medications may be prescribed that can help with memory, speech, and the ability to perform simpler tasks.

Contraindications

Alzheimer's Disease is not contraindicated for massage, although precautions may be taken in advanced stages of the disease. A person the client knows and is familiar with may stay in the room to assist with the client if the client becomes forgetful regarding their location.

Bell's Palsy
(palsy: paralysis)

Bell's Palsy is a condition affecting the **facial nerve**, causing **paralysis on one side of the face**.

Causes

The exact cause of Bell's Palsy is unknown, but is likely the result of an attack to the facial nerve(cranial nerve VII) by the herpes simplex virus. The inflammation damages the nerve, causing the muscles of the side of the face controlled by the facial nerve to become paralyzed or severely weakened. The side of the face affected may also become numb. Bell's Palsy is mostly a temporary condition, and should resolve over the course of a month or two. In some cases, it can become permanent.

Symptoms

Symptoms, which are usually only present on one side of the face, include the inability to close the eye, difficulty chewing, twitching of muscles in the face, and watery eyes. These symptoms typically resolve within three weeks at the earliest, but may persist for several months, or even become permanent.

Treatments

A person with Bell's Palsy may take corticosteroids to help treat the muscle weakness. Self care, including facial exercises, are recommended.

Contraindications

Bell's Palsy is indicated for massage. The side of the face that is paralyzed should be massaged lightly to avoid damaging any tissue. The client may not be able to tell the therapist if the massage is too deep around facial structures, so lighter massage on the affected area should be performed.

Paralysis of the left side of the patient's face

Carpal Tunnel Syndrome

Carpal Tunnel Syndrome is a condition caused by **compression of the median nerve between the carpals and the transverse carpal ligament.**

Causes

Several factors may contribute to the development of carpal tunnel syndrome, although the most common cause is **repetitive movements**. These repetitive movements can cause straining of the tendons that run through the carpal canal, which can place pressure on the median nerve. If the transverse carpal ligament tightens, it can also place pressure on the median nerve. When pressure is placed on the median nerve, numbness, pain, or tingling sensations may be experienced in the thumb, index, ring, and lateral side of the ring finger.

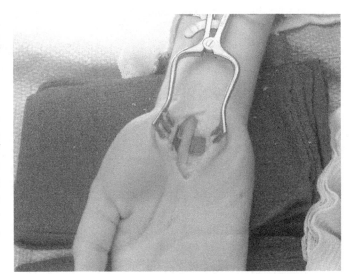

Carpal tunnel surgery, revealing the median nerve

Symptoms

Carpal tunnel syndrome often results in pain, numbness, and tingling sensations in the hand and wrist. Atrophy of the hand muscles may result due to lack of use.

Treatments

Several treatments are available for carpal tunnel syndrome. Self-care is recommended, including stretching the forearm and wrist flexors, massaging the transverse carpal ligament and hand muscles, and icing the area. Because carpal tunnel syndrome is often caused by repetitive actions, ceasing these actions is recommended. Non-steroidal anti-inflammatory medications may be prescribed. Surgery to remove the transverse carpal ligament may also be an option if the condition is severe.

Contraindications

Massage is indicated for carpal tunnel syndrome. Cross-fiber and circular friction on the transverse carpal ligament should be performed to help loosen adhesions in the area. Application of heat can help soften the ligament, and allow more space in the carpal canal.

Encephalitis
(encephal-: brain; -itis: inflammation)

Encephalitis is primarily a **viral infection** that results in **inflammation of the brain**.

Causes

Causes of encephalitis vary, but may include mosquito-borne viruses, such as West Nile, the Herpes Simplex virus, and the Rabies virus. Symptoms of encephalitis are usually mild, with the infected person suffering no more than flu-like symptoms, but severe cases may result in brain damage or death.

Symptoms

Symptoms of encephalitis vary depending on severity. Mild cases result in flu-like symptoms, such as fever, headache, general body ache, and fatigue. More severe cases may result in unconsciousness, seizures, weakness, and difficulty speaking or hearing.

Treatments

Most cases of encephalitis are mild, and treatment often consists of bed rest, and letting the virus work through its course. Antiviral medications may also be administered via an IV if the infection is more severe.

Contraindications

Because encephalitis is contagious and a serious medical condition, it is an absolute contraindication. Massage may be performed after the condition has completely resolved.

Meningitis

(mening-: meninges; -itis: inflammation)

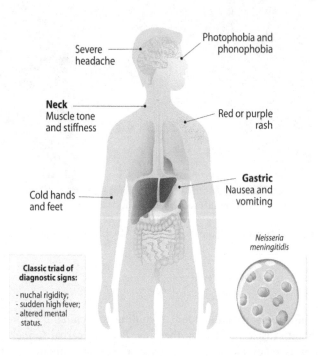

Severe headache

Photophobia and phonophobia

Neck
Muscle tone and stiffness

Red or purple rash

Cold hands and feet

Gastric
Nausea and vomiting

Neisseria meningitidis

Classic triad of diagnostic signs:
- nuchal rigidity;
- sudden high fever;
- altered mental status.

Meningitis is **inflammation of the meninges**, the protective connective tissue surrounding the brain and spinal cord. In the US, meningitis is most commonly caused by **viral infection**. However, certain **bacterial and fungal infections** may also cause meningitis. Bacterial meningitis is the most severe form of meningitis, usually preceded by a sinus or ear infection.

Causes

Being exposed to a pathogen, such as streptococci bacterium, or West Nile virus, are the causes of meningitis. Exposure to these may differ, and contracting them does not necessarily mean a person will develop meningitis. West Nile virus, which also may cause encephalitis, is often transmitted by mosquitoes. Rarely, meningitis may be caused by things that are not infectious, such as medications or allergies to certain chemicals.

Symptoms

Symptoms vary depending on the underlying cause. Viral meningitis may present with symptoms extremely similar to influenza, and will likely clear up on their own within a couple weeks. Fever, headache, nausea, vomiting, and an unusually stiff neck are symptoms to watch for. Meningitis is considered a medical emergency, and a person with suspected meningitis should be seen by a medical professional right away.

Treatments

Bacterial meningitis is treated with intravenous antibiotics to combat the infection, and a course of corticosteroids to prevent inflammation in the brain. Draining the infection from the sinuses may be helpful. Viral meningitis, however, is far less serious, and often clears up after a couple weeks. Treatment for viral meningitis is simply rest and increasing fluid intake. Pain relievers may also help if a person has general body aches or is suffering from mild fever.

Contraindications

Because meningitis is a contagious condition, it is an absolute contraindication to massage until it has completely resolved.

Multiple Sclerosis
(scler-: hard; -osis: condition)

Multiple Sclerosis is an **autoimmune disorder**, affecting the **myelin sheaths** that protect the axons of the Nervous System.

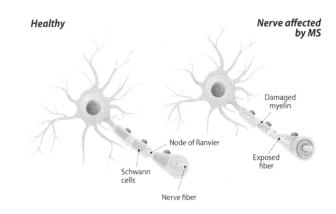

Causes

The cause of Multiple Sclerosis is unknown, but may be hereditary, and even environmental factors have been linked to the development of the disease. The disease begins with the body's immune system attacking the myelin sheaths, the protective fatty layers surrounding axons. These sheaths help to insulate the axons and prevent damage to the axons. When the myelin sheath is attacked and destroyed, it exposes the axons, which can have many different effects. Impulses traveling along an axon may terminate at the site of myelin degeneration, which may cause loss of functions. Scar tissue may form over the axons, which leads to extreme pain.

Symptoms

Symptoms of Multiple Sclerosis in acute stages include pain, weakness, fatigue, numbness(usually in the face), tingling sensation, blurry vision, and difficulty walking.

Treatments

There is no cure for Multiple Sclerosis. People may be prescribed disease-altering drugs that suppress the functions of the immune system. People may seek other means of managing Multiple Sclerosis and the accompanying pain and fatigue, including massage therapy, yoga, and meditation.

Contraindications

Massage in the acute stage of Multiple Sclerosis may be performed, but it is highly unlikely a client will seek massage because of the pain involved. Modalities that do not involve touching, such as Reiki, may be recommended and performed in these instances. In the post-acute stage, massage may be performed.

Parkinson's Disease

Parkinson's Disease is a motor disease that results in **trembling** due to a **loss of the neurotransmitter dopamine**.

Causes

There is no known cause of Parkinson's Disease. Neurons in the brain that produce dopamine are gradually destroyed. Dopamine is the neurotransmitter that stabilizes the body during motor movements, especially fine movements like writing. When dopamine levels in the body drop, trembling and shaking increases. Over time, as dopamine levels drop, the trembling increases. As dopamine continues to drop, larger movements become affected, like walking and talking.

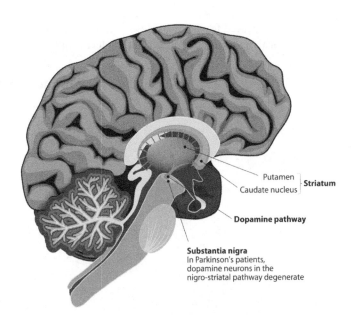

Symptoms

Symptoms of Parkinson's Disease include tremors, which usually begin in the hands and fingers and advance to larger body areas, difficulty writing, slower movement, difficulty in speech, and the loss of movements such as blinking.

Treatments

While there is no cure for Parkinson's Disease, treatments are available to help manage the condition, including dopamine replacement medications.

Contraindications

Massage is indicated for clients with Parkinson's Disease. In advanced stages, when a client is unable to lie on a table without the entire body trembling, a doctor's note may be requested. In these advanced stages, the therapist may need to help the client on and off the table.

Sciatica

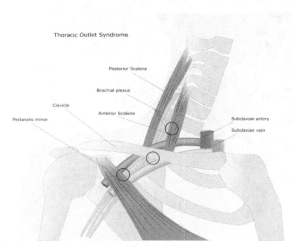

Vertebrae

Normal Disk

Herniated Disk

Sciatic Nerve

Nerve Compressed by Herniated Disk

Areas of Pain

Sciatica is a condition causing pain radiating down the buttocks, posterior thigh, and leg.

Causes

Sciatica is most commonly caused by a **herniated disc in the lumbar vertebrae**, which puts compression on the nerves that comprise the **sciatic nerve**. Bone spurs may also place pressure on the nerves.

Piriformis Syndrome is often confused with sciatica. Piriformis syndrome is caused by tightness in the piriformis muscle, which may place substantial pressure on the sciatic nerve.

Symptoms

The primary symptom of sciatica is pain in the posterior leg, thigh, and glutes, usually only on one side of the body. There may also be numbness and tingling in the affected area.

Treatments

Treatment for sciatica may include physical therapy, anti-inflammatory medications, or surgery if the condition is severe enough.

Contraindications

Massage is indicated for sciatica. However, if sciatica is the result of a herniated disc, the site of disc herniation should be considered a local contraindication. Stretching techniques, especially in the glutes, may help ease some pain associated with sciatica.

Thoracic Outlet Syndrome

Thoracic Outlet Syndrome

Posterior Scalene

Brachial plexus

Clavicle

Anterior Scalene

Pectoralis minor

Subclavian artery

Subclavian vein

Thoracic Outlet Syndrome is a condition caused by **compression of nerves and blood vessels passing through the thoracic outlet**.

Causes

Thoracic outlet syndrome may be caused by tight muscles, including **pectoralis minor and scalenes**, obesity, and tumors in the neck, such as those seen in Non-Hodgkin's Lymphoma.

Symptoms

Pressure placed on the nerves and blood vessels may cause pain, numbness, and weakness in the upper limb. If a blood vessel is compressed, it may cause the hand to become a bluish color due to lack of circulation, cause pain and fatigue in the arm, and coldness in the hands and fingers. If a nerve is compressed, numbness in the limb and atrophy of the muscles innervated by the nerve may result.

Treatments

Treatments primarily consist of stretching of the tight muscles to release pressure on the nerves and blood vessels. In the case of a tumor, surgery to remove the tumor may be required.

Contraindications

Massage is generally indicated for thoracic outlet syndrome. Massaging the scalenes and pectoralis minor may assist in releasing pressure on the area, returning sufficient blood supply to the area. Sensation may return to the upper limb as a result. If thoracic outlet syndrome is the result of tumors, the area should be avoided, and massage would be a local contraindication.

Trigeminal Neuralgia
(neur-: nerve; -algia: pain)

Trigeminal Neuralgia is a chronic condition causing **extreme pain in the face**.

Causes

The **trigeminal nerve**(cranial nerve V) sends sensory information from the face to the brain. When a blood vessel comes into contact with the trigeminal nerve at the brain stem, it results in dysfunction of the trigeminal nerve. This dysfunction results in hyper-sensitivity of the face, making even light touch extremely painful.

Symptoms

Extreme pain in the face, which may last from days to weeks, is the primary symptom of trigeminal neuralgia. This pain is typically only felt in one side of the face, but may worsen over time.

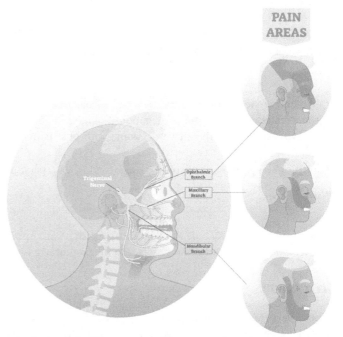

Treatments

Treatments for trigeminal neuralgia include medications to reduce pain, botox injections, or possible surgery to reduce pressure on the trigeminal nerve caused by blood vessels.

Contraindications

Massage for trigeminal neuralgia is generally not contraindicated, but everything is dependent on the severity of pain experienced by the client. If pain is severe, massage may be considered a local contraindication, or the client may not want to be massaged at all and the appointment would need to be rescheduled. If massage is able to be performed, the therapist should not use a face rest, instead opting to use a pillow for the client to rest their head upon while prone.

Respiratory Pathologies

Apnea
(a-: without; -pnea: breathing)

Patient utilizing a CPAP machine to assist in breathing

Apnea, commonly referred to as sleep apnea, is a **temporary cessation of breathing during sleep**. Apnea may be a serious condition, depending on the patient. There are three types of sleep apnea: central sleep apnea, obstructive sleep apnea, and complex sleep apnea syndrome.

People who are overweight have a much higher rate of occurrence than others. Advanced age and being male are also common demographics for the development of sleep apnea.

Causes

Central sleep apnea is the result of the brain not stimulating muscles responsible for breathing. A patient may experience shortness of breath due to lack of oxygen intake. This form of sleep apnea is not common.

Obstructive sleep apnea is the result of throat muscles relaxing, which causes the air passages to narrow or completely close upon inhalation. This reduces the amount of oxygen getting into the body. As a result, the brain may force the patient awake momentarily to unblock the airways. People with obstructive sleep apnea often snore, and may even sound as if they are choking.

Complex sleep apnea syndrome is diagnosed when a person experiences both central and obstructive sleep apnea.

Symptoms

Symptoms of apnea include snoring, shortness of breath upon waking, fatigue, and briefly waking at night. Another person may see the cessation of breathing and report it to the patient.

Treatments

Less severe forms of apnea may require less drastic forms of treatment, such as losing weight. In more severe forms, a person may be instructed to wear a CPAP(continuous positive airway pressure) machine during sleep, which increases air pressure in the airway, keeping the airways open enough for adequate oxygen intake to occur.

If other treatments are ineffective, surgery may be performed to remove tissue in and around the airway, which can increase the passageway for air to travel through.

Contraindications

Apnea is not contraindicated for massage.

Asthma

Asthma is a chronic respiratory disease that causes **constriction of the airways**, restricting oxygen intake. Asthma usually begins in childhood, but may disappear with age. Other times, it remains a chronic condition. Other factors such as smoking or obesity may lead to the development of asthma.

Causes

Asthma affects the **smooth muscle in the walls of the bronchial tubes**. Typically, when a person inhales an irritant(such as dust or smoke), the smooth muscle spasms and constricts in an effort to reduce the irritant moving further into the lungs. The bronchi will also produce an **excessive amount of mucous**, which further restricts the flow of oxygen into the lungs.

Symptoms

Symptoms include wheezing, chest tightness, and shortness of breath. Treatment varies depending on the severity in acute stages. If it is mild, medication may not be required. If symptoms are more severe, bronchodilators may be required to calm and open the airways. In extreme cases, where regular bronchodilators do not work, medical attention should be sought. A nebulizer, with inhalable steroids, should be used with asthma attacks.

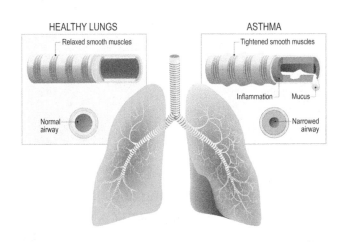

Treatments

Treatment for asthma primarily consists of the use of steroids and bronchodilators administered directly to the lungs via inhalers. If a person suffers from an asthma attack or has more severe forms of asthma, a nebulizer(which turns medication into a mist) may be required. Corticosteroids may also be used to lessen the chances of having an asthma attack.

Contraindications

In the acute stage, asthma is considered an absolute contraindication. Once breathing has returned to normal, massage may be performed. Tapotement may be performed on the back and chest to help loosen any excess phlegm that may be present.

Bronchitis
(bronch-: bronchi; -itis: inflammation)

Bronchitis is an inflammatory disease of the Respiratory System, restricting oxygen intake.

Causes

There are two different types of bronchitis: acute bronchitis and chronic bronchitis. **Acute bronchitis** is the result of a **primary infection** of the Respiratory System, such as influenza or pneumonia. These diseases affect the bronchial tubes, causing them to become irritated and inflamed. When these diseases resolve, the bronchitis will also resolve. **Chronic bronchitis** is the result of **constant irritation to the bronchial tubes**, caused by exposure to things such as **cigarette smoking or dust**. When exposure to the irritant ceases, the bronchitis will also cease.

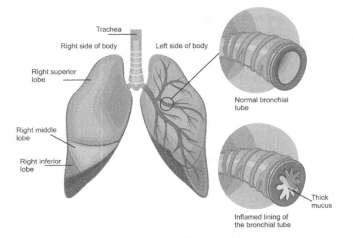

Symptoms

With both forms of bronchitis, there is an increased amount of mucous produced in the lungs, which makes breathing difficult. Increased coughing may be a side effect of the increase in mucous.

Treatments

Treatments vary depending on which type of bronchitis is involved. Acute bronchitis may require nothing more than a bronchodilator or cough suppressant. Because acute bronchitis is usually caused by a viral infection, antivirals may be prescribed to stop the advancement of the virus. Chronic bronchitis often requires the use of a bronchodilator, but not much else.

Contraindications

Acute bronchitis is considered an absolute contraindication, because it only appears as a secondary condition with another infection that is an absolute contraindication, such as influenza or pneumonia. Once these conditions resolve, the bronchitis will also resolve, and massage may be performed. Chronic bronchitis is indicated for massage. Tapotement may help loosen any excess phlegm as a result of the bronchitis, which can help breathing.

Emphysema
(emphyso: inflate)

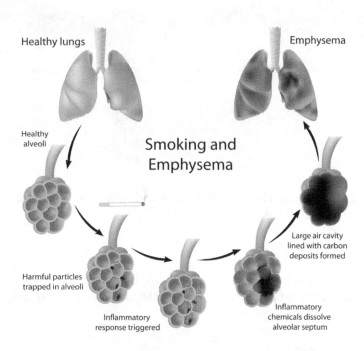

Healthy lungs

Emphysema

Healthy alveoli

Smoking and
Emphysema

Large air cavity
lined with carbon
deposits formed

Harmful particles
trapped in alveoli

Inflammatory
response triggered

Inflammatory
chemicals dissolve
alveolar septum

Emphysema is a chronic condition of the lungs, resulting in difficulty bringing oxygen into the body and eliminating carbon dioxide from the body.

Causes

Emphysema is caused by over-exposure to substances such as **cigarette smoke.** Constant irritation of the lungs by smoke can lead to **degeneration of the alveoli**, air sacs at the end of bronchial tubes where gas exchange takes place. When the alveoli degenerate, they lose surface area, which is what capillaries move across to eliminate carbon dioxide from the body and bring oxygen into the body. Lack of sufficient alveoli surface area makes gas exchange extremely difficult.

Symptoms

Emphysema causes shortness of breath. A person with emphysema may be much more likely to develop a collapsed lung due to damage to the lungs.

Treatments

Breathing exercises and oxygen supplementation may help control emphysema. If needed, bronchodilators can help relax the airways. If infections such as pneumonia occur, antibiotics may help.

Contraindications

Massage is indicated for emphysema.

Influenza
(Italian "influenza": influence)

Influenza is a **highly contagious viral infection** that primarily affects the lungs.

Causes

There are many different strains of the flu virus. It is constantly mutating, so treatment can be difficult. **Vaccinations** are the primary form of prevention for influenza.

During acute stages, influenza results in fever, general malaise, body aches, runny nose, and cough. Symptoms generally last no more than a week. Depending on the person involved, it can be a moderate infection, or can be life-threatening. Children and the elderly are much more likely to have serious cases of influenza than the general population.

Symptoms

Influenza typically has a sudden onset of symptoms, including fever, body ache, fatigue, sore throat, nasal congestion, body chills, and sweating.

Treatments

Treatment for influenza is usually nothing more than rest and increased fluid intake. Antiviral medication may be prescribed, and may help reduce the length of the infection. Influenza usually clears up on its own.

Contraindications

Influenza is highly contagious, and is considered an absolute contraindication.

Pneumonia

(pneumo: lung)

Pneumonia is a **highly contagious infection of the lungs**, resulting in a **buildup of fluid in the alveoli**.

Causes

The primary cause of pneumonia is **bacterial infection**(staphylococci), but may also be caused by a virus or fungi. The bacterium enters the body through breathing, which then infects the lungs.

Symptoms

Mild cases of pneumonia usually present with symptoms similar to those of influenza. Other symptoms may include pain in the chest upon breathing, coughing which may produce phlegm, fever, nausea, and shortness of breath. Symptoms can range from mild to severe, and even life threatening, based on the overall health and age of the person infected.

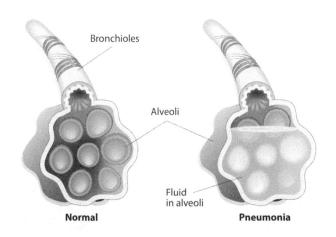

Treatments

Pneumonia is typically treated with antibiotics. Cough medicine and antipyretics may be prescribed to aid with coughing and to lower fever.

Contraindications

Pneumonia is a highly contagious condition, and is therefore an absolute contraindication.

Sinusitis

(sinus: sinus; -itis: inflammation)

Sinusitis is an acute condition causing **inflammation and swelling in the nasal sinuses**, which can result in **excessive mucous production**. It can also prevent mucous from properly draining from the sinuses, causing a person to feel a lot of pressure in the face around the nose and eyes. Bacterial infection may result, which can increase the amount of fluid present in the sinuses.

Causes

The most common cause of sinusitis is an acute viral infection, such as the common cold, which may in turn cause bacterial infection to take place.

Symptoms

A person with sinusitis may experience pressure in the face around the nose, eyes, and ears, headache, a thick mucous produced by the nose usually presenting with a yellow or green color, and congestion in the nasal cavity.

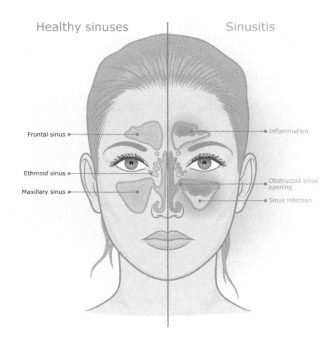

Treatments

Decongestants are effective at helping to drain the nasal cavities, which can help ease pressure in the area. Nasal sprays can help alleviate inflammation and clean out the nasal cavity, further helping to reduce pressure. If bacterial infection is present, antibiotics may be prescribed.

Contraindications

During the acute stage, and due to being caused by a contagious viral infection, sinusitis is considered an absolute contraindication. Once the condition has resolved, a client may receive massage.

Tuberculosis

(tubercul/o: tubercle; -osis: condition)

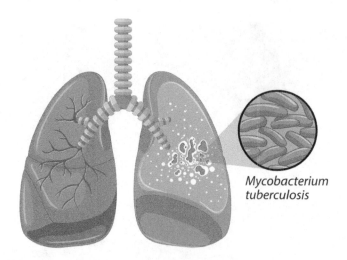

Mycobacterium tuberculosis

Tuberculosis is a **serious bacterial infection** of the Respiratory System, and is contagious. Exposure to tuberculosis may cause a person to acquire either **latent tuberculosis or active tuberculosis**. In latent tuberculosis, the bacteria enters the body but does not cause any problems or symptoms. This type is not contagious. However, if it becomes active tuberculosis, it becomes contagious. Active tuberculosis is when the bacteria is activated and symptoms of a tuberculosis infection are present.

Causes

Tuberculosis is contracted from another person through **microscopic droplets** spread through the air. This can be caused by actions such as **coughing and sneezing**.

Tuberculosis may have a better chance of becoming active in a person with HIV/AIDS, due to the compromised immune system.

Symptoms

Symptoms include chronic coughing, pain in the chest when breathing, fatigue, fever, and producing blood upon coughing. Night chills, sweating, and unexplained loss in weight may also be signs of an active tuberculosis infection. Tuberculosis may, in some instances, also affect structures and organs in the body such as the kidneys.

Treatments

The bacteria responsible for tuberculosis is extremely hard to destroy, so a person afflicted with the condition will need to take antibiotics for an extended period of time. This ensures the bacteria is completely destroyed and there is no chance of the bacteria becoming immune to the antibiotics being used.

Contraindications

Tuberculosis is a contagious condition, and is considered an absolute contraindication.

Skeletal Pathologies

Ankylosing Spondylitis
(ankyl/o: crooked; spondyl-: spine; -itis: inflammation)

Ankylosing Spondylitis is an **autoimmune disorder**, similar to rheumatoid arthritis, in which the body's immune system attacks and destroys the **annulus fibrosus of the intervertebral discs**. Over time, the curvature in the vertebrae is lost. Because the intervertebral discs are destroyed, the space between vertebral bodies lessens, eventually allowing the vertebral bones to sit directly atop one another. Movement between these bones is severely reduced, and eventually the bones can fuse together, which eliminates any movement between the bones at all.

A person with ankylosing spondylitis may appear to be hunched forward, and may present with kyphosis as a result. Another name for ankylosing spondylitis is "**Bamboo Spine**" because after fusion, the **vertebrae resembles a bamboo stalk.**

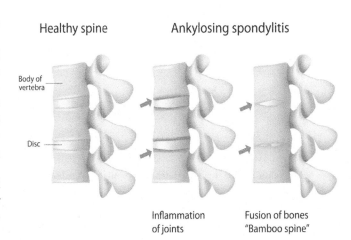

Healthy spine   Ankylosing spondylitis

Body of vertebra

Disc

Inflammation of joints

Fusion of bones "Bamboo spine"

Causes

Ankylosing spondylitis is caused by the body's immune system attacking the intervertebral discs for unknown reasons.

Symptoms

Pain is an extremely common symptom of ankylosing spondylitis, especially in the neck, base of the skull, and lumbar region. Lack of mobility is a secondary symptom, usually the result of pain.

Treatments

Non-steroidal anti-inflammatory medications may be prescribed to help reduce pain and inflammation in affected areas. Physical therapy, massage therapy, stretching, and range-of-motion exercises are all helpful in maintaining mobility in the vertebral joints and preventing bones from fusing together.

If the condition is severe, surgery may be performed to remove fused bone, or to insert metal rods to correct posture.

Contraindications

Massage is indicated for ankylosing spondylitis. Stretching and range-of-motion exercises should be performed within the client's pain tolerance. If the client has difficulty lying supine due to kyphosis, side-lying position may be needed.

Bunion

A bunion is a **subluxation of the big toe**, the result of the toe pushing back against the first metatarsal. Excessive force against this bone causes the **big toe to turn laterally**, with the **first metatarsal turning medially**, creating a **large bump.**

Causes

Tight fitting shoes may contribute to the development of bunions. Rheumatoid arthritis may also contribute. Foot injuries may also play a role.

Symptoms

Pain and swelling may present in the area of the bunion. With bunions, the big toe may cross under the second toe. This may cause calluses or corns to form on the area where these toes rub together. Movement in the big toe may reduce.

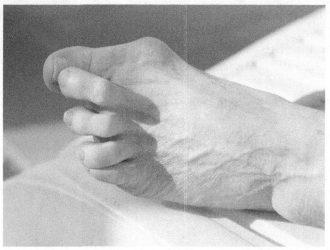

Subluxation forcing the big to laterally, creating a large bump

Treatments

How severe the bunion is determines the treatment. Less severe bunions may require only changing shoes or applying a splint to help reset the toe. More severe forms of a bunion may require surgery to correct the placement of the toe.

Contraindications

Massage is generally not contraindicated for a bunion. However, if the client is experiencing pain as a result of the bunion, massage in the area should be avoided.

Bursitis
(burs-: bursa; -itis: inflammation)

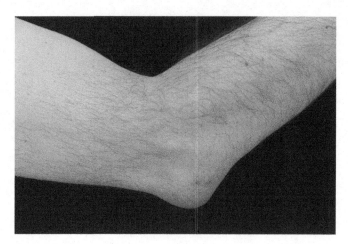

Bursitis is a condition that results in **inflammation of a bursa**, a small sac filled with synovial fluid.

Causes

Bursae are located all over the body, typically between a tendon and bone to prevent friction and irritation. When there is **repeated stress** placed on the bursa, it can become inflamed. Bursitis may affect many different joints, including the knee, shoulder, elbow, hip, and ankle.

Bursitis is most often caused by repetitive motions in the affected joint, which may irritate the bursa. **Trauma** may also result in bursitis, such as fractures or tendonitis.

Symptoms

Typically, a joint affected with bursitis will be inflamed and painful to move. The inflammation may be moderate or severe.

Treatments

Bursitis is easily treatable, primarily with rest and ice. Depending on the severity, the bursa may also need to be surgically drained or removed, or injected with corticosteroids to reduce the inflammation.

Contraindications

Bursitis is considered a local contraindication for massage. Cold packs may be used to help decrease inflammation in the area.

Dislocation

A dislocation is when a **bone at an articulation becomes displaced** from its normal location. A dislocation, in the acute stage, results in immobilization of the joint and temporary deformation. It may also be painful and result in inflammation around the joint.

Causes

Dislocations are most commonly the result of trauma to the joint, which pushes a bone out of place. The most common areas for dislocations are the fingers and shoulder, but dislocations may occur in many other joints as well, such as the knee or hip.

Dislocations may result in tearing of tendons, ligaments, muscles, or in the case of the shoulder or hip, the labrum(circular cartilage surrounding the joint). The dislocated joint, while most commonly returns to normal strength and function after being relocated, may become prone to dislocations in the future. This may cause arthritis to develop.

Symptoms

Dislocations are extremely painful, and often present with deformity of the joint and an inability to move the joint. Inflammation may be present in some cases.

Treatments

Treatment of a dislocation in the acute stage primarily involves trying to get the bone back to its normal position, known as reduction. After the joint has returned to its normal position, it is typically immobilized for a number of weeks to reduce recurrence of dislocation and to help the tissues around the joint to heal. If the dislocation is severe and unable to be returned to position, surgery may be required.

Contraindications

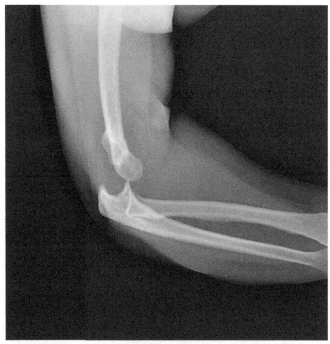

Dislocation at the elbow joint

In the acute stage, a dislocation is considered a local contraindication. If the joint has healed, massage may be performed on the area with caution. Stretching and range-of-motion should be avoided because the joint is much weaker after a dislocation.

Fracture

A fracture is a **break in a bone**. There are several different types of fractures, including transverse, greenstick, oblique, and spiral.

Causes

Fractures are the result of trauma to a bone. Despite many different types of fractures, every fracture is categorized as one of the following: Simple or Compound. A **simple fracture** is a fracture that **does not break through the skin**, and does not generally damage any surrounding tissue. A **compound fracture**, which is much more severe, **breaks through the skin and damages surrounding tissues**. Compound fractures are much more prone to infection due to exposure to the outside environment.

Symptoms

Fractures result in deformity of the affected bone, pain, immobilization of the area, and inflammation. In the case of compound fractures, external bleeding may also occur.

Despite most fractures being the result of blunt trauma, certain diseases that weaken the bones may also cause fractures, such as osteoporosis.

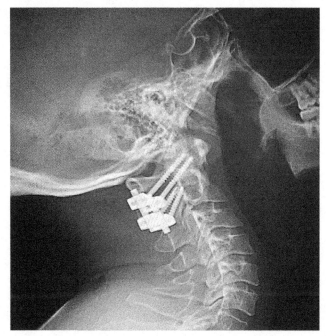

Spinal fusion surgery to repair fracture at C1-C2

Treatments

Fractures should be treated immediately. A cast or splint may be applied, depending on which bone is fractured. Other fractures, such as vertebrae fractures, may need more extensive treatment, including metal plates or bone grafts.

Contraindications

In the acute stage, a fracture should be considered a local contraindication. After the fracture has healed, massage may be performed on the area. If metal plates, rods, screws, or pins have been placed in the bone, caution should be taken in the area, but massage may still be performed.

Gout

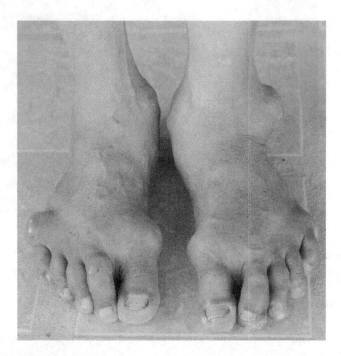

Gout is a form of arthritis, mostly seen around the **base of the big toe**, but may also affect other joints in the body, such as the hands and fingers.

Causes

Gout is the result of an **over-abundance of uric acid crystals** in the body. Gravity pulls the uric acid crystals down the body, where they collect in the most distal points in the limbs, the big toes, hands and fingers. Gout is typically the result of the kidneys not excreting enough uric acid, or the body producing too much uric acid.

Symptoms

Gout may be extremely painful in the acute stage as the crystals collect in the joints. Inflammation may set in, which can increase the pressure and pain in the joint. Loss of range-of-motion may also occur. Untreated, gout may result in kidney stones.

Treatments

Treatments for gout include non-steroidal anti-inflammatory drugs and/or corticosteroids to reduce pain and inflammation. Gout may also require the use of certain medications that prevent the creation of uric acid in the body.

Contraindications

Gout is considered a local contraindication.

Herniated Disc

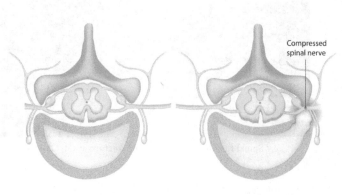

Compressed spinal nerve

Normal disc   Herniated disc

A herniated disc is a condition affecting the vertebral column, which may cause intense pain and numbness.

Causes

An intervertebral disc, located between two vertebrae, is made of two parts: the nucleus pulposus, and the annulus fibrosus. The nucleus pulposus is a gelatinous substance located in the center of the disc. The annulus fibrosus is the part of the disc made of thick cartilage. If a **tear occurs in the annulus fibrosus**, the **nucleus pulposus may protrude through the torn section**, which may place pressure on spinal nerves emerging from the spinal cord.

A herniated disc is primarily caused by degeneration of a disc, which takes place gradually. This makes injury of the disc much easier in actions such as lifting and twisting. Other times, trauma may cause a herniated disc, such as in car accidents.

Symptoms

Herniated discs may result in pain and/or numbness due to the disc placing pressure on the spinal nerves. Because numbness may occur, weakness in the muscles innervated by the nerves may also set in due to impaired function.

Treatments

Treatment for a herniated disc varies depending on the severity. Pain medication may help control pain. Muscle relaxers may help take pressure off the area of the herniation. Physical therapy may also contribute to lessening the effects of the herniated disc. Very rarely, surgery may be required.

Contraindications

Herniated discs are considered local contraindications. The area around the hernia may be massaged, but the disc itself should be avoided.

Kyphosis
(kyph-: hill; -osis: condition)

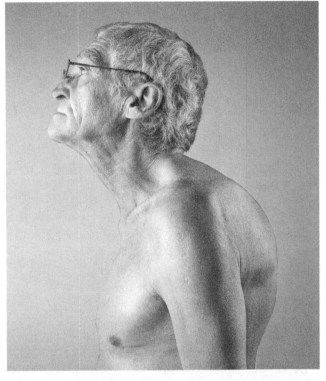

Kyphosis is a condition affecting the **thoracic vertebrae**, resulting in **hyper-curvature**. Another name for kyphosis is "**Dowager's Hump**".

Causes

A kyphotic curvature in the vertebrae is a curvature that moves posteriorly. If the curvature is exaggerated, it is known as kyphosis. Kyphosis has many different causes. Kyphosis may be caused by extremely tight muscles(such as **pectoralis minor and serratus anterior**) pulling the scapulae anteriorly, which rounds the back. It may also be the result of bone degeneration(osteoporosis), disc degeneration(ankylosing spondylitis), or even birth defects.

Symptoms

Kyphosis may cause pain in the back, and difficulty in movement and breathing as a result. It may also result in the lumbar vertebrae losing its curvature, a condition known as **flat back**.

Treatments

Kyphosis may vary from mild to severe, depending on the cause. Treatments include exercises that strengthen the muscles of the back, stretching of tight muscles that may contribute to kyphosis, braces to keep the vertebrae properly aligned, and possibly even surgery if it's warranted.

Contraindications

Kyphosis is not contraindicated for massage. A person with kyphosis may be uncomfortable lying supine, and may need to be placed into side-lying position for comfort. Massage of the pectoralis minor and serratus anterior muscles may help the scapulae return to their normal locations, which can help straighten the vertebrae.

Lordosis
(lord-: curve; -osis: condition)

Lordosis is a condition affecting the **lumbar vertebrae**, resulting in **hyper-curvature**. Another name for lordosis is "**Swayback**".

Causes

A lordotic curvature in the vertebrae is a curvature that moves anteriorly. If the curvature is exaggerated, it is known as lordosis. Lordosis has many different causes. Lordosis may be caused by tight muscles(such as **psoas major, iliacus, quadratus lumborum**, and **rectus femoris**), weak muscles(such as **rectus abdominis and the hamstrings**), obesity, or bone diseases(such as osteoporosis).

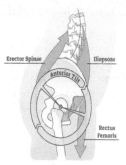

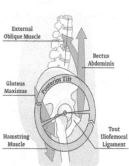

Pregnancy is also a common cause of lordosis, but the condition typically subsides post-pregnancy.

Symptoms

Lordosis may place excessive pressure on the vertebrae, and alter a person's stance and gait. Lordosis may result in pain in the back, and cause difficulty moving.

Treatments

Treatment primarily includes strengthening weak muscles, stretching tight muscles, and lifestyle changes such as adjusting posture, diet, and exercise.

Contraindications

Lordosis is not contraindicated for massage. Stretching exercises on the psoas major, iliacus, and quadratus lumborum muscles may help return the lumbar spine back to its normal curvature.

Lyme Disease

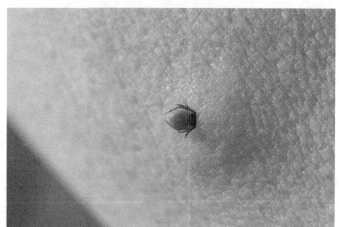

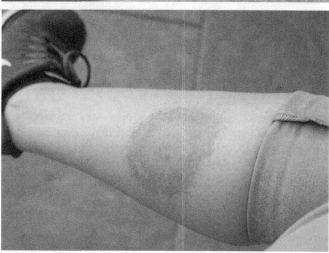

Lyme Disease is a **bacterial infection spread by deer ticks**, and contracting the infection is much more common in grassy or wooded areas where deer ticks are found. The condition may affect a person for months, and lead to symptoms that may last for years afterwards.

Causes

The bacteria responsible for Lyme Disease is spread through a bite from deer ticks. The bacteria is usually only transmitted if the bite lasts longer than **36 hours**.

Symptoms

Symptoms of Lyme Disease vary depending on the stage of infection. In the early stages, a bump may appear where the person has been bitten. Sometime later, within 30 days, a rash may appear that forms a bullseye pattern. It may spread outward from that area over a few days. A person may experience flu-like symptoms when the rash appears. In advanced stages, conditions may begin occurring such as pain and inflammation in joints, meningitis, and paralysis in different parts of the body such as the face.

Treatments

Lyme Disease is a bacterial infection, and therefore is treated with antibiotics. Advanced stages of Lyme Disease, where there may be some sort of paralysis, require the use of intravenous antibiotics. Otherwise, oral antibiotics may be taken. The course of treatment usually lasts up to three weeks to completely destroy all bacteria.

Contraindications

Massage largely depends on the symptoms a client experiences.

DID YOU KNOW?

Lyme Disease is named after the towns of Lyme and Old Lyme, Connecticut due to an outbreak of the disease in the areas in 1975!

Lesser symptoms, such as aches and joint inflammation, may allow for massage while avoiding general local contraindications. If a client is experiencing flu-like symptoms, the massage should be postponed until the client is feeling better.

Osgood-Schlatter Disease

Osgood-Schlatter Disease is a repetitive strain injury, caused by **over-use of the patellar tendon.**

Causes

Osgood-Schlatter Disease primarily affects **adolescents**, particularly those involved in sports. **Over-use of the quadriceps** during activities such as running and jumping can cause tightness in the patellar tendon. When the patellar tendon tightens, it pulls proximally on the tibial tuberosity. Because the bone is still growing, the force of the patellar tendon on the tibial tuberosity can cause an **over-growth of bone**, resulting in a bony lump. Males are more likely to develop this condition than females, but instances in females are increasing as participation in sports by females increases.

Symptoms

Osgood-Schlatter Disease may cause pain, but it varies from person-to-person. The pain may be mild, or it may be more intense in some cases, making movement of the knee difficult.

Despite complications from Osgood-Schlatter Disease being rare, inflammation of the area may persist over time. The bony lump produced by increased bone production may also remain.

Treatments

Treatment is mild, usually nothing more than pain relievers, rest, and ice. Exercises that stretch the quadriceps are recommended.

Contraindications

In the acute stage, massage of the tibial tuberosity is a local contraindication. If the client is beyond the age of 21, and bone is no longer being produced at the tibial tuberosity, massage on the area may be performed.

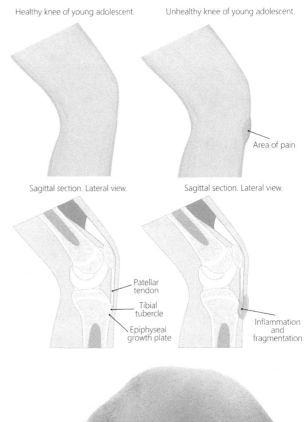

Healthy knee of young adolescent.   Unhealthy knee of young adolescent.

Area of pain

Sagittal section. Lateral view.   Sagittal section. Lateral view.

Patellar tendon

Tibial tubercle

Epiphyseal growth plate

Inflammation and fragmentation

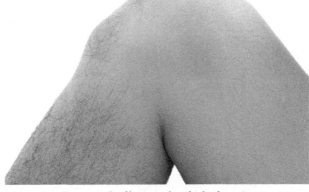

Overgrowth of bone at the tibial tuberosity

In the acute stage, massage and stretching techniques should be performed on the quadriceps to loosen the muscles and take pressure off the patellar tendon, which can reduce the excessive development of bone at the tibial tuberosity.

Osteoarthritis
(osteo-: bone; arthr-: joint; -itis: inflammation)

Osteoarthritis is the most common form of arthritis, which is **inflammation of a joint.**

Causes

Osteoarthritis, also known as "**wear-and-tear arthritis**", is caused by damage to the **hyaline cartilage** separating one bone from another. The cartilage between bones reduces friction between the bones, and absorbs shock in the joint. Over time, the articular cartilage may begin to break down and wear away. This causes irritation in the joint and increases friction between the bones, which causes inflammation. As this persists, damage to the bone may take place. The most common location of osteoarthritis is the knee, but in **massage therapists**, it may also affect the **carpometacarpal joint of the thumb(saddle joint).**

DESTRUCTION OF CARTILAGE

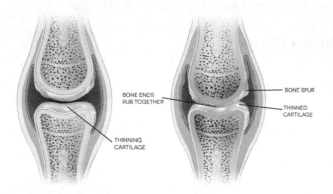

BONE ENDS RUB TOGETHER

THINNING CARTILAGE

BONE SPUR

THINNED CARTILAGE

Symptoms

Osteoarthritis may cause pain, difficulty moving the affected joint, and bone spurs in the joint due to increased friction between the bones. When the condition advances to the point of the joint being mostly unusable, joint replacement surgery may be recommended.

Treatments

Treatment includes non-steroidal anti-inflammatory drugs, lifestyle and dietary changes if caused by obesity, and alternative methods such as yoga.

Contraindications

In the acute stage, massage is considered a local contraindication for any form of arthritis because it can bring more blood into the area and increase inflammation. In the post-acute stage, massage should be performed on the area usually affected to bring fresh blood and nutrients into the area, and to increase production of synovial fluid in the joint. This can help reduce irritation in the joint and lessen the effects of arthritis.

Osteoporosis
(osteo-: bone; por-: porous; -osis: condition)

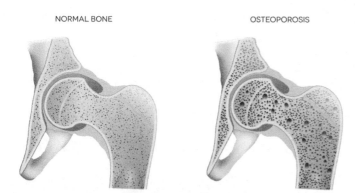

NORMAL BONE

OSTEOPOROSIS

Osteoporosis is a condition that causes **weakness and degeneration in the bones**.

Causes

Osteoporosis mainly affects **post-menopausal women**. After menopause, a woman's body produces **less estrogen**. During growth stages of a person's life, estrogen helps the bones grow and mature. When estrogen levels drop post-menopause, osteoclast levels increase and more bone is destroyed than is created. When this occurs, the bones become brittle, weak, and prone to fracture.

In addition to making bones brittle, osteoporosis may also contribute to the development of kyphosis and back pain. One of the most common places for fracture to occur is in the neck of the femur. The femur, which is normally the strongest bone in the body, should be able to support roughly 2,000 pounds of pressure per square inch. When the femur becomes weakened, it makes it incredibly easy to break. If a fracture takes place around the hip joint, joint replacement surgery is often required.

Symptoms

In the early stages of osteoporosis, there are usually no symptoms. As bone loss increases over time, a person may experience back pain, hunched posture(kyphosis), and bones that fracture easier than usual. These symptoms often become worse as the disease progresses and more bone tissue is lost.

Treatments

Treatments for osteoporosis include estrogen replacement therapy, and weight-bearing exercise earlier in life before any symptoms of osteoporosis surface. Weight-bearing exercise, such as squats and dead-lifts, helps to strengthen the bones, which substantially reduces the risk of developing osteoporosis in older age.

Contraindications

Massage is indicated for osteoporosis. However, precautions should be taken, such as performing a lighter massage, and not performing techniques such as tapotement to avoid damaging bone.

Rheumatoid Arthritis

Rheumatoid Arthritis is an **autoimmune disorder**, resulting in **inflammation**, **pain**, and **deformity of the joints around the hands and wrists**.

Causes

Around synovial joints, there is a membrane called the synovial membrane, which supplies joints with synovial fluid. In rheumatoid arthritis, the body's immune systems attacks the **synovial membranes**, destroying them. This is especially common in the metacarpophalangeal joints. After the synovial membranes have been destroyed, extremely thick, fibrous material replaces them, which not only makes movement painful and difficult, but can also cause deformity, turning the fingers into an adducted position.

Symptoms

Rheumatoid arthritis can produce pain and discomfort in the affected joints, as well as cause pain and stiffness after long periods of inactivity in the joints. Fever and fatigue may also be symptoms of general rheumatoid arthritis. Less commonly, some people may experience symptoms in structures completely unrelated to the affected joints, such as the eyes, heart, lungs, and kidneys.

Treatments

There is no cure for rheumatoid arthritis, but treatments include non-steroidal anti-inflammatory drugs, corticosteroids, and physical therapy.

Contraindications

In the acute stage, rheumatoid arthritis is considered a local contraindication, as the pain may be too intense for the client to receive massage on the affected area. In general, however, a client with rheumatoid arthritis may receive massage to help ease pain associated with inflammation if the body can tolerate a light-to-medium pressured massage.

Scoliosis

(scoli-: crooked; -osis: condition)

Scoliosis is a condition causing the vertebral column, usually in the thoracic region, to be pulled into a **lateral position**.

Causes

The causes of scoliosis are unknown, but there may be a hereditary link. Scoliosis typically develops around the beginning stages of puberty. Scoliosis is mostly mild in severity, but can become much more prominent, which can put incredible strain on the ribs, vertebrae, and hips. With scoliosis, one hip may be higher than the other, which causes a discrepancy in gait. Tight muscles may also contribute to the development of scoliosis, as seen in cases such as a hypertonic rhomboid major and minor unilaterally, which pulls the vertebrae to one side.

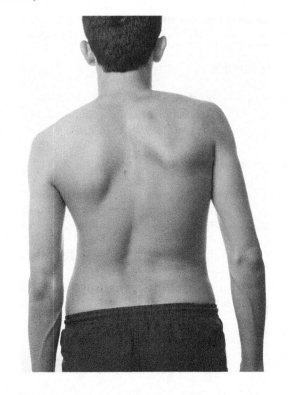

Symptoms

If scoliosis is severe, damage to the heart or lungs may occur, due to the deformity of the rib cage. Back pain may also persist.

Treatments

Treatment, while commonly unnecessary, may include the use of braces to correct posture, the use of chiropractic therapy, massage therapy, or in severe cases, surgery with metal rod implantation.

Contraindications

Scoliosis is indicated for massage. In instances where scoliosis is caused by hypertonic muscles, such as the rhomboids unilaterally, massage may help loosen the muscles and allow the bones to realign themselves. If surgery has been performed and metal rods have been placed in the back, massage should be performed lighter on the area, and the use of cold packs should be avoided.

Sprain

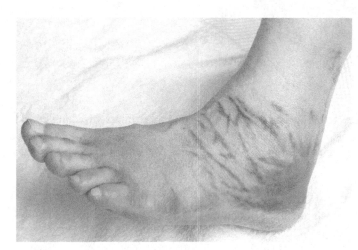

A sprain is an **injury to a ligament**.

Causes

Sprains are much less likely to be caused by repetitive motions, unlike strains. Sprains typically occur quickly, causing tears in a ligament. Like strains, sprains may be broken down in severity by using grades: grade 1, grade 2, and grade 3.

A **grade 1 sprain** is caused by **stretching of a ligament**, but does not cause major tearing. Common grade 1 sprains may be caused by activities such as running. After 24-48 hours, the ligament should return to normal, and any pain and/or inflammation should subside.

A **grade 2 sprain**, such as a high ankle sprain, causes **tearing of a ligament** and presents with **bruising and inflammation**. Grade 2 sprains may require surgery to repair, or they may heal on their own, depending on the severity of the tear.

A **grade 3 sprain** is a **complete rupture of a ligament**, and much like a grade 3 strain, **does require surgery to repair.** The most common form of grade 3 sprain is a torn anterior cruciate ligament(ACL, the ligament holding the femur and tibia together), most commonly caused by sports or automobile accidents.

Symptoms

Symptoms of sprains are very similar to symptoms of strains, including inflammation, pain, and potential bruising depending on the grade of sprain. If the sprain is severe, a pop in the joint may be heard or felt at the time of injury.

Treatments

Sprains take much longer to heal than strains, due to ligaments being avascular, compared to muscles and tendons, which have a rich blood supply. Treatment for sprains vary depending on the severity of the sprain. The less severe, the more likely it is that rest, ice, and elevation will suffice. Surgery is only required when there is no chance of the ligament repairing itself.

Contraindications

In the acute stage, sprains are local contraindications. If inflammation has subsided from a first degree sprain, gentle massage in the area may be performed to bring fresh blood and nutrients into the area and speed healing. Contrast therapy may be performed in addition to gentle massage to reduce any inflammation that may occur due to the massage.

Temporomandibular Joint Dysfunction

Temporomandibular Joint Dysfunction(TMJD) is a condition affecting the mandible, causing simple tasks such as **chewing to become painful and difficult.**

Causes

The temporomandibular joint is the joint that connects the mandible to the temporal bone. Between the bones, there is a small disc of cartilage, used to prevent friction between the bones and to make movement smooth. If there is arthritis in the joint, or the disc is damaged, it can result in temporomandibular joint dysfunction. This can cause pain, difficulty in moving the jaw, and produce a clicking sensation when the jaw opens. Often times, the muscles that connect to the mandible(temporalis, lateral pterygoid) may tighten and pull the mandible out of place.

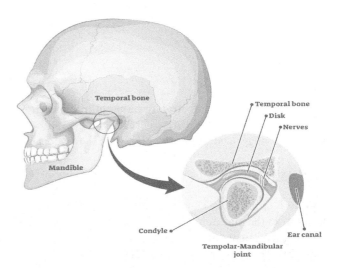

Symptoms

Temporomandibular joint dysfunction can produce pain in the face, a clicking or popping sound when closing the mouth, and difficulty in opening the mouth. The jaw may become locked while open.

Treatments

Treatments vary depending on the primary cause, ranging from prescription muscle relaxants and pain relievers, to physical and massage therapy.

Contraindications

Massage is indicated for temporomandibular joint dysfunction. Massage of the temporalis may help the jaw realign and reduce the pain and clicking.

─────────────────── **Whiplash** ───────────────────

Whiplash is an **injury to the neck**, resulting from a **quick, forceful movement of the head forward and back**. This results in the **tendons and ligaments in the neck to become stretched further than normal**, damaging the tissue and making the neck much less stable than normal.

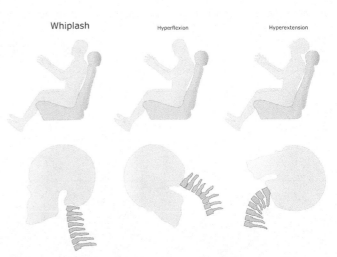

Causes

The most common cause of whiplash is a car accident. Injuries during sport or physical abuse may also cause whiplash. Shaking a baby may result in whiplash, and is one of the reasons shaking a baby should never happen.

Symptoms

The neck can become stiff and painful, especially upon movement. Headaches may occur. Pain may radiate to the shoulders, and range-of-motion may be restricted. Numbness may be experienced in the upper limbs due to possible injury to nerves emerging from the brachial plexus.

Treatments

Rest and ice are effective treatments for whiplash. The use of pain relievers can help eliminate pain associated with the condition. Inflammation in the area may be present, and contrast therapy on the neck may be performed to assist with reduction of inflammation. Physical therapy may also be performed to help strengthen the tendons and ligaments affected.

Contraindications

In the acute stage, massage is considered a local contraindication for a client with whiplash. Once the symptoms have subsided, gentle massage in the are may be performed. Stretching of the neck should be avoided to prevent injuring the tissue.

Urinary Pathologies

Cystitis
(cyst-: bladder; -itis: inflammation)

Cystitis is a **bacterial infection** resulting in **inflammation of the bladder**. It can often involve the entire Urinary System, and is then known as a Urinary Tract Infection(UTI). Cystitis is most common in women, as the female urethra is shorter than the male urethra, giving bacteria a shorter passage to the bladder.

Causes

Cystitis is caused most commonly by E. Coli entering the urethra, then reproducing. The increased amount of bacterium in the urethra causes the infection to spread upwards into the bladder. Cystitis can cause numerous symptoms, including blood in the urine, burning sensations while urinating, and a frequent urge to urinate. If untreated, the infection may spread to the kidneys. When this happens, it is known as pyelonephritis.

Symptoms

Symptoms of cystitis include a frequent urge to urinate, a painful burning sensation upon urination, urinating small amounts at a time, fever, and blood in the urine.

Treatments

Because cystitis is a bacterial infection, it is treated with antibiotics.

Contraindications

In the acute stage of infection, massage is contraindication for cystitis. Once the infection has cleared, massage may be performed.

Kidney Stones

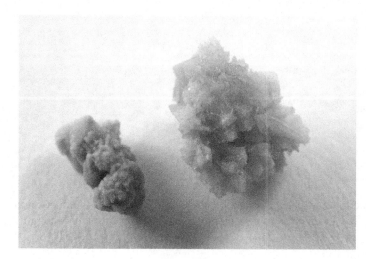

Kidney Stones, also known as Nephrolithiasis, are **deposits of salts and minerals** created inside the kidney, which are hard and rough. Stones vary in size, and may cause many differing health complications.

Kidney stones are more common in people who are obese or have a family history of kidney stone development. Diet may play a role as well.

Causes

Kidney stones may be caused by numerous factors. Most commonly, they are caused by increased amounts of calcium oxalate, which is found in many types of food. Excessive amounts of calcium oxalate can cause stones to develop. Uric acid may also produce stones if a person does not drink enough fluids. A high protein diet may contribute to the development of uric acid stones.

Less commonly, struvite stones may form, which are the result of bacterial infections of the urinary tract.

Symptoms

Kidney stones are largely asymptomatic until they leave the kidney and enter the ureter. When this occurs, pain may be felt around the abdomen, groin, back, and sides. Painful urination may take place as the stone blocks the ureter. The urine may have a pink or brown appearance due to blood in the urine. An inadequate amount of urine may be produced due to blockages.

Treatments

Many treatment options are available. In less severe cases, increasing water intake can help flush the kidneys of the increased calcium and help move the stones out of the body. To aid in moving the stone out of the body, a doctor may prescribe medications that help to relax the smooth muscle in the ureter, known as alpha blockers.

In more severe cases, stones may be destroyed while still inside the body using a treatment known as **extracorporeal shock wave lithotripsy**. The stones are broken down using sound waves, and then are able to be passed out of the body easier. If the stones are too big to be destroyed using sound waves, they may be removed surgically.

Contraindications

Kidney stones are not considered a contraindication for massage therapy.

Pyelonephritis
(pyel/o: renal pelvis; nephr/o: kidney; -itis: inflammation)

Pyelonephritis is a **bacterial infection of the kidney**, usually beginning in the urethra or bladder. The infection spreads upwards through the ureters and **into the kidneys**. Pyelonephritis is considered a serious condition, and if suspected, should be seen by a doctor immediately for treatment.

Causes

Bacteria enters the urethra. Usually, urinating cleans out the urethra. Rarely, it does not, and bacteria can reproduce in the urethra. The bacteria then can spread upwards into the bladder, then move further up into the ureters and kidneys. Women are more likely than men to develop urinary tract infections due to a shorter urethra.

Symptoms

Symptoms of an acute infection in the kidneys include pain in the back, groin, or abdomen, nausea, vomiting, fever, blood in the urine, burning during urination, and an urge to constantly urinate. Cloudy urine may also be a sign of an infection, especially if there is a foul odor.

Treatments

Antibiotics are used to combat pyelonephritis. They are typically administered orally, but in more severe cases that require hospitalization, they may be administered via IV. Pain relievers may be used to aid with associated pain.

Contraindications

Pyelonephritis is considered an absolute contraindication. A client who suspects a kidney infection should seek medical treatment.

Renal Failure

Renal failure is **kidney failure**, where the kidneys stop functioning properly. This can lead to the body being **unable to eliminate waste, electrolytes**, and **excessive fluid**. This can lead to dangerous, even fatal levels of these substances in the body.

Causes

Renal failure is commonly the result of another condition damaging the kidney enough to impair function. Examples are hypertension, glomerulonephritis, pyelonephritis, diabetes, and polycystic kidney disease.

Symptoms

Usually, renal failure occurs gradually, and symptoms become more known as the kidney begins to lose function. Fatigue, nausea, vomiting, hypertension, increased fluid accumulation in the lower limbs, and loss of appetite are common symptoms.

Treatments

As the kidneys begin failing, treatment usually revolves around treating the symptoms to try and slow the disease. Once the kidneys have experienced too much damage and the body is unable to eliminate waste and fluid effectively, dialysis may be performed to remove these substances, either through the blood or through the peritoneum.

Kidney transplants may be performed. Instead of removing the damaged kidneys, a doctor will leave the damaged kidneys in the body and attach another kidney. Despite not functioning optimally, the damaged kidneys can still assist the new kidney in filtering waste and fluid, even though it may only be a small amount.

Contraindications

Because massage may increase the load on kidneys by helping rid the body of waste, massage is considered an absolute contraindication in clients with renal failure. There is debate amongst kidney specialists on this matter though, and some believe massage therapy does not do harm in people with renal failure.

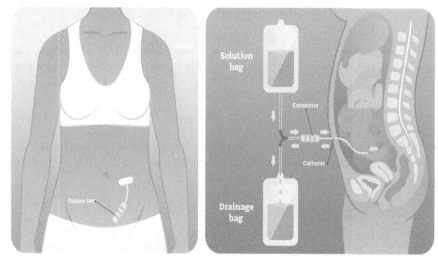

Peritoneal dialysis

Urethritis
(urethr/o: urethra; -itis: inflammation)

Urethritis is **inflammation of the urethra**, usually caused by a **bacterial infection**. It is extremely treatable.

Causes

Urethritis is caused by a bacterial infection. Bacteria enters the urethra and reproduces, resulting in an infection. The infection may spread up the urinary tract, and may lead to cystitis or pyelonephritis if left untreated.

Less commonly, urethritis may be caused by herpes simplex.

Symptoms

Pain upon urination is the primary symptom of urethritis. A less common symptom is inability to effectively urinate, known as dysuria. Discharge from the vagina may present, and the urine may contain blood.

Treatments

Because urethritis is most commonly caused by bacterial infection, antibiotics are prescribed to destroy the bacteria and prevent the infection from moving further into the Urinary System.

Contraindications

Massage is indicated for clients with urethritis.

Cancer

When the body produces an **abnormal amount of a specific tissue**, it develops what is known as a **tumor**. Tumors are also known as neoplasms. Tumors may be either benign or malignant. **Benign tumors** are considered noncancerous, and do not spread to other areas of the body. **Malignant tumors** are considered **cancerous**, and will **spread to other areas of the body**. The most common type of cancer is skin cancer.

Benign tumors typically **grow slowly**. These tumors do not invade other tissues or structures in the body. Benign tumors may cause harm, however, by placing pressure on regions of the body that contain major blood vessels, lymph vessels, or nerves. Benign tumors are often removed before they get to this point if there is a risk of damaging other structures. Other benign tumors may be left alone if they do not cause problems.

Malignant tumors spread through the body and affect other tissues and structures through a process known as metastasis. Cancerous cells spread through the body by entering into the **blood stream and lymph vessels**, allowing the cells to easily transport to another region. Once these cells settle in another region or structure, they continue to reproduce at a rapid, uncontrolled rate. The **original site** of the tumor is known as the **primary tumor**, while the tumor that has **developed elsewhere** is known as a **secondary tumor**. Some cancers, such as leukemia, do not result in any tumor growing. Malignant cancers commonly spread through the Lymphatic System and can result in tumors in major lymph nodes. This is especially common in areas like the breasts and neck.

There are three main classifications for cancer: carcinoma, sarcoma, and cancers of the blood stream/Lymphatic System. **Carcinoma** is cancer that occurs in the **epithelial tissue**, which can be found in the skin, digestive tract, and respiratory tract. A common form of carcinoma is basal cell carcinoma. **Sarcoma** is cancer that occurs in the body's **connective tissues**, such as bone and cartilage. Examples include bone cancer and Kaposi's Sarcoma. Examples of cancers that involve the blood stream and Lymphatic System include leukemia and Non-Hodgkin's Lymphoma.

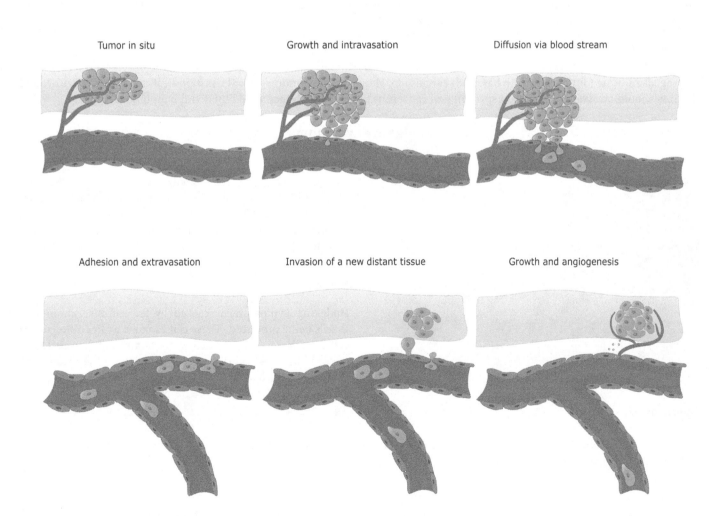

Tumor in situ   Growth and intravasation   Diffusion via blood stream

Adhesion and extravasation   Invasion of a new distant tissue   Growth and angiogenesis

Basal Cell Carcinoma
(carcin-: cancer; -oma: tumor)

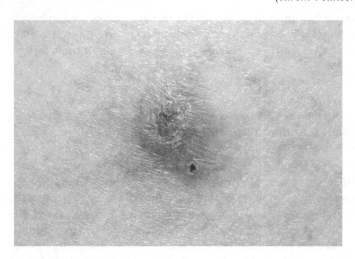

Basal Cell Carcinoma is a type of **skin cancer** typically seen around the **face**, **head**, **neck**, and **arms**.

Causes

Basal cell carcinoma is the **most common form of skin cancer**, caused by exposure to **ultraviolet light**. The tumor grows **extremely slowly**, which makes basal cell carcinoma much more treatable than other types of skin cancer. Because it is much more treatable, it is considered the **least serious form of skin cancer**.

Basal cell carcinoma is considered a malignant form of cancer, due to its ability to spread to the tissues immediately surrounding it. It will very rarely spread to other organs, however.

Symptoms

Basal cell carcinoma tumors may appear to have blood vessels in them, and vary in color from black to brown to pink. These growths may bleed easily.

Treatments

Treatment for basal cell carcinoma includes surgical excision of the tumor, freezing the tumor, or in more serious cases, medications that prevent the cancerous cells from spreading to other tissues.

Contraindications

Massage is indicated for a client with basal cell carcinoma. However, the tumor is a local contraindication, and massage around the area should be avoided to prevent spreading of cancerous tissue through increased blood and lymph flow.

Hodgkin's Lymphoma
(lymph-: lymph; -oma: tumor)

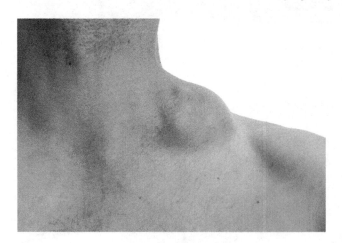

Hodgkin's Lymphoma is a **malignant cancer** affecting the Lymphatic System, specifically the **lymph nodes in the upper limb, chest, and neck**. Hodgkin's Lymphoma usually follows lymph channels in a predictable manner, moving from one lymph node to the next.

Causes

Hodgkin's Lymphoma is caused by an excessive amount of B-cells being produced. These cells, known as **Reed-Sternberg cells**, are larger than normal and contain multiple nuclei, as opposed to non-cancerous B-cells, which are smaller and only contain one nucleus.

Symptoms

Symptoms of Hodgkin's Lymphoma include swelling of lymph nodes in the neck, upper limb, and axilla that may be painless, weight loss, fever, and fatigue. A person may also experience sensitivity to alcohol.

Treatments

Surgery isn't usually performed for a patient with Hodgkin's Lymphoma. Instead, chemotherapy and radiation therapy are used to destroy the cancerous lymphocytes. Bone marrow transplants may also be performed, stimulating production of non-cancerous cells.

Contraindications

A massage therapist should obtain a doctor's note approving massage. Afterwards, massage may be performed, avoiding any tumors, lymph nodes, or other areas affected.

Leukemia
(leuk/o: white; -emia: blood condition)

Leukemia is a cancer of the **bone and lymph** involving **excessive production of non-functioning leukocytes**. These leukocytes do not function the way normal leukocytes should, leaving the body with a compromised immune system. These cancerous cells may spread to other parts of the body such as the liver and brain.

Causes

There is no known cause for the development of leukemia.

Symptoms

Common symptoms of leukemia include pain in the bone, swollen lymph nodes, fatigue, fever, chills, increased likelihood of developing infections, the appearance of small red spots in the skin, and bruising or bleeding easily. A doctor should be seen if any of these symptoms persist.

Treatments

Treatment for leukemia largely depends on the advancement of the condition. If the cancer has metastasized to other parts of the body, treatment would be performed on those areas in conjunction with treating the leukemia. Chemotherapy and radiation therapy are used to target and destroy cancerous cells throughout the body. After chemotherapy and/or radiation therapy, stem cell transplant may be performed to supply the bone with stem cells that grow healthy marrow, which produces functioning leukocytes. Bone marrow itself may also be transplanted into the patient to accomplish the same goal.

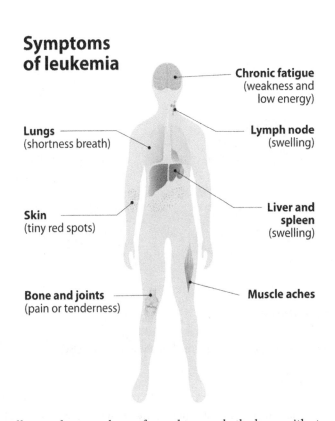

Symptoms of leukemia

- **Chronic fatigue** (weakness and low energy)
- **Lungs** (shortness breath)
- **Lymph node** (swelling)
- **Skin** (tiny red spots)
- **Liver and spleen** (swelling)
- **Bone and joints** (pain or tenderness)
- **Muscle aches**

Contraindications

A massage therapist should obtain a doctor's note approving massage. Afterwards, massage may be performed, avoiding any tumors, lymph nodes, or other areas affected.

Malignant Melanoma
(melan-: black; -oma: tumor)

Malignant Melanoma is a type of **skin cancer** that may affect any part of the skin, and can also affect other tissues such as the eyes and internal organs.

Causes

Malignant melanoma is the **least common** form of skin cancer, but it is the **most serious**. It is caused by exposure to **ultraviolet light**. The cells in the body that produce skin pigment, **melanocytes**, become stimulated by exposure to ultraviolet light and reproduce, causing darker skin. In malignant melanoma, the melanocytes reproduce uncontrolled. This uncontrolled reproduction results in a tumor, and these cancerous cells can easily spread throughout the body and damage other organs and tissues.

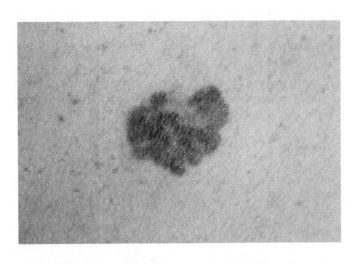

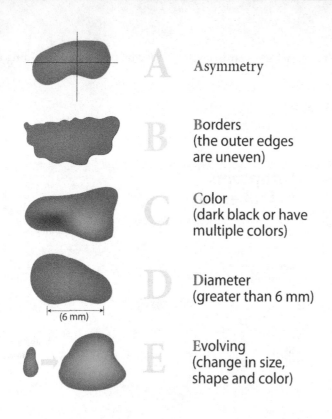

A   Asymmetry

B   Borders
(the outer edges
are uneven)

C   Color
(dark black or have
multiple colors)

D   Diameter
(greater than 6 mm)

(6 mm)

E   Evolving
(change in size,
shape and color)

Dermatologists use the ABCDE method to diagnose malignant melanoma:

A: Asymmetrical; moles are typically symmetrical, but melanoma tumors have an unusual shape, and the sides don't match.

B: Borders; the borders of the growth change over time and are uneven. This is a sign of significantly increased melanin production.

C: Color; moles are typically some shade of brown. If there are multiple shades or colors, or if the tumor is black, this may be a sign of increased melanin production.

D: Diameter; if a growth is 6mm or greater in diameter(the distance through it), this may be a sign of melanoma.

E: Evolving; moles typically look the same over time. If a mole or growth begins to evolve or change in any way, this may be a sign of melanoma.

Malignant melanoma most commonly begins to appear on a part of the body that doesn't have any prior lesions, like moles. If a new growth appears where there was nothing prior, this may be a sign of melanoma. Less commonly, moles may become cancerous.

Symptoms

Symptoms of melanoma are all included in the ABCDE's.

Treatments

Malignant melanoma, if caught early enough, is easily treatable. Later stages, where it has grown beyond the skin, need more advanced treatments, including surgery to remove any tumors or cancerous lymph nodes, chemotherapy, and radiation therapy.

Contraindications

A client with malignant melanoma should obtain permission from a doctor before proceeding with any type of massage, because the cancerous cells are easily spread throughout the body through the blood and lymph. The site of tumor growth should be avoided.

Non-Hodgkin's Lymphoma
(lymph-: lymph; -oma: tumor)

Non-Hodgkin's Lymphoma is a type of cancer of the Lymphatic System, caused by the development of **tumors by lymphocytes**.

Causes

In the body, lymphocytes, like every cell, go through their normal life cycle, and die when they are supposed to. In Non-Hodgkin's Lymphoma, the **lymphocytes don't die**, but **continue reproducing**. This causes an **excessive amount of lymphocytes** to build up in the lymph nodes.

Symptoms

People with Non-Hodgkin's Lymphoma may experience swollen lymph nodes around the neck, groin, and axilla, fatigue, weight loss, and fever.

Treatments

Often times, Non-Hodgkin's Lymphoma isn't serious, and treatment is only required when it becomes advanced. Advanced Non-Hodgkin's Lymphoma is treated with chemotherapy and radiation therapy to destroy the cancerous cells.

Contraindications

A massage therapist should obtain a doctor's note approving massage. Afterwards, massage may be performed, avoiding any tumors, lymph nodes, or other areas affected.

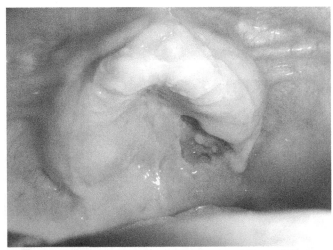

Tumor appearing in the hard and soft palate of the maxilla

Squamous Cell Carcinoma

(carcin-: cancer; -oma: tumor)

Squamous Cell Carcinoma is a form of **skin cancer** that in many cases is not serious, but has the ability to spread to other parts of the body. Squamous cell carcinoma is **more serious and less common than basal cell carcinoma**, but **not as serious and more common than malignant melanoma**.

Causes

Squamous cell carcinoma, much like basal cell carcinoma and malignant melanoma, is most often caused by exposure to ultraviolet light. Tumors most commonly develop on areas of the body commonly exposed to sunlight, such as the head, neck, arms, and hands. Tumors may be flat, scaly, and firm, and appear around the mouth, in the mouth, and on the lips.

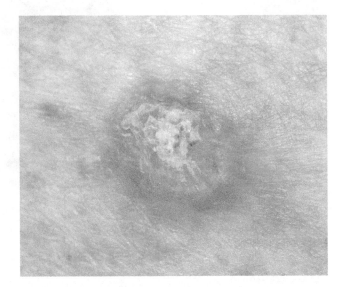

Symptoms

Squamous cell carcinoma tumors are typically shaped like a dome, and tend to bleed easily. They appear red and scaly, with a rough texture. If the tumor is large, pain may be present around the area.

Treatments

Much like basal cell carcinoma, treatment for squamous cell carcinoma is relatively easy, with several different methods, from surgical excision and freezing of the tumor, to radiation therapy for more advanced tumors.

Contraindications

A client with squamous cell carcinoma may receive massage, but the site of the tumor should be avoided due to possible spreading of cancerous tissue.

Psychological Pathologies

Anorexia Nervosa

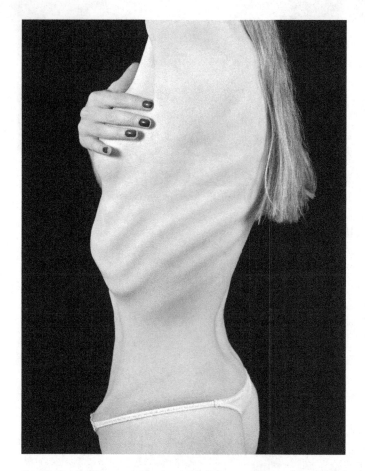

Anorexia nervosa is a condition marked by **severe weight loss** resulting from an **unhealthy restricting of caloric intake**. In conjunction with eating an inadequate amount of food, a person with anorexia may also try losing weight by taking diuretics, laxatives, and vomiting after eating. This can cause a severe lack of nutrition, resulting in the body thinning far beyond a healthy level.

Causes

Anorexia is a psychological disorder in which a person's perception of their weight is distorted. Contributing factors towards the development of anorexia include environmental influences that put an over-emphasis on being thin, and psychological issues such as obsessive compulsive disorder that make it easier to not eat by sticking to set goals.

Symptoms

Symptoms are wide-ranging, from severe thinness and weight loss, to problems with tooth decay from excessive vomiting.

A lack of proper nutrition can lead to fatigue, weakness, thinning hair, and dehydration. A person with anorexia may develop anemia, osteoporosis, abnormalities in hormone production and regulation, issues with kidney function, and muscle atrophy.

Psychologically, a person may withdraw socially, and try to hide their anorexia by wearing clothing to hide their weight loss. A person may become irritable and skip meals. When confronted, a person may deny skipping meals or lie about how much food they have eaten.

Treatments

Treatment for anorexia may include hospitalization in severe cases, where the body is not receiving adequate nutrition over a long period of time. While in the hospital, a person will be given fluids to balance dehydration and electrolyte levels, and be treated for issues possibly relating to the heart, liver, and kidneys. A feeding tube may be inserted to ensure a person is receiving enough nutrients.

Aside from a stay in the hospital, a person may be seen by a mental health professional to deal with underlying causes of anorexia. A person may work closely with a dietician to maintain a healthy diet.

Contraindications

Massage therapy is not contraindicated in clients with anorexia. A lighter massage should be performed to prevent damage to bones and other structures in the body.

Anxiety Disorders

Anxiety disorders are a group of disorders in where a person experiences an **increased amount of anxiety**, often at a level where the person feels they are in a **life-or-death situation**. These anxious moments can adversely affect a person's daily life and relationships. Different types of anxiety disorders include panic disorder, social anxiety disorder, and general anxiety disorder.

A person with an anxiety disorder may also suffer from addiction, depression, chronic pain, or even attempt suicide.

Causes

Often times, underlying medical issues may be the cause of anxiety disorders. Some examples include cardiovascular diseases, substance withdrawal, asthma, and hyperthyroidism. Medications may also induce anxiety.

Symptoms

Symptoms vary depending on the type of anxiety a person suffers from. General symptoms include nervousness, increased breathing and heart rate, shaking, trembling, digestive issues, and the inability to stop thinking about whatever it is that is putting a person into a state of anxiety.

Panic anxiety may leave a person with a feeling of fear or terror, and lead to chest pain, shortness of breath, and a rapid heart beat. Social anxiety may lead a person to avoid contact with others as a means to protect themselves from situations they might find themselves being embarrassed or self-conscious in.

Treatments

Psychotherapy is the primary treatment for anxiety disorders. Cognitive Behavioral Therapy is used to help treat social anxiety by exposing a person to situations they may experience in real life, giving them exposure and helping them learn how to cope with the situation when it arises. Medications may be prescribed, such as antidepressants, that can help a person from feeling anxious.

Contraindications

Anxiety disorders are not contraindicated for massage therapy.

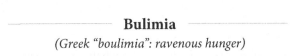

Bulimia
(Greek "boulimia": ravenous hunger)

Bulimia is a psychological disorder in which a person ingests **abnormally large portions of food**, followed by **purging of the food ingested**. Purging of food can be caused by **self-induced vomiting**, **consuming laxatives or diuretics**, and/or **excessive exercise**. This is all done in an effort to avoid weight gain.

The use of self-induced vomiting and laxatives/diuretics is known as Purging Bulimia. These involve ridding the body of the ingested food in some way that doesn't allow it to be properly digested. The use of excessive exercise is known as Non-Purging Bulimia.

Causes

The exact cause of bulimia is unknown, although there are several contributing factors that may lead to the development of the condition. Stress, history of abuse, trauma, low self-esteem, and having a negative image of one's body can all be contributing factors.

Symptoms

Common symptoms may include dehydration, imbalances in electrolyte levels, fluctuating weight, lesions in the mouth due to excessive vomiting, chronic heart burn, and infertility.

People with bulimia may exhibit some of the following traits and behaviors: frequent bathroom usage after eating, eating privately, smelling of vomit, and lacking control when eating.

Treatments

Bulimia is most commonly caused by low self-esteem and negative body image. Therefore, the primary treatment is therapy to help the patient overcome these psychological issues.

Contraindications

Bulimia is not contraindicated for massage. Massage may help psychologically and improve self esteem and body image. A lighter massage may be indicated, as the client may have atrophied muscles and a weakened body due to lack of nutrients.

Depression

Depression is a disorder affecting **mood**, causing a person to feel **sad**, usually over a **prolonged period of time**. A person may become disinterested in normal daily activities, and become more distant. Depression usually develops during teenage years, but may occur at any time. If a person is experiencing depression, they should seek help from a mental health professional.

Causes

There are many different causes for depression, and no one person is the same as another. Causes include a change in the body's hormone levels, such as during and after pregnancy, changes in the function of neurotransmitters in the brain, and even may be genetically passed down.

Symptoms

Symptoms are wide-ranging, and people experience depression differently. Symptoms may include a feeling of sadness, fatigue, disinterest in eating, anxiety, insomnia, irritability, and consistently thinking about death and suicide. A person with depression may attempt suicide.

Treatments

If a person is diagnosed with depression, antidepressants known as selective serotonin reuptake inhibitors, or SSRIs, are usually prescribed to help manage hormone levels and increase serotonin levels in the blood. Talking with a mental health professional may help a person feel better. Exercise and a healthy diet may help with hormone imbalances and increase a person's self esteem, which can aid in lowering depression. Other relaxation techniques, such as massage therapy and yoga, may be sought.

Contraindications

Depression is not contraindicated for massage therapy. Massage may help relax a person with depression, increase self-esteem and body image, and help manage hormone levels in the body. The National Suicide Prevention Lifeline is 1-800-273-8255.

Insomnia
(in-: not; somnus: sleep)

Insomnia is a disorder causing a **lack of sufficient sleep**. This may be the result of a person having **difficulty falling asleep**, **staying asleep**, or **waking too early**. This can lead to many health complications.

Causes

There are many reasons a person's sleep may be affected. Stress is the most common cause of insomnia, making it difficult to "turn off" thoughts when it's time to sleep. Having an irregular sleep schedule may make it difficult for the body to adjust when it's time to sleep. Jet lag may also cause insomnia. Certain medications may interfere with normal sleep. Pain associated with medical conditions may also keep a person from sleeping.

Symptoms

Common symptoms include trouble falling asleep, trouble staying asleep, waking too early, general fatigue, irritability, increased stress and anxiety, and depression. A person with insomnia may develop other health conditions as a result of not getting enough sleep, such as hypertension.

Treatments

Determining and treating the root cause of the insomnia is the primary treatment for insomnia. Reducing stress, getting a person on a set sleep schedule, increasing exercise, meditation, yoga, and massage therapy can all aid in eliminating insomnia. If these methods do not accomplish the goal, medications to help a person sleep may be prescribed. Over-the-counter sleep aids may help a person sleep, but should not be used long-term as a person may develop a dependency on them.

Contraindications

Insomnia is not a contraindication for massage. Massage may aid a person in reducing stress and obtaining a normal sleep cycle.

Other Pathologies

Conjunctivitis
(conjunctiv/o: conjunctiva; -itis: inflammation)

Conjunctivitis is **inflammation and/or infection of the conjunctiva**, the clear membrane that lines the inner eyelid and covers the sclera of the eye. Conjunctivitis is also known as **pinkeye**, due to the appearance of the conjunctiva when the blood vessels inside become irritated and inflamed.

Causes

The most common cause of conjunctivitis is a **bacterial or viral infection**. In infants, conjunctivitis may occur if tear ducts become blocked. Allergens may also cause conjunctivitis.

Symptoms

The affected eye may appear red, producing a **discharge**. This discharge may crust over and make it difficult to open the eye in the morning after sleep. The eye may feel itchy. Vision is not affected by conjunctivitis, but an increased amount of tears may be produced.

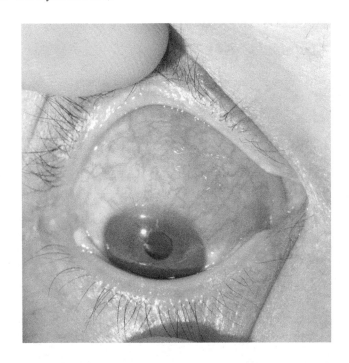

Treatments

Treating conjunctivitis is dependent on the cause. If it is caused by bacteria, antibiotic eye drops are prescribed. Antiviral medications may be prescribed in certain cases, such as a herpes simplex outbreak. If conjunctivitis is caused by an irritant such as contact lenses, a person will stop using contacts until the conjunctivitis clears up.

Contraindications

Conjunctivitis is generally not a contraindication, unless it is caused by bacteria or a virus. If this is the case, massage is considered an absolute contraindication, and should be rescheduled until after the condition has resolved.

Glaucoma
(Greek glaukos: bluish-green; -oma: tumor)

Glaucoma is a **degenerative eye disorder** in which the **optic nerve is progressively damaged by increased pressure** in the eye, eventually resulting in blindness. It is more common in people over the age of 60.

Causes

Inside the eye, there is fluid known as aqueous humor that is normally produced and drained from the eye. In people with glaucoma, this fluid does not properly drain, but keeps being produced, which adds pressure inside the eye. This pressure damages the optic nerve. When the optic nerve is damaged extensively, vision is lost.

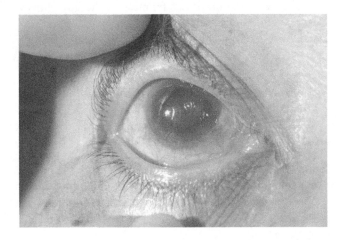

Symptoms

Symptoms vary depending on the advancement of the condition. Earlier stages may be relatively asymptomatic. Advanced stages can see a person develop tunnel vision, lose vision in the peripheral edges, experience headaches, nausea, vomiting, pain in the eye, and blurred vision.

Treatments

Treatment for glaucoma mainly focuses on reducing pressure inside the eye. Eyedrops can be prescribed that increase the amount of fluid being drained from the eye. Other eye drops may reduce the production of fluid in the eye. If these aren't useful, surgery may be performed. Laser surgery helps to open any blocked fluid draining channels. Small tubes may be put into the eye itself to help drain excess fluid.

Contraindications

Glaucoma is not contraindicated for massage.

Tinnitus
(Latin "tinnire": to ring like a bell)

Tinnitus is the presence of a **sound in the ear**, typically **ringing, without an external auditory source**. Tinnitus is usually related to another cause, such as an injury to the ear or hearing loss. It is usually not serious, but may be somewhat irritating. Tinnitus may always be present, or may come and go. The volume and pitch of the sound may be low or high, and may be loud enough to interfere with a person's ability to hear properly.

Causes

Common causes of tinnitus include exposure to loud noises, such as music, machinery, and firearms, hearing loss related to aging, and Meniere's disease. Less commonly, conditions that affect the Cardiovascular System may contribute to tinnitus, such as athero-sclerosis and hypertension. With these conditions, more pressure is being placed on the blood vessels, which can harm the blood vessels in the ears, making them more susceptible to developing tinnitus.

Symptoms

The main symptom is a sound in the ear that only the person can hear. This sound can be a ringing, clicking, humming, roaring, or buzzing sound. Depending on the cause, it may be heard in one or both ears.

Treatments

Treatment for tinnitus is often treating the underlying cause, which should alleviate the ringing in the ear. If a cardiovascular issue is suspected, medications may be prescribed to help treat these, which can eliminate the tinnitus. Less commonly, excessive ear wax may produce tinnitus. If this is the case, impacted ear wax may be removed. Avoiding loud noises will also help alleviate tinnitus.

Contraindications

Tinnitus is not contraindicated for massage therapy. However, if a client complains of ringing in the ear, other conditions should be assessed for contraindications.

Vertigo

Vertigo is the sensation that a person's **surroundings are moving or spinning**, which may cause **dizziness**. This can be especially prevalent if a person is looking down from a tall height.

Causes

Commonly, vertigo is the result of a problem with the **inner ear**. **Meniere's disease**, which causes **fluid buildup that changes pressure inside the ear**, is a common cause. A buildup of calcium deposits in the inner ear can alter balance. Viral infections, such as vestibular neuritis, may also cause vertigo. Less commonly, tumors in the ear may cause vertigo.

Symptoms

Vertigo presents with a feeling of the environment around a person spinning, moving, swaying, or tilting. A person may become unbalanced, become nauseated, vomit, or develop headaches.

Treatments

Treatment for vertigo is usually dependent on the cause. If calcium is present in the inner ear, certain head and neck movements may be performed to aid the calcium in leaving the inner ear, allowing it to be broken down by the body. Medications may be prescribed to aid with nausea and fluid build up associated with Meniere's disease. Surgery may be performed if there is a tumor present. Often times, no treatment is necessary, as the brain becomes acclimated to vertigo and the symptoms lessen or disappear.

Contraindications

Vertigo is not contraindicated for massage. The massage therapist may need to help the client on and off the table to avoid accidental falls due to dizziness.

First Aid and Response to Emergencies

First Aid

There are many different ways to care for a person with a medical emergency, depending on the type of injury and the severity. When using first aid, **universal precautions** should be administered. Universal precautions are treating every person and fluid as if they were **contaminated or infectious**. Universal precautions are extremely important in containing blood-borne pathogens. Any time there is exposure to any type of bodily fluid, **gloves and other personal protective equipment** should be worn, and contact with blood should be avoided at all costs.

CAB refers to the initial assessment steps that should be taken when coming into contact with an unconscious person. **Circulation** should be checked using pulse points. If no circulation is detected, the **airway** should be checked to determine if there is an obstruction that is causing the person to be unable to **breathe**. If there is an obstruction, it should try to be removed using a gentle finger swipe. If there is no circulation, the airway is not blocked, and the person is not breathing, CPR should be performed and EMS should be notified.

Responding to Emergencies

Bleeding

If a person is bleeding, a **sterile bandage** should be placed on the wound to promote **blood clotting**, which stops bleeding. If the bleeding is severe, a **tourniquet** may be applied, which should significantly reduce the bleeding. The person should lie down and be kept warm using a blanket, if available.

Cardiac and Pulmonary Arrest

If a person is suspected of suffering from cardiac arrest, CPR should be performed immediately. CPR, which stands for **Cardiopulmonary Resuscitation**, is extremely important to know and understand how to perform. CPR consists of alternating **chest compressions and breathing support** in cases where cardiac arrest has occurred. Refer to American Red Cross guidelines for appropriate instruction, techniques, and requirements.

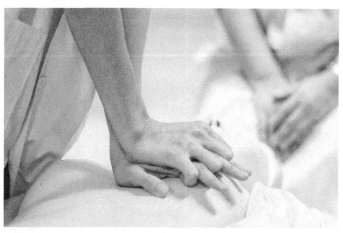

Choking

If a swallowed object or piece of food enters the **larynx or trachea, choking** will occur. A person who is choking may have extreme difficulty in coughing or talking, and may place their **hands to their throat** to indicate they are choking. This person should be treated immediately, utilizing **five blows to the back**, followed by **five abdominal thrusts**. This process should be repeated until the object is dislodged. If the person loses consciousness, they should be placed on the ground, and the throat should be checked for blockages. If the blockage is able to be removed without pushing it further into the respiratory tract, a **finger sweep** should be utilized. If not, CPR should be performed until paramedics arrive.

Demonstrating abdominal thrusts

Diabetic Ketoacidosis

Diabetic ketoacidosis occurs when a **diabetic** person has **too many ketones** in the body, caused by **hyperglycemia**. A person may have problems breathing, be fatigued, exhibit pain in the abdomen, and experience nausea and vomiting. If this person is unconscious as a result, EMS should be notified immediately. If they are not breathing, CPR should be administered until paramedics arrive.

Insulin Shock

If a person has **diabetes**, they need to take insulin to help manage their body's blood sugar. If **blood sugar levels fall too far**, it is known as **hypoglycemia**, and may result in **insulin shock**. A person may develop insulin shock for several reasons, such as injecting too much insulin, not increasing blood sugar levels, not eating, or exercising without increasing carbohydrate consumption. **Mild drops in blood sugar levels** can be treated quickly by **ingesting high carbohydrate food or liquid**. Severe hypoglycemia may result in insulin shock, however, and a person may develop seizures, muscle tremors, or they may lose consciousness. If a person loses consciousness, EMS should be notified immediately. If a shot of glucose is available, it should be administered immediately.

Fractures

Tending to a broken bone depends on the severity of the fracture. All fractures should be seen by a medical professional right away. If a fracture breaks through the skin, bleeding should be stopped. The area of the fracture should be **immobilized**, as movement in the area may cause damage to other structures in the body. The person may **develop shock**, and wrapping them in an **insulating blanket** may help. An ice pack may help reduce inflammation and pain in the area. The person should be taken to a hospital to have the bone reset, and the ensure there isn't major damage to other structures such as blood vessels inside the body that may cause internal hemorrhaging.

Seizures

If a person is having a seizure, the seizure should be **allowed to run its course**. Afterwards, the patient should be placed into a **seated position**, where they can rest and recover. If the seizure lasts for **five minutes or longer**, it is the person's **first seizure**, or the person is **unable to effectively walk or breathe** afterwards, **EMS should be contacted**.

Shock

If a person is in shock, **EMS should be notified immediately**. The person should **lie down**, keeping the **head flat**. A **blanket** or other clothing should be applied to keep the person's body temperature up. If the person is **vomiting**, they should be **placed on their side** to prevent choking. If any injuries are apparent, they should be treated.

Cerebral Vascular Accident

If a person is suspected of suffering a cerebral vascular accident, they may be exhibiting symptoms commonly seen with **strokes**, including **drooping face**, **difficulty speaking**, **weakness in the arms** that occurs suddenly, **sudden headache**, and sudden problems with **vision**. **EMS should be notified immediately**, as a cerebral vascular accident is a life-threatening condition. If the person is unconscious and not breathing, CPR should be performed. If the person is still conscious, they should be kept as calm as possible. They should not be given food or drink, to avoid vomiting.

Syncope

Syncope, also known as **fainting**, is usually not a serious condition. It is caused by the brain very **temporarily losing blood flow**. However, **injuries caused by falling** may occur. If a person has fainted, any restrictive clothing should be removed, and the legs should be elevated at least one foot above the heart. If the person is unconscious and not breathing, EMS should be notified, and CPR should be performed. If the person has not regained consciousness after one minute, EMS should be notified. Injuries sustained during a fall should also be treated, such as bleeding.

Asthma Attack

During an asthma attack, a person may have **extreme difficulty breathing** due to constriction of the bronchial tubes. The person may be **unable to effectively speak**, and the lips and fingers may turn a blueish color. Constrictive clothing should be removed or loosened. If the person has an **inhaler**, it should be utilized. The person should be taken to a hospital for treatment, as an asthma attack may actually worsen despite symptoms seemingly disappearing, such as wheezing.

Hyperventilation

Hyperventilation is a **psychological disorder** that causes a person to **breathe extremely rapidly or deeply**. This creates a **surplus of carbon dioxide** in the body, as the person is **not effectively exhaling**. Because hyperventilation is a common symptom of **panic attacks**, helping the person calm down is the primary treatment. Using a calm, reassuring tone can help a person regain proper breathing. The person should try holding their breath, as this may help reset the breathing pattern. If hyperventilation persists, EMS should be notified.

Concussion

A concussion occurs when there is a **blow to the head** that causes an **injury to the brain**. While a concussion is not always obvious, if a person suffers a head injury, assuming a concussion has occurred is recommended. The person should **keep the head and neck immobilized**, and **simple questions** should be asked to **determine cognitive function**. These questions can include asking the person their name, their age, and their location.

If the person is unconscious, CAB should be checked. If the person is not breathing, the throat should be checked for an obstruction. If there is an obstruction, it should try to be removed using a gentle finger swipe. If there is no obstruction, CPR should be performed and EMS should be notified.

Heat Injuries

There are three main types of heat injuries that don't involve burns: heat exhaustion, heat cramps, and heat stroke. **Heat exhaustion** is caused by a person having a **high body temperature with excessive sweating**. Sweating is a product of homeostasis, which is trying to cool the body. If the person continues to sweat, it means the body isn't properly cooling down. This can lead to **heat cramps**, which cause **tightening and involuntary spasms** of the muscles due to **dehydration and loss of electrolytes**, such as sodium and potassium. **Heat stroke** is when a person has an **extremely high body temperature**, with a **lack of sweating**. This occurs when a person is **severely dehydrated**, and has no more fluid to use as sweat to try cooling the body down. This can be potentially fatal.

Cold Injuries

There are two main types of cold injuries: hypothermia and frostbite. **Hypothermia** is caused by the **body temperature dropping below 90 degrees**. This can be potentially fatal. **Frostbite** is caused by a **formation of ice crystals in soft tissues**, typically the fingers, toes, and parts of the face such as the nose and ears. If the tissues are frozen for too long, they experience **necrosis**.

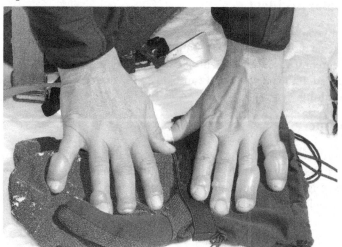

Blistering commonly seen with frostbite

Rule of 9's

The **Rule of 9's** is used to determine the **extent of burns by the total body area involved**. Each percentage represents the percentage of the body damaged by burns:

- Head and Neck: 9%
- Right Arm : 9%
- Left Arm: 9%
- Right Leg: 18%
- Left Leg: 18%
- Thorax: 18%
- Abdomen: 9%
- Lower Back: 9%
- Groin: 1%

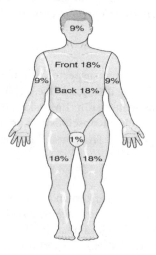

Orthopedic Injuries

Strains, sprains, and dislocations are all forms of **orthopedic injuries**. Strains and sprains are primarily treated with the use of **PRICE: Protect, Rest, Ice, Compression, Elevation**. The damaged area should be protected from further injury, rested to allow proper healing, iced to reduce inflammation, compressed to help further reduce inflammation, and elevated to assist in proper circulation and reduce inflammation. If a bone is **dislocated**, it should be **relocated if possible**. If not, the area should be **stabilized and protected**. If a fracture has taken place in conjunction with the dislocation, the fracture should be treated as normal, and the person should be taken to a hospital for treatment.

Poisoning

Poisoning may occur in several different ways. Poisoning via **inhalation**, such as **carbon monoxide poisoning**, may require the person be given an **antidote**, or require **breathing support** by way of an **oxygen mask**. **Injection poisoning** introduces harmful substances into the body via **needles, insect stings, sharp objects**, or **bites**. The poison usually requires the use of an **antidote** to treat. **Absorption** of poison typically includes exposure to substances such as **pesticides**. The area affected should be cleansed thoroughly with water.

Ingestion is introducing harmful substances through **swallowing**. Depending on the substance ingested, the person may be required to **induce vomiting**, or need to **drink milk or water**.

Bites and Stings

If an **animal bite** occurs that results in a **puncture**, **bleeding should be forced** from the wound to try clearing out as much bacteria as possible. The area should be **cleansed with soap and water**, and a **sterile dressing** should be applied to control bleeding and allow for proper healing.

Insect stings, such as from bees, should be **scraped with a sharp flat surface to remove any stinger** left behind that may be in the skin. The area should be **cleansed with soap and water**. If asphyxiation is suspected, EMS should be contacted immediately.

Snake bites should be **cleansed with soap and water**. The **area of the bite should be immobilized below the heart** to decrease the ease of blood flow to the heart from the area that contains venom. EMS should be notified.

Spider bites should be **cleansed with soap and water**. The **area of the bite should be immobilized below the heart**. The patient should be advised to seek medical attention.

Scorpion stings should be **cleansed with soap and water**. The **area of the sting should be immobilized below the heart**. The patient should be advised to seek medical attention.

Bee sting with stinger left in skin

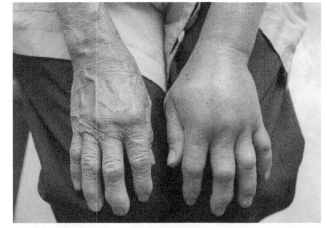

Snake bite

Spider bite

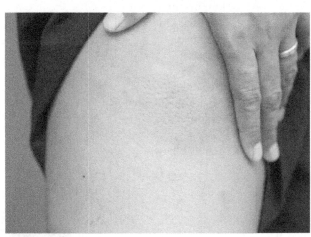

Scorpion sting

Pathology Matching

_____: Hyper-curvature of the thoracic vertebrae caused by tight pectoralis minor and serratus anterior

_____: Protrusion of the nucleus pulposus through the annulus fibrosus

_____: Inflammation of the liver

_____: Erosion of the articular cartilage, causing inflammation in a joint

_____: Swelling of veins due to malfunctioning valves

_____: Injury to a ligament caused by over-stretching

_____: Lack of cortisol production caused by damage to the adrenal cortex

_____: Epidermal growth caused by the human papilloma virus

_____: Fungal infection of the skin causing a circular rash

_____: Autoimmune disorder causing dry, scaly patches to form on the skin

_____: Bacterial infection of the kidneys presenting with back pain and fever

_____: Swelling of a limb due to excessive interstitial fluid in an area

_____: Subluxation of the distal phalange of the big toe forcing the first metatarsal to turn medially and the big toe to turn laterally

_____: Constriction of blood vessels in the hands and feet, reducing blood flow

_____: Bacterial infection causing inflammation of the bladder

_____: Paralysis of one side of the face due to damage to the facial nerve

_____: Necrosis of heart tissue

_____: Compression of the brachial plexus and blood vessels caused by tight scalenes and pectoralis minor

_____: Bacterial infection of a hair follicle, also known as a furuncle

_____: Form of tendonitis causing inflammation at the lateral epicondyle of the humerus

_____: Highly contagious viral infection of the respiratory tract

_____: Degeneration of alveoli, reducing gas exchange

A: Varicose Veins
B: Emphysema
C: Thoracic Outlet Syndrome
D: Kyphosis
E: Psoriasis
F: Boil
G: Hepatitis
H: Myocardial Infarction
I: Bunion
J: Wart
K: Tennis Elbow

L: Bell's Palsy
M: Cystitis
N: Sprain
O: Pyelonephritis
P: Herniated Disc
Q: Influenza
R: Lymphedema
S: Ringworm
T: Addison's Disease
U: Osteoarthritis
V: Raynaud's Disease

Answer Key on Page 308

Pathology Crossword

Across

3. A cancer that spreads to other tissues or regions in the body
4. Scar that is raised off the skin due to excessive scar tissue production
8. Bacterial infection in the lungs causing coughing with blood, fever, and chills
10. The most common, slowest growing, least serious form of skin cancer
13. Constriction of blood vessels in the fingers, reducing circulation
14. Fungal infection affecting the feet
16. Medications used to lower cholesterol and assist in lowering hypertension
17. Bacterial infection in the kidneys that begins in the urethra
18. Disease a person obtains at some point after birth
19. Substances released by damaged tissue to dilate blood vessels in an area and produce inflammation
20. Inflammation of the gallbladder typically caused by the development of gallstones that block the bile duct

Down

1. Subluxation causing the big toe to turn laterally and the first metatarsal to turn medially, producing a large bump
2. Disease a person is born with
5. In a person with diabetes, this hormone is either not produced in enough quantity, or the body becomes desensitized to it
6. Overgrowth of bone at the tibial tuberosity
7. Medical device used to regulate heart rhythm in a person with arrhythmia
9. An injury to a muscle or tendon
11. Hypercurvature of the lumbar vertebrae
12. The process of a cell eating another structure
15. Hypercurvature of the thoracic vertebrae

Answer Key on Page 310

Pathology Practice Test

1. During a pre-massage interview, a client is noticeably tired, has a slight cough, and claims that they experience wheezing and occasional tightness in the lungs. The client states they have been prescribed a steroid inhaler to take once per day to help treat the condition they are currently experiencing. Based on the information provided, what is the most likely condition the client is presenting with
A. Chronic bronchitis
B. Emphysema
C. Influenza
D. Cystic fibrosis

2. Substances released by T-cells and B-cells after binding to an antigen that communicate with the immune system to bring other T-cells and B-cells to the area of infection
A. Paratopes
B. Immunoglobulins
C. Antibodies
D. Cytokines

3. A client greets a massage therapist, and the massage therapist observes a large lump on the client's anterior neck. On the intake form, the client details that they suffer from hyperthyroidism. The large lump on the client's neck is a symptom of hyperthyroidism. What may be a contributing factor in this lump appearing
A. The client may have a diet high in carbohydrates
B. The client may have a diet low in iodine
C. The client may have a diet low in vitamin C
D. The client may have a diet high in beta carotene

4. Sean is baking a delicious cake, and the timer goes off, letting him know the cake is done baking. Sean reaches in to the oven and accidentally touches the side of the oven with his forearm. He immediately pulls his arm out, and sees skin has already begun peeling away in the area. After a trip to the emergency room, Sean's wound is bandaged, and he is sent home to recover. Several months pass, and the wound has healed, but scar tissue has formed to fill in the area where tissue has suffered necrosis. What is this type of scarring known as
A. Keloid
B. Contracture
C. Striae
D. Hypertrophic

5. A patient has recently had surgery, and in the process, the peritoneum had to be cut and repaired. This causes the client an increased buildup of fluid in the abdomen. In response to the increased fluid, surgeons insert a tube into the abdomen to help drain excess fluid in the days after surgery. What is this tube known as
A. Endoscope
B. Centrifuge
C. Arthroscope
D. Catheter

6. A patient is experiencing nausea, pain in the low back, and bloody urine. After performing imaging, the doctor diagnoses the patient with kidney stones. The kidney stones appear large, and are unable to pass without treatment. Which treatment is utilized to break the kidney stones into smaller pieces to allow the stones to pass easier
A. Dialysis
B. Arthroscopy
C. Lithotripsy
D. Chemotherapy

7. Which of the following describes meningitis
A. Paralysis of one side of the body due to infection of the Herpes Simplex virus
B. Inflammation of the brain, causing increased pressure placed on the cranium
C. Degeneration of brain tissue, resulting in loss of memory
D. Inflammation of the meninges, resulting in pressure being placed on the brain

8. A client indicates to a massage therapist that they occasionally experience extremely cold fingers that have a pins and needles sensation, usually when they are experiencing some sort of mental stress. The cold fingers typically return to normal after a short time. The client also states that they smoke cigarettes, and they are unsure if this contributes to their fingers becoming cold. Which is the most likely explanation for the client's symptoms
A. The client is experiencing intermittent vasoconstriction in the fingers, known as Raynaud's syndrome
B. The client is experiencing peripheral vascular disease most commonly seen with diabetes mellitus
C. The client is experiencing the early stages of myocardial infarction
D. The client is experiencing tightness in the pectoralis minor and scalenes that is contributing to the development of thoracic outlet syndrome

9. An injury that tears skin or other structures from the body, such as nails
A. Avulsion
B. Incision
C. Laceration
D. Puncture

10. A client states they have been diagnosed with Meniere's disease, with vertigo as an associated symptom. Which of the following describes vertigo
A. Ringing in the ears
B. Bacterial infection of the mucous membranes
C. Dizziness
D. Abnormal lateral curvature of the cervical vertebrae

11. A heart rate of 140-220 beats per minute resulting from abnormal electrical impulses stimulating the ventricles to contract rapidly
A. Bradycardia
B. Atrial fibrillation
C. Heart murmur
D. Tachycardia

12. A client has recently completed a full course of warfarin and heparin, two common blood thinners. If the client seeks massage treatment, how should the massage therapist proceed
A. The therapist should perform hacking and cupping on the back and chest to help loosen phlegm that may be built up in the lungs
B. The therapist should cancel the massage and not reschedule until the client resumes their prescribed medication
C. The therapist should perform a lighter massage to prevent potential bruising
D. The therapist should increase room temperature as the client may feel cold

13. In a pre-massage assessment, a therapist performs a posture analysis, and makes note that the scapulae appear to be in a fixed protracted state. This causes a rounded appearance in the upper back. The rhomboids and trapezius appear to be stretched. What condition is the client experiencing
A. Kyphosis
B. Thoracic outlet syndrome
C. Scoliosis
D. Adhesive capsulitis

14. A client explains to a massage therapist that they feel a lot of pain around their thumb. The client states that they are also a massage therapist, and feel as if they are using their thumb too much while providing treatment. The therapist observes the thumb and notices inflammation in the area, and the client is unable to move the joint without pain. Which of the following is the most likely condition associated with the client's symptoms
A. Osteoarthritis
B. Dupuytren's contracture
C. Rheumatoid arthritis
D. De Quervain's tenosynovitis

15. A secondary tumor
A. Forms into a primary tumor
B. Is the original tumor of a malignant cancer
C. Is also called a metastasis
D. Is made of epithelial cells

16. Rapid production of epithelial cells resulting in thick silvery patches, caused by an autoimmune response
A. Psoriasis
B. Rosacea
C. Melanoma
D. Papilloma

17. Anemia, scurvy, and osteoporosis may all be considered
A. Hereditary diseases
B. Idiopathic diseases
C. Deficiency diseases
D. Autoimmune diseases

18. A client lists on an intake form that they suffer from peripheral vascular disease. Which of the following describes peripheral vascular disease
A. Constriction of blood vessels in the fingers and toes, increasing circulation
B. Degeneration of blood vessels in the arms and legs, restricting circulation
C. Dilation of blood vessels in head and neck, resulting in hypoxia
D. Constriction of extracranial blood vessels, producing migraine headaches

19. A patient was recently on a walk in the desert when they were attacked by a coyote. The coyote managed to bite the patient twice in the forearm, but the patient was able to fight off the coyote and scare it away. The patient went to the hospital for treatment, suffering only a couple puncture wounds but nothing too severe. What type of healing would be required for this type of wound
A. Primary intention healing
B. Secondary intention healing
C. Quadrilateral intention healing
D. Tertiary intention healing

20. Thickening of arterial walls, leading to conditions such as hypertension
A. Angina pectoris
B. Arteriosclerosis
C. Phlebitis
D. Scleroderma

21. Which of the following cells produce antibodies
A. B-cells
B. Lymphocytes
C. Monocytes
D. T-cells

22. In a patient with renal failure, blood may need to be filtered through the following machine to eliminate harmful substances
A. Pacemaker
B. Centrifuge
C. Dialyzer
D. Defibrillator

23. Wear-and-tear arthritis, resulting in destruction of hyaline cartilage between articulating bones, increasing friction
A. Osteoarthritis
B. Rheumatoid arthritis
C. Gouty arthritis
D. Arthralgia

24. Dilation of blood vessels during the inflammatory stage is controlled by
A. Leukocytes
B. Histamines
C. Neutrophils
D. Fibrosis

25. All of the following are forms of parasites except
A. Pinworm
B. Tapeworm
C. Hookworm
D. Ringworm

Answer Key on Page 322

What we face may look insurmountable, but what I
learned is that we are always stronger than we know.

- Arnold Schwarzenegger

Kinesiology

Muscle Actions

Mandible Elevation

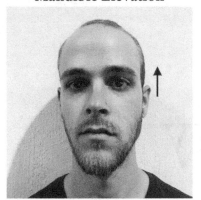

Muscles:
Masseter
Temporalis

Plane:
Frontal/
Coronal

Mandible Depression

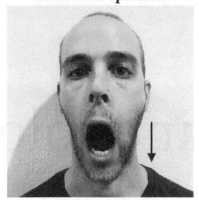

Muscles:
Lateral Pterygoid

Plane:
Frontal/
Coronal

Head/Neck Rotation

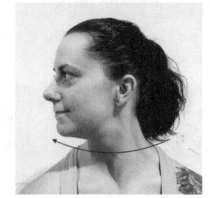

Muscles:
Sternocleidomastoid
Longissimus Capitis
Scalenes

Plane:
Transverse/
Horizontal

Head/Neck Flexion

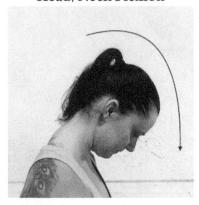

Muscles:
Sternocleidomastoid
Scalenes

Plane:
Sagittal

Head/Neck Extension

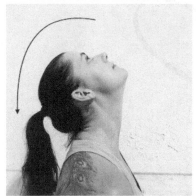

Muscles:
Longissimus Capitis
Splenius Capitis

Plane:
Sagittal

Head/Neck Lateral Flexion

Muscles:
Sternocleidomastoid
Scalenes

Plane:
Frontal/
Coronal

Scapula Retraction/Adduction

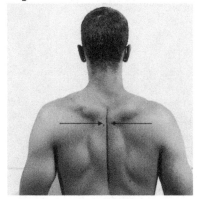

Muscles:
Rhomboids
Trapezius

Plane:
Frontal/
Coronal

Scapula Protraction/Abduction

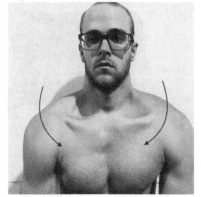

Muscles:
Pectoralis Minor
Serratus Anterior

Plane:
Frontal/
Coronal

Scapula Elevation

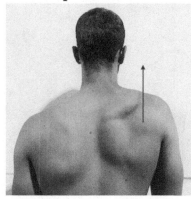

Muscles:
Levator Scapulae
Trapezius

Plane:
Frontal/
Coronal

Scapula Depression

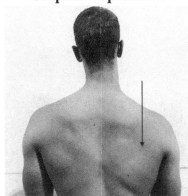

Muscles:
Serratus Anterior
Trapezius

Plane:
Frontal/
Coronal

Shoulder Flexion

Muscles:
Biceps Brachii
Anterior Deltoid
Pectoralis Major
Coracobrachialis

Plane:
Sagittal

Shoulder Extension

Muscles:
Latissimus Dorsi
Teres Major
Subscapularis
Triceps Brachii

Plane:
Sagittal

Shoulder Abduction

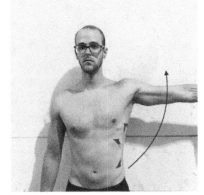

Muscles:
Deltoid
Supraspinatus

Plane:
Frontal/
Coronal

Shoulder Adduction

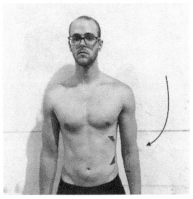

Muscles:
Latissimus Dorsi
Teres Major
Subscapularis

Plane:
Frontal/
Coronal

Shoulder Medial Rotation

Muscles:
Latissimus Dorsi
Teres Major
Subscapularis
Pectoralis Major

Plane:
Transverse/
Horizontal

Shoulder Lateral Rotation

Muscles:
Infraspinatus
Teres Minor

Plane:
Transverse/
Horizontal

Shoulder Horizontal Adduction

Muscles:
Pectoralis Major
Coracobrachialis

Plane:
Transverse/
Horizontal

Shoulder Horizontal Abduction

Muscles:
Infraspinatus
Teres Minor

Plane:
Transverse/
Horizontal

Elbow Flexion

Muscles:
Brachialis
Biceps Brachii
Brachioradialis

Plane:
Sagittal

Elbow Extension

Muscles:
Triceps Brachii
Anconeus

Plane:
Sagittal

Forearm Supination

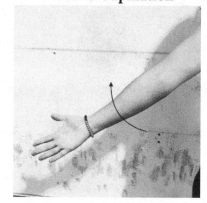

Muscles:
Biceps Brachii
Supinator

Plane:
Transverse/
Horizontal

Forearm Pronation

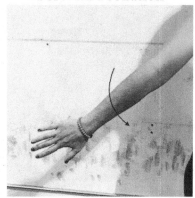

Muscles:
Pronator Teres

Plane:
Transverse/
Horizontal

Trunk Flexion

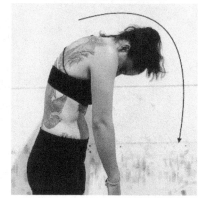

Muscles:
Rectus Abdominis

Plane:
Sagittal

Trunk Extension

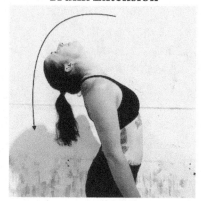

Muscles:
Longissimus
Spinalis
Iliocostalis

Plane:
Sagittal

Hip Flexion

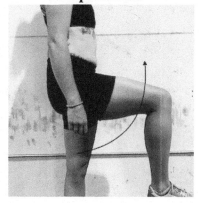

Muscles:
Psoas Major
Iliacus
Rectus Femoris
Sartorius

Plane:
Sagittal

Hip Extension

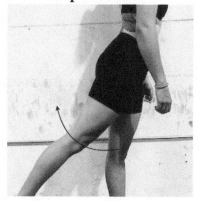

Muscles:
Semimembranosus
Semitendinosus
Biceps Femoris
Gluteus Maximus

Plane:
Sagittal

Hip Abduction

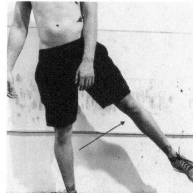

Muscles:
Gluteus Maximus
Piriformis

Plane:
Frontal/
Coronal

Hip Adduction

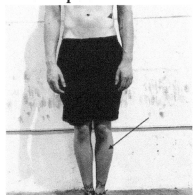

Muscles:
Adductor Magnus
Gracilis

Plane:
Frontal/
Coronal

Knee Flexion

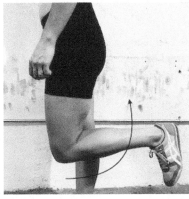

Muscles:
Semimembranosus
Semitendinosus
Biceps Femoris
Gastrocnemius

Plane:
Sagittal

Knee Extension

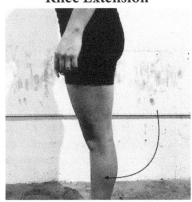

Muscles:
Rectus Femoris

Plane:
Sagittal

Ankle Plantarflexion

Muscles:
Gastrocnemius
Soleus
Peroneus Longus

Plane:
Sagittal

Ankle Dorsiflexion

Muscles:
Tibialis Anterior

Plane:
Sagittal

Foot Inversion/Supination

Muscles:
Tibialis Anterior
Tibialis Posterior

Plane:
Frontal/
Coronal

Foot Eversion/Pronation

Muscles:
Peroneus Longus

Plane:
Frontal/
Coronal

Bony Landmarks

Bony landmarks are specific locations on bones where muscles attach. There are many different kinds on landmarks, from tubercles and tuberosities, to condyles and epicondyles.

- **Condyle**: A rounded projection coming off a bone at an articulation.
- **Epicondyle**: Part of the bone located proximal to the condyle.
- **Crest**: A thin ridge of a bone.
- **Facet**: A smooth articular surface of a bone.
- **Fissure**: A narrow opening, resembling a crack.
- **Formina(foramen)**: A hole or opening in a bone.
- **Fossa**: A shallow depression in a bone.
- **Linea**: A narrow ridge, less pronounced than a crest.
- **Meatus**: A canal-like passage.
- **Process**: A prominent structure on a bone.
- **Ramus**: An elongated, seemingly stretched-out part of a bone.
- **Sinus**: A cavity created by bones.
- **Suture**: A type of synarthrotic joint that doesn't allow movement.
- **Trochanter**: A very large process, only found on the femur.
- **Tubercle**: A small, rounded projection.
- **Tuberosity**: A large, rounded, often rough projection.

Bones have numerous different types of landmarks. Landmarks are not only named after their **type**(above), but often what they **look like**(example, "coracoid" means "resembling a crow's beak"), what muscles **attach to them**(example, deltoid tuberosity), or even where they're **located in the body**(example, anterior superior iliac spine).

Origins

Muscles have two different attachments, origins and insertions. The **origin** of a muscle is where the muscle "**begins**". It is the **anchor point** of the muscle. The origin of a muscle **does not produce movement**, except in certain cases where the insertion is locked in place. For example, if the shoulders are locked in an adducted position, the latissimus dorsi's origin at the iliac crest may elevate the hip unilaterally, with the shoulder staying in place and not moving.

In regards to position, if the muscle being referenced is a **muscle that controls a limb**, the **origin will always be more proximal than the insertion**. For example, the origins of the biceps brachii are both located on the scapula, and the insertion is located on the radius. The scapula is more proximal than the radius. In regards to **muscles that control the trunk**, the origin is generally going to be **more medial than the insertion**. For example, the rhomboids originate on the spinous processes of C7-T5, and insert onto the medial border of the scapula. The medial border of the scapula is more lateral than the spinous processes of C7-T5. Unfortunately this rule doesn't apply to every muscle of the trunk.

Insertions

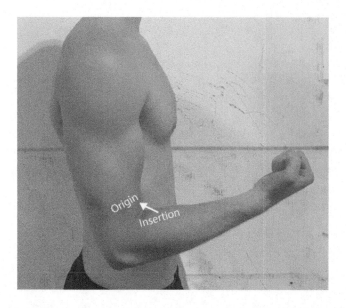

Insertions are the part of the muscle **where action takes place**. When the muscle contracts, it **pulls on the tendon attaching to the bony landmark at the insertion point**. This results in the **insertion being pulled toward the origin** as the **muscle length decreases** due to the concentric contraction. For example, when brachialis contracts, its insertions located at the coronoid process of the ulna and ulnar tuberosity will be pulled toward the origin, located at the anterior distal shaft of the humerus.

When a muscle performs a concentric contraction, an action will occur. This is the result of the **muscle crossing a joint**. If a muscle crosses a joint, such as brachialis crossing the elbow, the elbow will move when the insertion is pulled to the origin. In this specific example, a concentric contraction of brachialis will produce elbow flexion.

Head

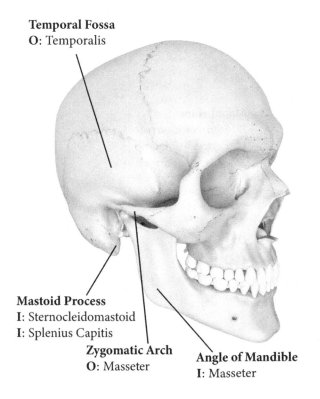

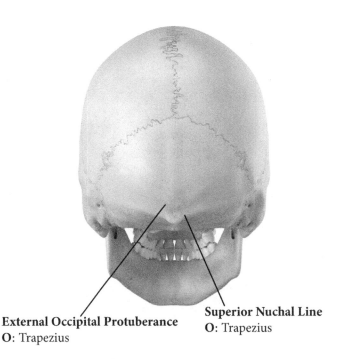

Temporal Fossa
O: Temporalis

Mastoid Process
I: Sternocleidomastoid
I: Splenius Capitis

Zygomatic Arch
O: Masseter

Angle of Mandible
I: Masseter

External Occipital Protuberance
O: Trapezius

Superior Nuchal Line
O: Trapezius

Vertebrae

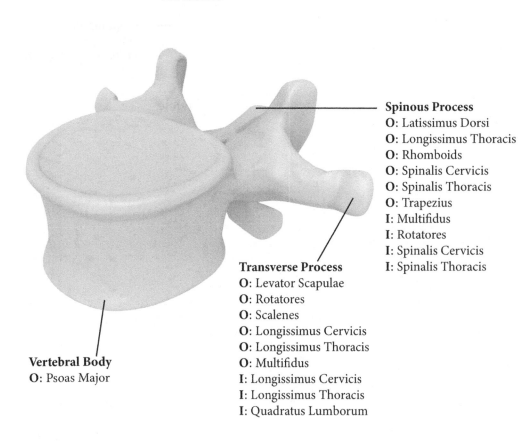

Spinous Process
O: Latissimus Dorsi
O: Longissimus Thoracis
O: Rhomboids
O: Spinalis Cervicis
O: Spinalis Thoracis
O: Trapezius
I: Multifidus
I: Rotatores
I: Spinalis Cervicis
I: Spinalis Thoracis

Transverse Process
O: Levator Scapulae
O: Rotatores
O: Scalenes
O: Longissimus Cervicis
O: Longissimus Thoracis
O: Multifidus
I: Longissimus Cervicis
I: Longissimus Thoracis
I: Quadratus Lumborum

Vertebral Body
O: Psoas Major

Chest

Sternum

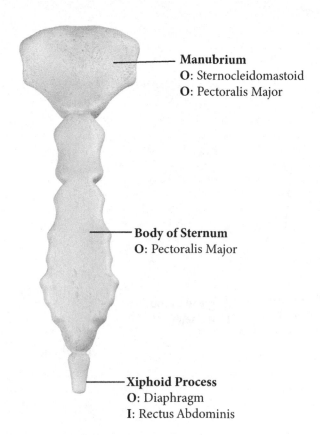

Manubrium
O: Sternocleidomastoid
O: Pectoralis Major

Body of Sternum
O: Pectoralis Major

Xiphoid Process
O: Diaphragm
I: Rectus Abdominis

Clavicle

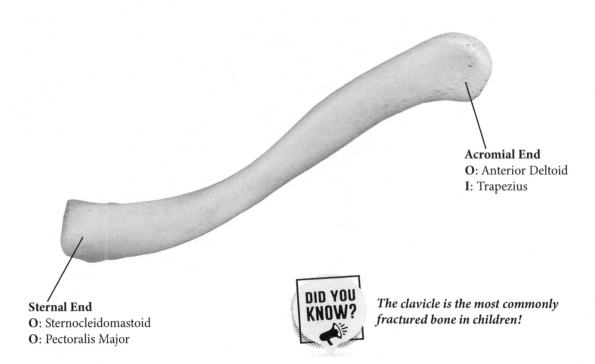

Acromial End
O: Anterior Deltoid
I: Trapezius

Sternal End
O: Sternocleidomastoid
O: Pectoralis Major

DID YOU KNOW?

The clavicle is the most commonly fractured bone in children!

Scapula(Anterior)

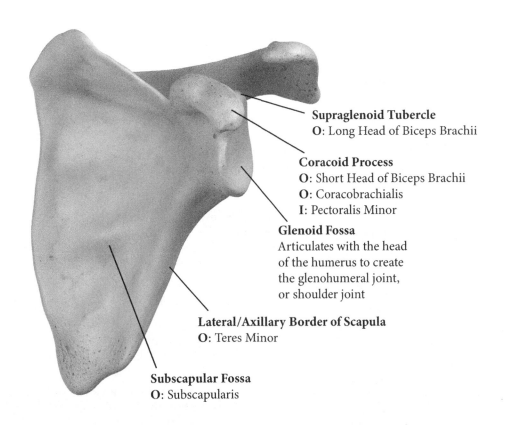

Supraglenoid Tubercle
O: Long Head of Biceps Brachii

Coracoid Process
O: Short Head of Biceps Brachii
O: Coracobrachialis
I: Pectoralis Minor

Glenoid Fossa
Articulates with the head
of the humerus to create
the glenohumeral joint,
or shoulder joint

Lateral/Axillary Border of Scapula
O: Teres Minor

Subscapular Fossa
O: Subscapularis

Scapula(Posterior)

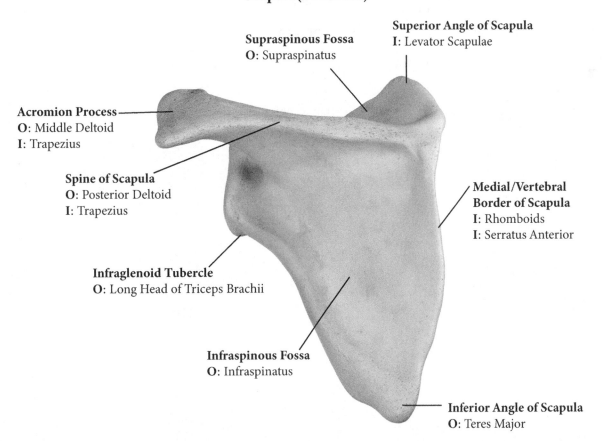

Suttpraspinous Fossa
O: Supraspinatus

Superior Angle of Scapula
I: Levator Scapulae

Acromion Process
O: Middle Deltoid
I: Trapezius

Spine of Scapula
O: Posterior Deltoid
I: Trapezius

**Medial/Vertebral
Border of Scapula**
I: Rhomboids
I: Serratus Anterior

Infraglenoid Tubercle
O: Long Head of Triceps Brachii

Infraspinous Fossa
O: Infraspinatus

Inferior Angle of Scapula
O: Teres Major

Arm

Humerus(Anterior)

Head of Humerus
Articulates with the glenoid fossa to create the glenohumeral joint, or shoulder joint

Lesser Tubercle
I: Subscapularis

Greater Tubercle
I: Supraspinatus
I: Infraspinatus
I: Teres Minor

Intertubercular/Bicipital Groove
I(Medial Lip): Latissimus Dorsi
I(Medial Lip): Teres Major
I(Lateral Lip): Pectoralis Major

Deltoid Tuberosity
I: Deltoid

Trochlea

Humerus(Posterior)

Lateral Supracondylar Ridge
O: Brachioradialis

Lateral Epicondyle
O: Wrist Extensors
O: Anconeus
Medical Condition:
Tennis Elbow

Olecranon Fossa

Medial Epicondyle
O: Wrist Flexors
O: Pronator Teres
Medical Condition:
Golfer's Elbow

Forearm

Radius

Head of Radius

Radial Tuberosity
I: Biceps Brachii

Styloid Process of Radius
I: Brachioradialis

Ulna(Lateral View)

Olecranon Process
I: Triceps Brachii
I: Anconeus

Coronoid Process
I: Brachialis

Ulnar Tuberosity
I: Brachialis

Styloid Process of Ulna

Head of Ulna

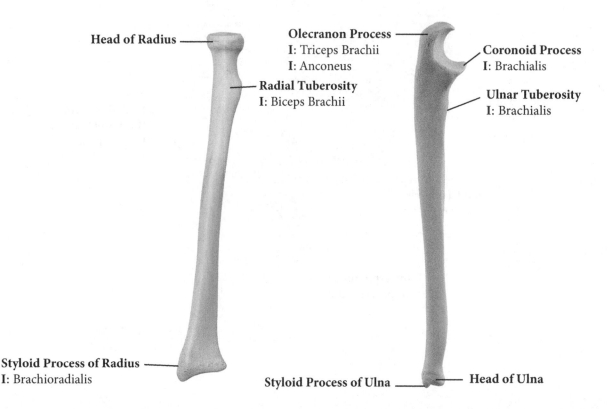

Pelvis

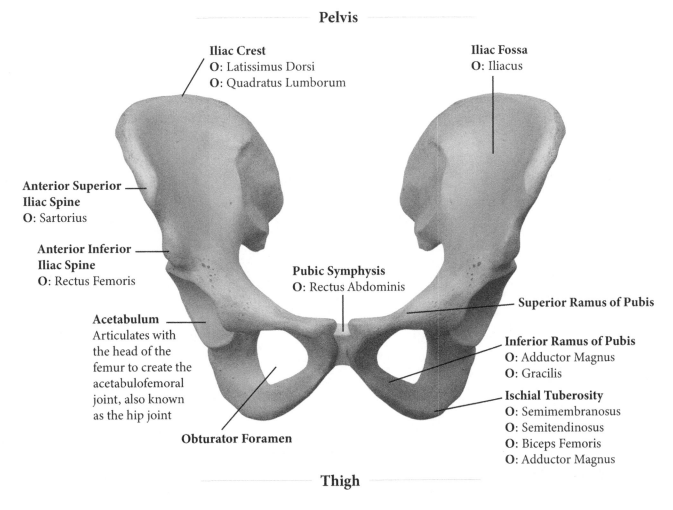

Iliac Crest
O: Latissimus Dorsi
O: Quadratus Lumborum

Iliac Fossa
O: Iliacus

Anterior Superior Iliac Spine
O: Sartorius

Anterior Inferior Iliac Spine
O: Rectus Femoris

Pubic Symphysis
O: Rectus Abdominis

Superior Ramus of Pubis

Acetabulum
Articulates with the head of the femur to create the acetabulofemoral joint, also known as the hip joint

Inferior Ramus of Pubis
O: Adductor Magnus
O: Gracilis

Ischial Tuberosity
O: Semimembranosus
O: Semitendinosus
O: Biceps Femoris
O: Adductor Magnus

Obturator Foramen

Thigh

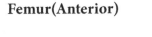

Femur(Anterior)

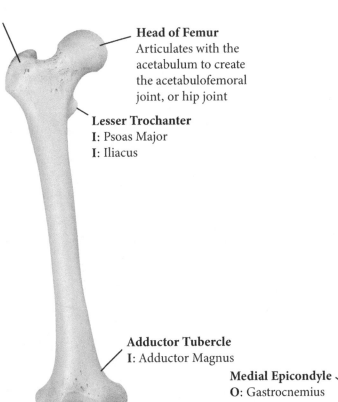

Greater Trochanter
I: Gluteus Maximus
I: Piriformis

Head of Femur
Articulates with the acetabulum to create the acetabulofemoral joint, or hip joint

Lesser Trochanter
I: Psoas Major
I: Iliacus

Adductor Tubercle
I: Adductor Magnus

Medial Epicondyle
O: Gastrocnemius

Femur(Posterior)

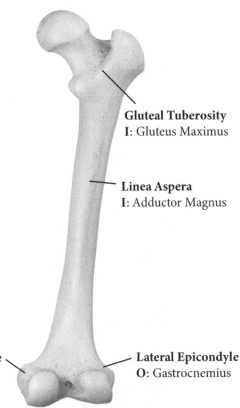

Gluteal Tuberosity
I: Gluteus Maximus

Linea Aspera
I: Adductor Magnus

Lateral Epicondyle
O: Gastrocnemius

Leg

Fibula

Head of Fibula
O: Soleus
O: Peroneus Longus
I: Biceps Femoris

Lateral Malleolus

Tibia

Tibial Tuberosity
I: Rectus Femoris
Medical Condition:
Osgood-Schlatter
Disease

Pes Anserinus
I: Sartorius
I: Gracilis
I: Semitendinosus

Medial Malleolus

Carpals

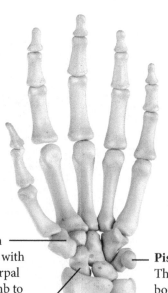

Trapezium
Articulates with
the metacarpal
of the thumb to
create the saddle
joint

Pisiform
The only carpal
bone that is a
sesamoid bone

Scaphoid
Articulates with the
radius to create the
radiocarpal joint

Tarsals

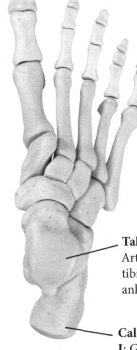

Talus
Articulates with the
tibia to create the
ankle joint

Calcaneus
I: Gastrocnemius
I: Soleus

Muscles of the Head

Muscles to Know:
Buccinator
Masseter
Temporalis

Terms to Know:
bucc/o: Cheek

Actions to Know:
Mandible Elevation
Cheek Compression

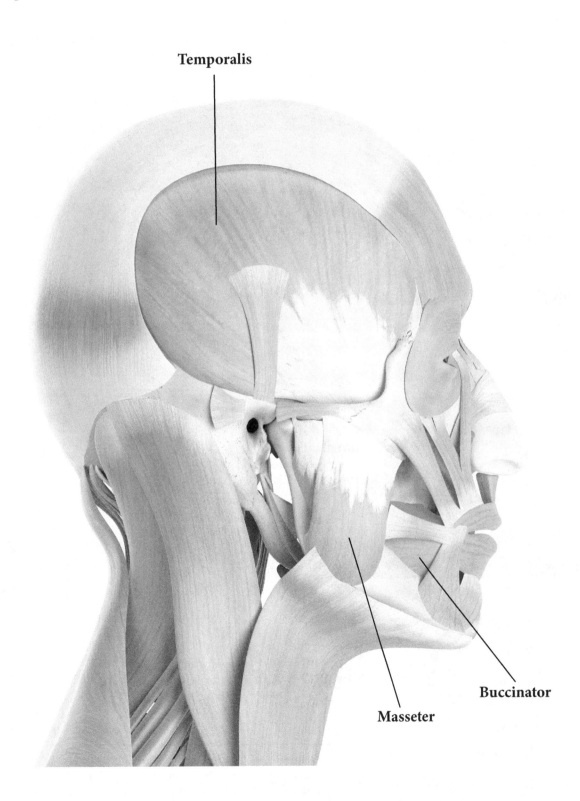

Temporalis

Masseter

Buccinator

Buccinator

Buccinator is a muscle of the face located in the area of the cheek, also known as the "buccal" region. The term "bucc/o" means "cheek".

Buccinator originates on the alveolar processes of the mandible and maxilla, and inserts onto the angle of the mouth and the orbicularis oris muscle.

Buccinator primarily assists in chewing by squeezing the cheeks closer together while the jaw is depressed. This forces the food back in towards the teeth, allowing proper mastication to take place upon elevation of the mandible. Buccinator is also the muscle primarily used for whistling, again by squeezing the cheeks together, and it also assists in smiling.

Smiling

Mandible Elevation

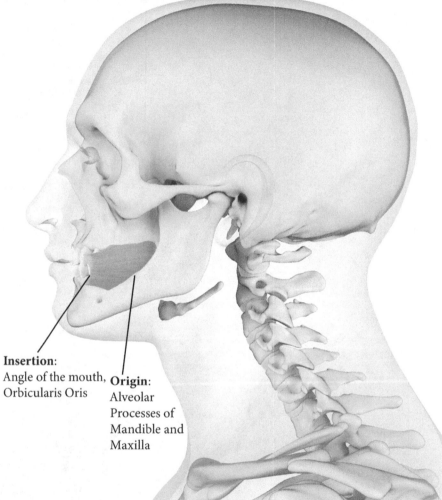

Insertion:
Angle of the mouth,
Orbicularis Oris

Origin:
Alveolar
Processes of
Mandible and
Maxilla

DID YOU KNOW?

If a person is affected by Bell's Palsy, the buccinator becomes paralyzed, which produces slurred speech!

Origin: Alveolar Processes of Mandible and Maxilla
Insertion: Angle of the mouth, Orbicularis Oris
Action(s): Elevation of Mandible, Compresses Cheeks against Teeth
Innervation: Buccal Branch of Facial Nerve
Synergist: Masseter
Antagonist: Lateral Pterygoid

Masseter

Masseter, named after its primary action of mastication, is a muscle of the face that attaches to the mandible. When it contracts, it elevates the mandible and allows chewing to take place. It works with other muscles, such as buccinator, to perform mastication.

Masseter originates on the zygomatic arch and maxilla, and inserts onto the coronoid process and ramus of the mandible.

Masseter is one muscle primarily involved in TMJ(Temporomandibular Joint) Dysfunction, along with temporalis and pterygoid.

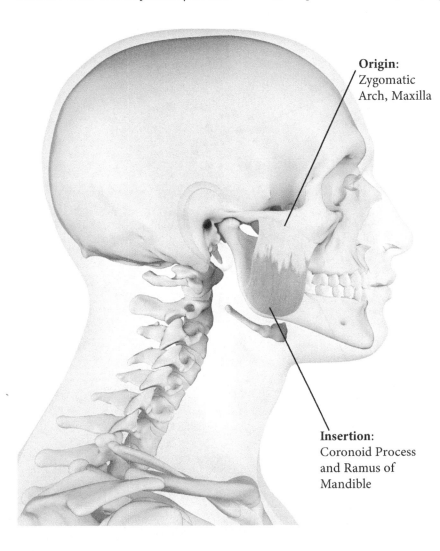

Origin: Zygomatic Arch, Maxilla

Insertion: Coronoid Process and Ramus of Mandible

Mandible Elevation

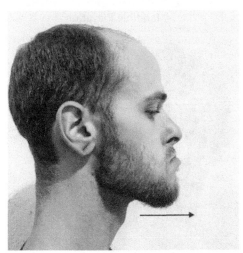

Mandible Protraction

DID YOU KNOW?

Masseter is the strongest muscle in the body by proportional size!

Origin: Zygomatic Arch, Maxilla
Insertion: Coronoid Process and Ramus of Mandible
Action(s): Elevation, Protraction of Mandible
Innervation: Mandibular Nerve
Synergist: Buccinator
Antagonist: Lateral Pterygoid

Temporalis

Temporalis is a muscle of the cranium, named after the temporal bone, which is its origin. Temporalis inserts onto the coronoid process of the mandible. "Coronoid" means "resembling a crown".

Inserting onto the mandible allows the temporalis to assist in elevating the mandible and performing mastication, along with masseter.

If a person is affected by TMJ(Temporomandibular Joint) Dysfunction, temporalis may be involved.

Mandible Elevation

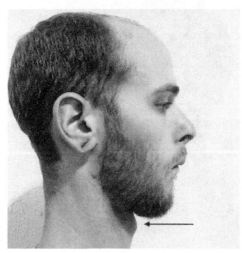

Mandible Retraction

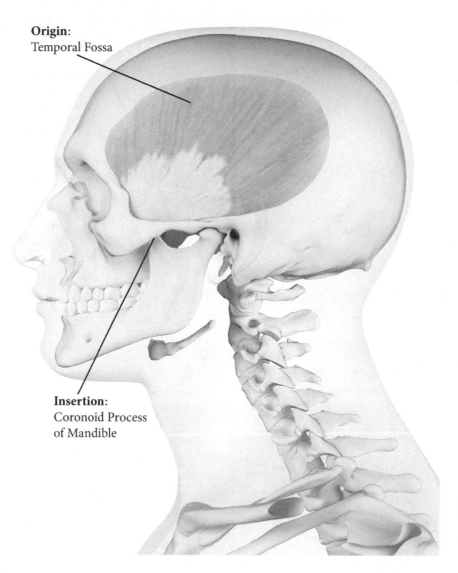

Origin:
Temporal Fossa

Insertion:
Coronoid Process
of Mandible

Origin: Temporal Fossa
Insertion: Coronoid Process of Mandible
Action(s): Elevation, Retraction of Mandible
Innervation: Facial Nerve
Synergist: Masseter
Antagonist: Lateral Pterygoid

Muscles of the Neck

Muscles to Know:
Levator Scapulae
Scalenes
Splenius Capitis
Sternocleidomastoid

Terms to Know:
Capitis: Head
Skalenos: Uneven
Splenion: Bandage
stern/o: Sternum
cleid/o: Clavicle
mast/o: Breast
-oid: Resembling

Actions to Know:
Scapula Elevation
Head/Neck Lateral Flexion
Head/Neck Flexion
Head/Neck Rotation
Head/Neck Extension

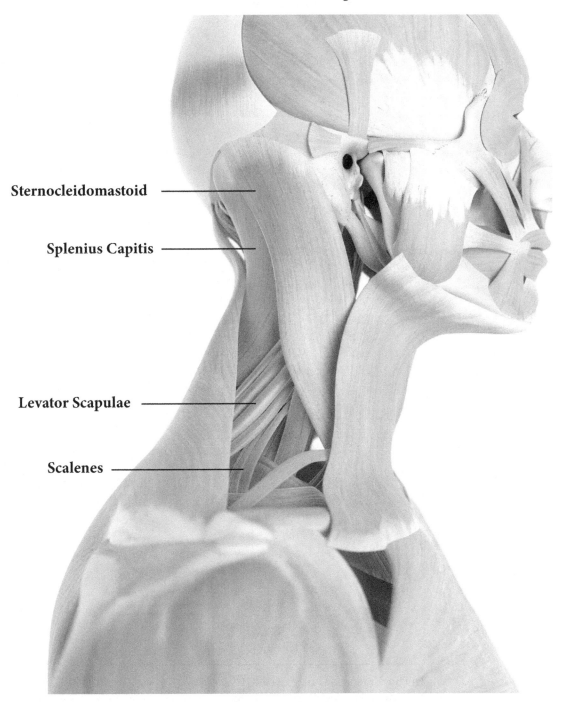

Sternocleidomastoid

Splenius Capitis

Levator Scapulae

Scalenes

Lateral View

Levator Scapulae

Levator scapulae is a muscle of the posterior neck, named after its action(elevation), and insertion(scapula).

Levator scapulae originates on the transverse processes of C1-C4, and inserts onto the superior angle of the scapula.

Levator scapulae is one of the prime movers of scapular elevation, such as shrugging the shoulders. It also may slightly downwardly rotate the scapula.

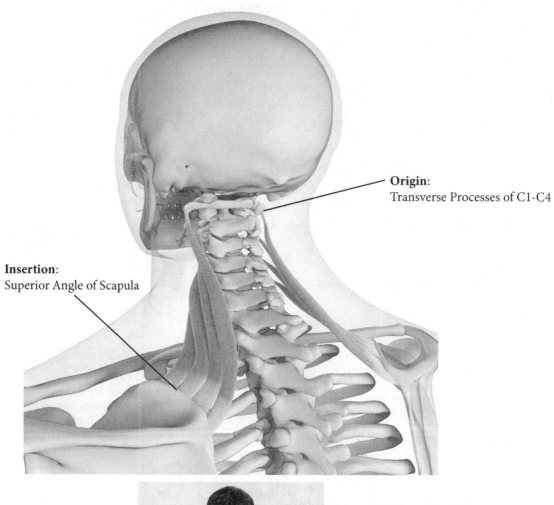

Origin:
Transverse Processes of C1-C4

Insertion:
Superior Angle of Scapula

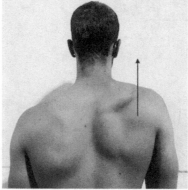

Scapula Elevation

Origin: Transverse Processes of C1-C4
Insertion: Superior Angle of Scapula
Action(s): Elevation of Scapula
Innervation: Dorsal Scapular Nerve
Synergist: Upper Trapezius
Antagonist: Lower Trapezius, Serratus Anterior

Scalenes

The scalenes are muscles of the anterior neck. The scalenes are split into three parts: anterior scalene, middle scalene, and posterior scalene. The name "scalene" comes from the Greek word "skalenos", which means "uneven". All three scalene muscles are a different size.

The scalenes originate on the transverse processes of C1-C7, and insert onto ribs 1 and 2.

Unilaterally, the scalenes laterally flex the cervical vertebrae, bringing the ear to the shoulder. The scalenes also elevate the ribs. Bilaterally, the scalenes bring the neck into flexion.

The scalenes are neurovascular entrappers. Conditions such as Thoracic Outlet Syndrome, where the brachial plexus, subclavian artery, and subclavian vein are compressed, can be caused by hypertonic scalenes. This condition may result in loss of sensation in the upper limb and reduced blood flow.

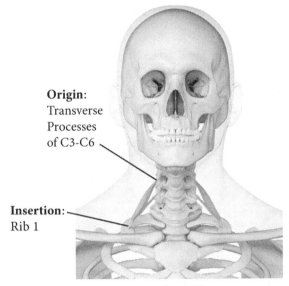

Origin:
Transverse Processes of C3-C6

Insertion:
Rib 1

Anterior Scalene

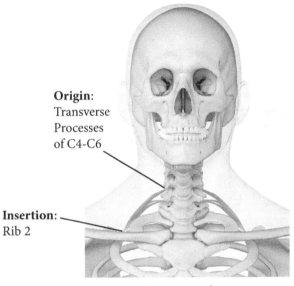

Origin:
Transverse Processes of C4-C6

Insertion:
Rib 2

Posterior Scalene

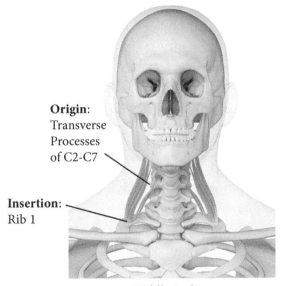

Origin:
Transverse Processes of C2-C7

Insertion:
Rib 1

Middle Scalene

Head/Neck Lateral Flexion

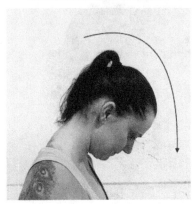

Head/Neck Flexion

Origin: Transverse Processes of C1-C7
Insertion: Ribs 1 and 2
Action(s): Unilaterally: Lateral Flexion of Cervical Vertebrae; Bilaterally: Head/Neck Flexion
Innervation: Branches of Cervical Plexus and Brachial Plexus
Synergist: Sternocleidomastoid
Antagonist: Spinalis Cervicis, Splenius Capitis

Splenius Capitis

Splenius capitis is a muscle of the posterior neck, named after its appearance("splenius" derives from the Greek word "splenion", which means "bandage"), and its insertion("capitis" refers to the head).

Splenius capitis originates on the spinous processes of C7-T3. Splenius capitis inserts onto the mastoid process of the temporal bone, and the occipital bone.

Unilaterally, the splenius capitis will laterally flex the neck, and rotate the cervical vertebrae to the same side. Bilaterally, splenius capitis assists in extension of the head/neck.

Head/Neck Lateral Flexion

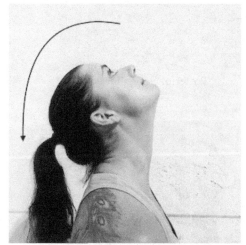

Head/Neck Extension

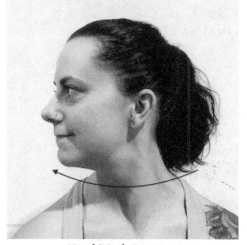

Head/Neck Rotation

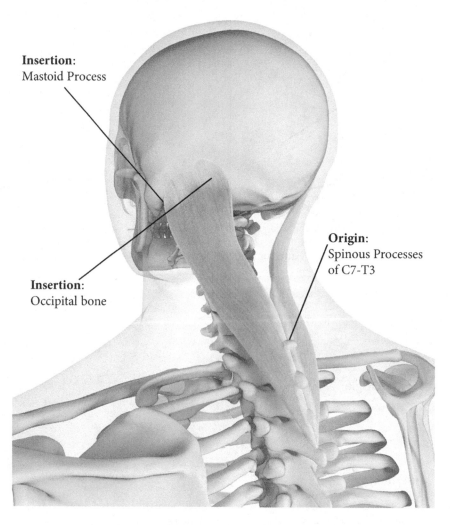

Insertion: Mastoid Process

Insertion: Occipital bone

Origin: Spinous Processes of C7-T3

Origin: Spinous Processes of C7-T3
Insertion: Mastoid Process of Temporal bone, Occipital bone
Action(s): Unilaterally: Lateral Flexion, Rotation of Cervical Vertebrae to same side; Bilaterally: Extension of Head
Innervation: Dorsal Primary Rami of Spinal Nerves C2-C6
Synergist: Spinalis Cervicis
Antagonist: Sternocleidomastoid

Sternocleidomastoid

Sternocleidomastoid is a muscle of the anterior neck, named after its origins(sternum, clavicle) and insertion(mastoid process). This muscle may also be known as "sternomastoid".

Sternocleidomastoid has numerous actions. Unilaterally, it rotates the cervical vertebrae to the opposite side of the contracting muscle. It also laterally flexes the cervical vertebrae to the same side of the contracting muscle. Bilaterally, it flexes the cervical vertebrae, allowing the chin to come to the chest.

Sternocleidomastoid establishes the borders of the anterior triangle of the neck, creating a V shape.

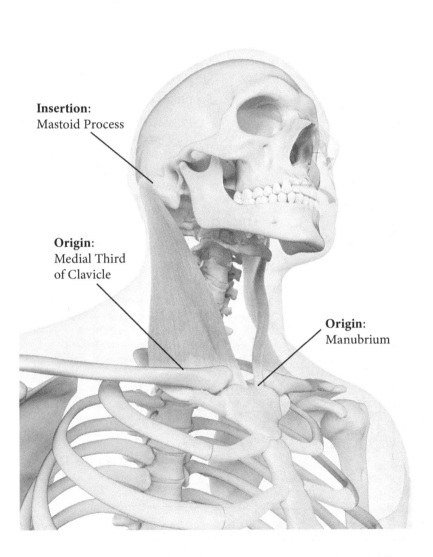

Insertion:
Mastoid Process

Origin:
Medial Third
of Clavicle

Origin:
Manubrium

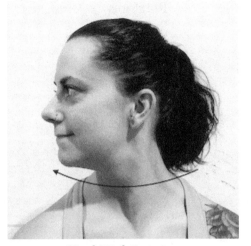

Head/Neck Rotation

Head/Neck Flexion

Head/Neck Lateral Flexion

Origin: Manubrium, Medial Third of Clavicle
Insertion: Mastoid Process of Temporal bone
Action(s): Unilaterally: Rotation of Cervical Vertebrae to opposite side, Lateral Flexion of Cervical Vertebrae to same side; Bilaterally: Flexion of Cervical Vertebrae
Innervation: Accessory Nerve
Synergist: Scalenes
Antagonist: Splenius Capitis, Trapezius

Muscles of the Back

Muscles to Know:
Infraspinatus
Latissimus Dorsi
Longissimus
Multifidus
Quadratus Lumborum
Rhomboids
Rotatores
Spinalis
Subscapularis
Supraspinatus
Teres Major
Teres Minor
Trapezius

Terms to Know:
Latissimus: Wide
Dorsi: Back
Teres: Round and Long
lumb/o: Lumbar
quadr/o: Four
infra-: Below
sub-: Under
supra-: Above

Actions to Know:
Shoulder Lateral Rotation
Shoulder Medial Rotation
Shoulder Flexion
Shoulder Extension
Shoulder Horizontal Adduction
Shoulder Horizontal Abduction
Shoulder Adduction
Shoulder Abduction
Trunk Lateral Flexion
Trunk Extension
Trunk Rotation
Scapula Retraction
Scapula Protraction
Scapula Elevation
Scapula Depression

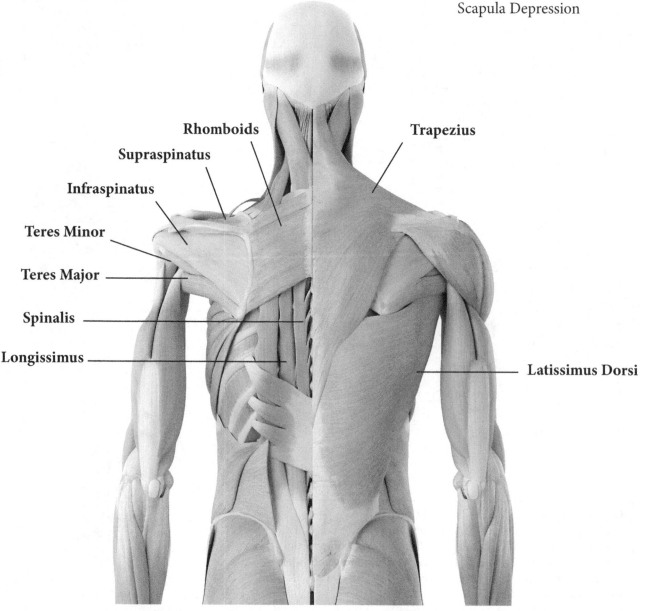

Not Pictured: Multifidus, Rotatores, Quadratus Lumborum, Subscapularis

Infraspinatus

Infraspinatus is a muscle of the back, named after its location(inferior to the spine of scapula). Infraspinatus is a member of the rotator cuff muscle group, along with supraspinatus, teres minor, and subscapularis.

Infraspinatus originates on the infraspinous fossa, located on the posterior surface of the scapula. Infraspinatus inserts onto the greater tubercle(sometimes also known as the greater tuberosity) of the humerus.

Infraspinatus is primarily responsible for lateral rotation, extension, and horizontal abduction of the shoulder. Infraspinatus and teres minor have the same actions.

Shoulder Lateral Rotation

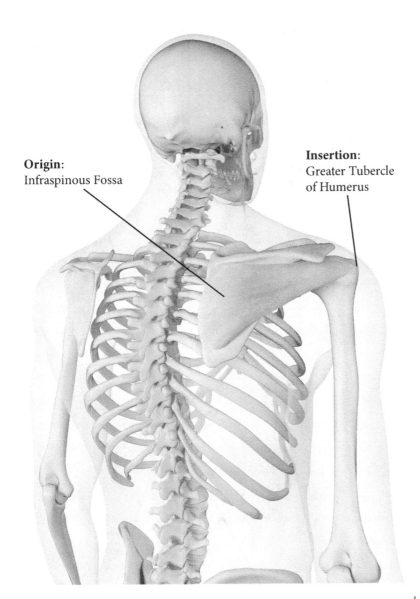

Origin:
Infraspinous Fossa

Insertion:
Greater Tubercle
of Humerus

Shoulder Horizontal Abduction

 Easy to Remember: To remember the muscles of the rotator cuff, think "SITS"! This stands for:
Supraspinatus
Infraspinatus
Teres Minor
Subscapularis

Origin: Infraspinous Fossa
Insertion: Greater Tubercle of Humerus
Action(s): Lateral Rotation, Horizontal Abduction of Shoulder
Innervation: Suprascapular Nerve
Synergist: Teres Minor, Latissimus Dorsi, Posterior Deltoid
Antagonist: Anterior Deltoid, Subscapularis, Pectoralis Major

Latissimus Dorsi

Latissimus dorsi is a muscle of the back, named after its size("latissimus" means "wide") and location("dorsi" refers to the back). Latissimus dorsi is the widest muscle in the body.

Latissimus dorsi originates on the iliac crest, thoracolumbar aponeurosis, and the spinous processes of T7-T12. Latissimus dorsi inserts onto the medial lip of the intertubercular groove(also may be known as the bicipital groove).

Latissimus dorsi is the muscle primarily responsible for performing adduction of the shoulder. If a person were to perform pull-up exercises, it would be latissimus dorsi contracting strongest. Latissimus dorsi also medially rotates and extends the shoulder. Latissimus dorsi, teres major, and subscapularis all perform the same actions. When the insertion is fixed in place, latissimus dorsi may elevate the hip.

Latissimus dorsi is often referred to as the "swimmer's muscle" due to its actions, which are used when swimming.

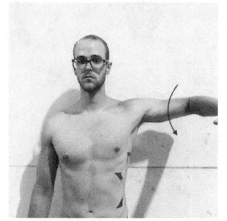

Shoulder Medial Rotation

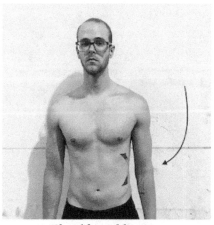

Shoulder Adduction

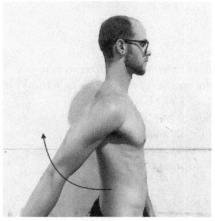

Shoulder Extension

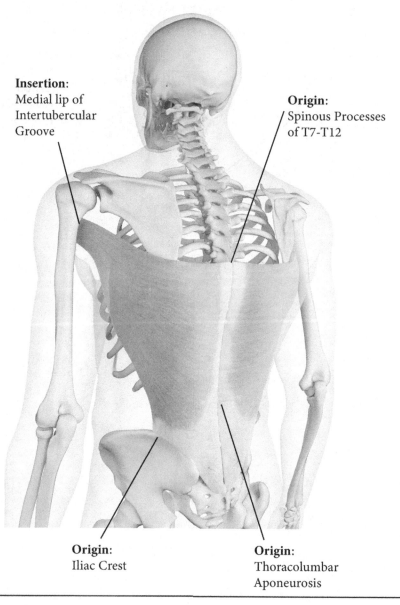

Insertion:
Medial lip of
Intertubercular
Groove

Origin:
Spinous Processes
of T7-T12

Origin:
Iliac Crest

Origin:
Thoracolumbar
Aponeurosis

Origin: Iliac Crest, Thoracolumbar Aponeurosis, Spinous Processes of T7-T12
Insertion: Medial lip of Intertubercular Groove
Action(s): Extension, Adduction, Medial Rotation of Shoulder
Innervation: Thoracodorsal Nerve
Synergist: Teres Major, Subscapularis
Antagonist: Pectoralis Major, Coracobrachialis

Longissimus

Longissimus is a group of three muscles, longissimus cervicis, longissimus capitis, and longissimus thoracis, which are all part of the erector spinae muscle group. Each muscle is named after the region of the body it is located on or attaches to.

Longissimus capitis originates on the articular surfaces of C4-C7, and inserts onto the mastoid process. Longissimus cervicis originates on the transverse processes of T1-T5, and inserts onto the transverse processes of C2-C6. Longissimus thoracis originates on the transverse and spinous processes of L1-L5, the iliac crest, and the sacrum, and inserts onto the transverse processes of T1-T12.

Unilaterally, the longissimus laterally flexes the trunk. Bilaterally, longissimus extends the trunk.

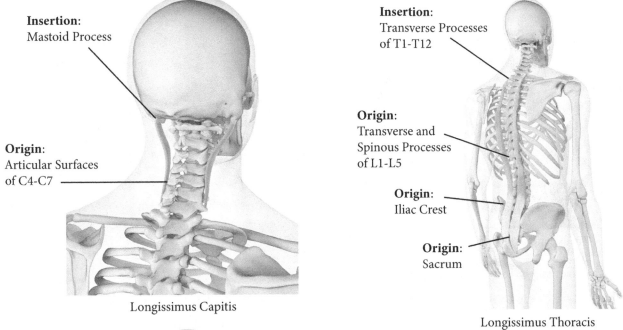

Insertion: Mastoid Process

Origin: Articular Surfaces of C4-C7

Longissimus Capitis

Insertion: Transverse Processes of T1-T12

Origin: Transverse and Spinous Processes of L1-L5

Origin: Iliac Crest

Origin: Sacrum

Longissimus Thoracis

Origin: Transverse Processes of T1-T5

Insertion: Transverse Processes of C2-C6

Longissimus Cervicis

Trunk Lateral Flexion

Trunk Extension

Origin: Longissimus Capitis: Articular Surfaces of C4-C7,
Longissimus Cervicis: Transverse Processes of T1-T5,
Longissimus Thoracis: Transverse and Spinous Processes of L1-L5, Iliac Crest, Sacrum
Insertion: Mastoid Process, Transverse Processes of C2-C6, Transverse Processes of T1-T12
Action(s): Unilaterally: Lateral Flexion of Trunk; Bilaterally: Extension of Trunk
Innervation: Dorsal Primary Rami of T1-L5
Synergist: Spinalis
Antagonist: Rectus Abdominis

Multifidus

Multifidus is a muscle of the back, often grouped together with other multifidus muscles to create the multifidi.

The multifidi as a group originate on the posterior surface of the sacrum, the posterior superior iliac spine(PSIS), mamillary processes of L1-L5, the transverse processes of T1-T12, and the articular processes of C4-C7. The multifidi insert on the transverse processes of C2-L5, spanning essentially the entire vertebral column.

Unilaterally, the multifidi will laterally flex the trunk, and rotate the trunk. Bilaterally, the multifidi extend the trunk. The multifidi span the most number of vertebrae of any muscle.

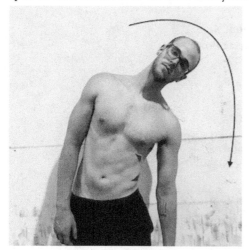

Trunk Lateral Flexion

Trunk Extension

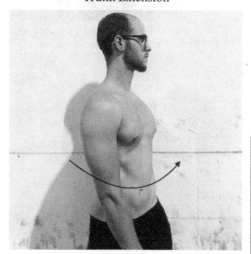

Trunk Rotation

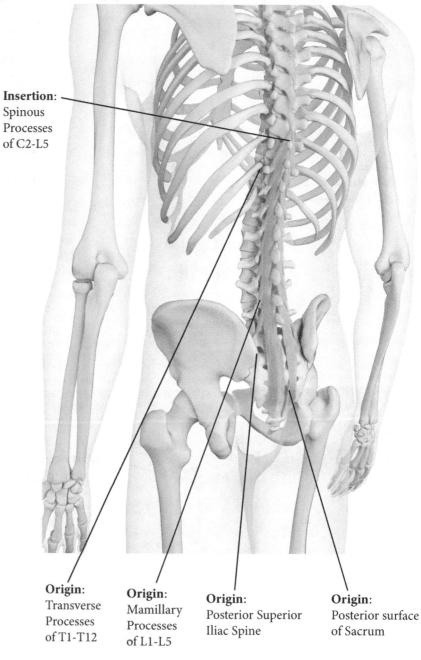

Insertion: Spinous Processes of C2-L5

Origin: Transverse Processes of T1-T12

Origin: Mamillary Processes of L1-L5

Origin: Posterior Superior Iliac Spine

Origin: Posterior surface of Sacrum

Origin: Posterior surface of Sacrum, Posterior Superior Iliac Spine, Mamillary Processes of L1-L5, Transverse Processes of T1-T12, Articular Processes of C4-C7
Insertion: Spinous Processes of C2-L5
Action(s): Unilaterally: Lateral Flexion of Trunk, Rotation of Trunk; Bilaterally: Extension of Trunk
Innervation: Dorsal Rami of Spinal Nerves
Synergist: Longissimus, Spinalis
Antagonist: Rectus Abdominis

Quadratus Lumborum

Quadratus lumborum is a muscle of the lower back, named after its shape(four sides), and its location(in the lumbar region).

Quadratus lumborum originates on the iliac crest, and inserts onto the 12th rib, and the transverse processes of L1-L4.

Quadratus lumborum, unilaterally, will assist in lateral flexion of the trunk. Bilaterally, it will assist in extension of the trunk. If a person suffers from lordosis(also known as swayback), it may be caused by hypertonicity in the quadratus lumborum, pulling the pelvis anteriorly, thus increasing the curvature of the lumbar vertebrae.

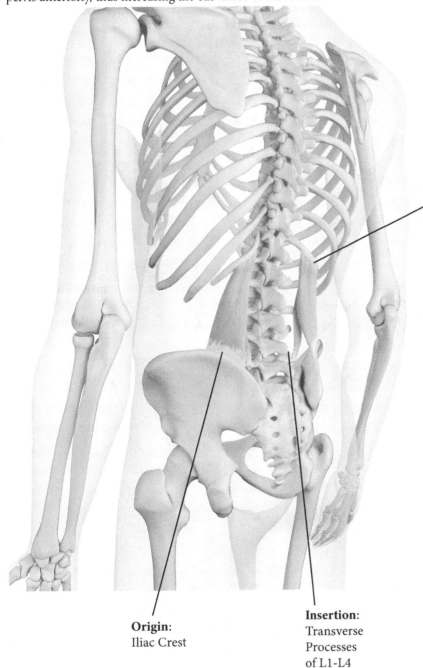

Insertion:
12th Rib

Origin:
Iliac Crest

Insertion:
Transverse
Processes
of L1-L4

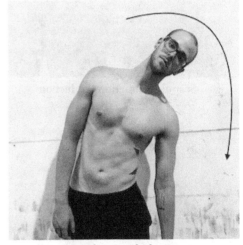

Trunk Lateral Flexion

Trunk Extension

Origin: Iliac Crest
Insertion: 12th Rib, Transverse Processes of L1-L4
Action(s): Unilaterally: Lateral Flexion of Trunk;
Bilaterally: Extension of Trunk
Innervation: Ventral Primary Rami of T12-L3
Synergist: Longissimus, Spinalis
Antagonist: Rectus Abdominis

Rhomboids

The rhomboids(rhomboid major and rhomboid minor) are two muscles located on the back. They are named after their shape(rhombus).

Rhomboid major originates on the spinous processes of T3-T5. Rhomboid minor originates on the spinous processes of C7-T2. Together, the rhomboids insert onto the medial/vertebral border of the scapula.

When the rhomboids contract, they pull the scapula towards the vertebrae. This action is known as retraction/adduction. Two primary antagonists to the rhomboids are serratus anterior and pectoralis minor. Both of these muscles protract/abduct the scapula. If the rhomboids are hypertonic on one side, it may contribute to the development of Scoliosis.

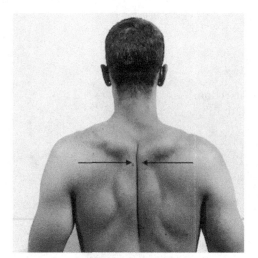

Scapula Retraction/Adduction

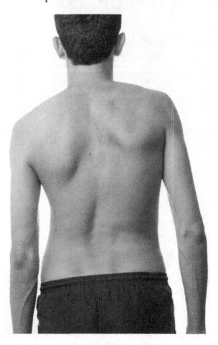

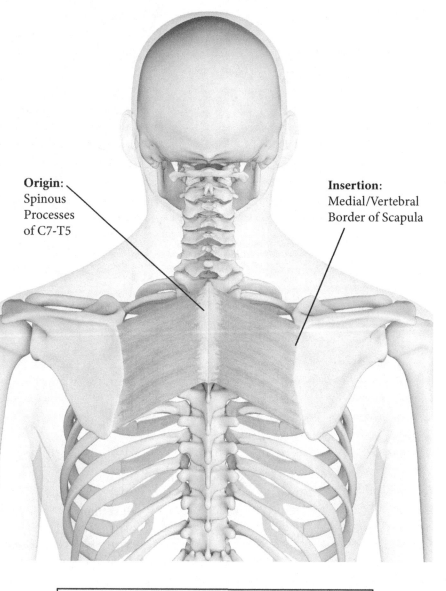

Origin: Spinous Processes of C7-T5

Insertion: Medial/Vertebral Border of Scapula

Origin: Rhomboid Minor: Spinous Processes of C7-T2; Rhomboid Major: Spinous Processes of T3-T5
Insertion: Medial/Vertebral Border of Scapula
Action(s): Retraction/Adduction of Scapula
Innervation: Dorsal Scapular Nerve C5
Synergist: Middle Trapezius
Antagonist: Serratus Anterior, Pectoralis Minor

Rotatores

The rotatores are a group of muscles that span the entire vertebral column. They are named after their action.

The rotatores originate on the transverse processes of C1-L5, and insert onto the spinous processes of the vertebrae just superior. An example, the rotator muscle that originates on the transverse process of C2 would insert onto the spinous process of C1.

Unilaterally, the rotatores will rotate the trunk to the opposite side. Bilaterally, the rotatores assist in extension of the trunk.

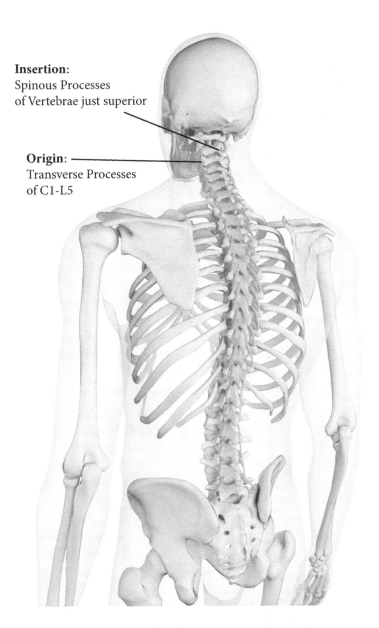

Insertion:
Spinous Processes
of Vertebrae just superior

Origin:
Transverse Processes
of C1-L5

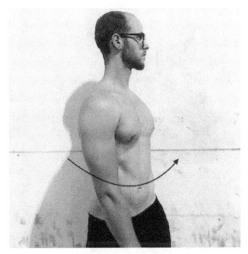

Trunk Rotation

Trunk Extension

Origin: Transverse Processes of C1-L5
Insertion: Spinous Processes of Vertebrae just superior
Action(s): Unilaterally: Rotate Trunk to opposite side; Bilaterally:
Extension of Trunk
Innervation: Dorsal Primary Rami of Spinal Nerves C1-T12
Synergist: Spinalis, Longissimus
Antagonist: Rectus Abdominis

Spinalis

Spinalis is a group of two muscles, both located on the back. Each muscle is named after its location: spinalis thoracis(in the thoracic region), spinalis cervicis(in the cervical region).

Spinalis cervicis originates on the nuchal ligament, and spinous process of C7. Spinalis cervicis inserts onto the spinous process of C2. Spinalis thoracis originates on the spinous processes of T11-L2. There may be slight variation of the origin, however, ranging from T10-L3. Spinalis thoracis inserts onto the spinous processes of T3-T8.

Unilaterally, the spinalis muscles laterally flex and rotate the trunk to the same side. Bilaterally, they assist in extending the trunk.

Trunk Flexion

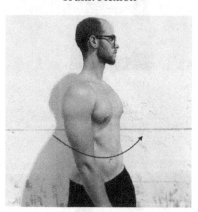

Trunk Rotation

Trunk Extension

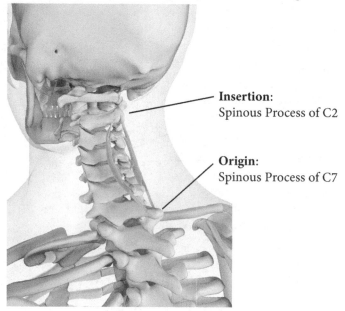

Insertion:
Spinous Process of C2

Origin:
Spinous Process of C7

Spinalis Cervicis

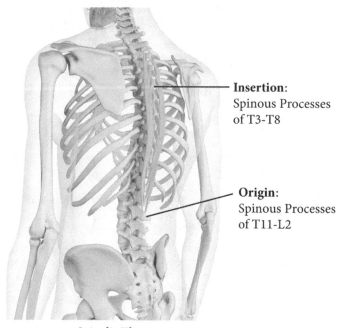

Insertion:
Spinous Processes
of T3-T8

Origin:
Spinous Processes
of T11-L2

Spinalis Thoracis

Origin: Spinalis Cervicis: Nuchal Ligament, Spinous Process of C7;
Spinalis Thoracis: Spinous Processes of T11-L2
Insertion: Spinalis Cervicis: Spinous Process of C2; Spinalis Thoracis: Spinous Processes of T3-T8
Action(s): Unilaterally: Flex and Rotate Spine to the same side; Bilaterally: Extend the Trunk
Innervation: Dorsal Rami of Cervical and Thoracic Spinal Nerves
Synergist: Longissimus
Antagonist: Rectus Abdominis

Subscapularis

Subscapularis is a muscle of the back, named after it's location(under the scapula).

Subscapularis originates on the subscapular fossa, located on the anterior surface of the scapula. Subscapularis inserts onto the lesser tubercle(sometimes also called the lesser tuberosity of the humerus). It is part of the rotator cuff muscle group, along with infraspinatus, teres minor, and supraspinatus.

Subscapularis is a synergist to latissimus dorsi, performing the same actions on the shoulder. These actions are adduction, extension, and medial rotation. If a person is affected by adhesive capsulitis(frozen shoulder), there may be hypertonicity in the subscapularis, reducing the range-of-motion during actions such as shoulder flexion.

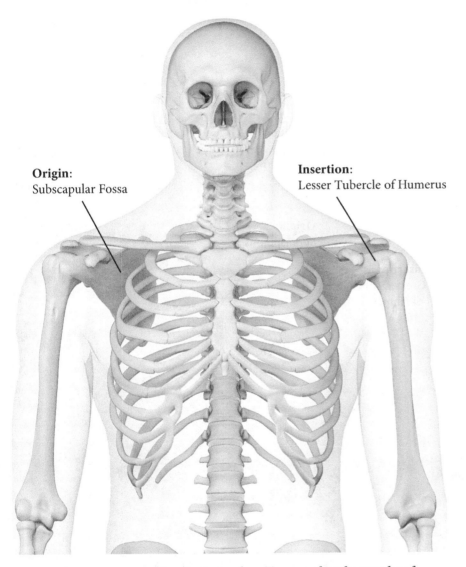

Origin:
Subscapular Fossa

Insertion:
Lesser Tubercle of Humerus

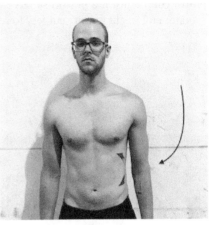

Shoulder Adduction

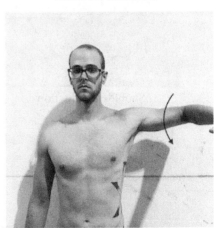

Shoulder Medial Rotation

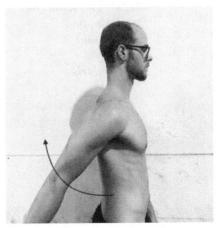

Shoulder Extension

 Easy to Remember: To remember the muscles of the rotator cuff, think "SITS"! This stands for:
Supraspinatus
Infraspinatus
Teres Minor
Subscapularis

Origin: Subscapular Fossa
Insertion: Lesser Tubercle of Humerus
Action(s): Medial Rotation, Adduction, Extension of the Shoulder
Innervation: Upper and Lower Subscapular Nerves
Synergist: Latissimus Dorsi, Teres Major
Antagonist: Pectoralis Major, Coracobrachialis

Supraspinatus

Supraspinatus is a muscle of the back, named after it's location(superior to the spine of the scapula).

Supraspinatus originates on the supraspinous fossa, just above the spine of the scapula. Supraspinatus inserts onto the greater tubercle(sometimes called the greater tuberosity of the humerus). It is part of the rotator cuff muscle group, along with infraspinatus, teres minor, and subscapularis.

Supraspinatus has one primary action: abduction of the shoulder. It is a synergist to the deltoid in performing this action. Supraspinatus also helps hold the humerus in place against the glenoid fossa, providing stability to the shoulder joint.

Most commonly, if a person suffers from a torn rotator cuff, it likely involves the supraspinatus more than other muscles. A torn rotator cuff might require surgery to repair, depending on the severity.

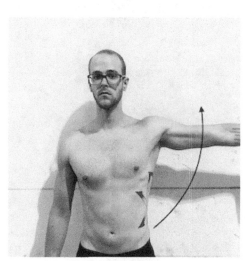

Shoulder Abduction

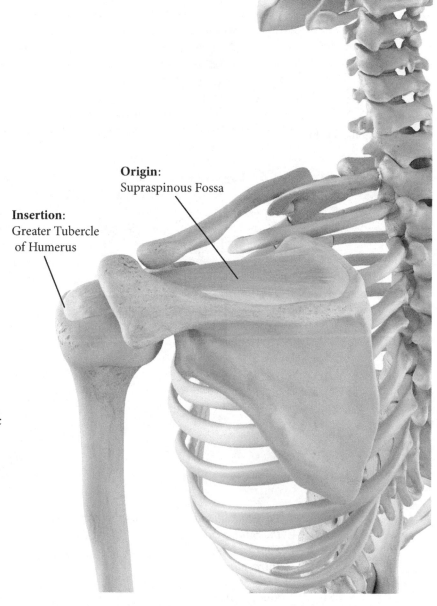

Origin:
Supraspinous Fossa

Insertion:
Greater Tubercle
of Humerus

Easy to Remember: To remember the muscles of the rotator cuff, think "SITS"! This stands for:
Supraspinatus
Infraspinatus
Teres Minor
Subscapularis

Origin: Supraspinous Fossa
Insertion: Greater Tubercle of Humerus
Action(s): Abduction of Shoulder
Innervation: Suprascapular Nerve
Synergist: Deltoid
Antagonist: Latissimus Dorsi, Teres Major

Teres Major

Teres major is a muscle of the back. The name "teres" means "round and long". Teres major has a long, round shape.

Teres major originates on the inferior angle of the scapula, and inserts onto the medial lip of the intertubercular groove. It shares its insertion with latissimus dorsi.

Teres major and latissimus dorsi both perform the same actions: medial rotation, extension, and adduction of the shoulder.

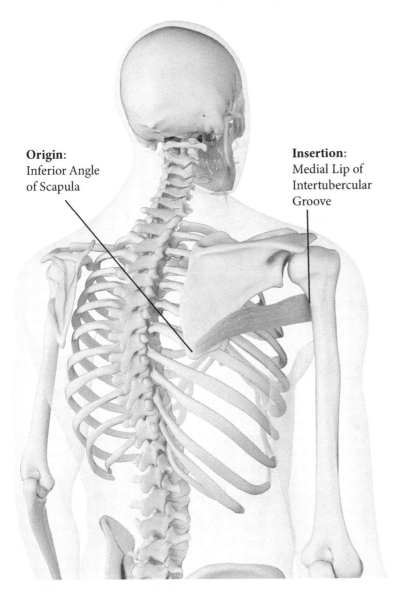

Origin:
Inferior Angle
of Scapula

Insertion:
Medial Lip of
Intertubercular
Groove

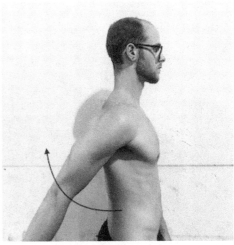

Shoulder Extension

Shoulder Medial Rotation

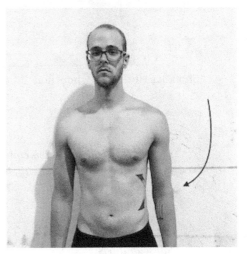

Shoulder Adduction

Origin: Inferior Angle of Scapula
Insertion: Medial Lip of Intertubercular Groove
Action(s): Medial Rotation, Adduction, Extension of Shoulder
Innervation: Lower Subscapular Nerve
Synergist: Latissimus Dorsi, Subscapularis
Antagonist: Pectoralis Major, Coracobrachialis

Teres Minor

Teres minor is a muscle of the back. The word "teres" means "round and long". Teres minor has a long, round shape.

Teres minor originates on the lateral/axillary border of the scapula. The term "axillary" refers to the armpit, which teres minor is located next to. Teres minor inserts onto the greater tubercle(sometimes known as the greater tuberosity) of the humerus.

Teres minor is a member of the rotator cuff muscle group, along with infraspinatus, subscapularis, and supraspinatus. Teres minor and infraspinatus are located immediately next to one another, and sometimes may even fuse together. These muscles perform the same actions: lateral rotation, extension, and horizontal abduction of the shoulder.

Shoulder Lateral Rotation

Shoulder Horizontal Abduction

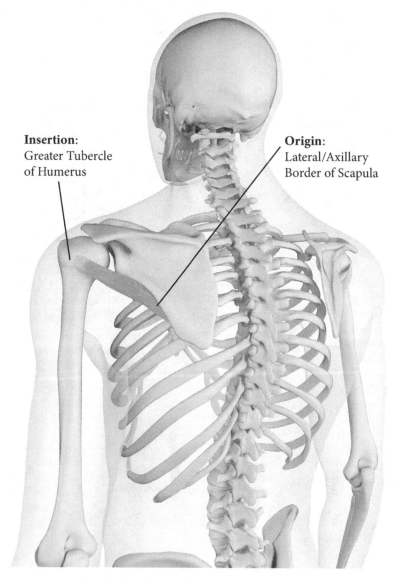

Insertion:
Greater Tubercle
of Humerus

Origin:
Lateral/Axillary
Border of Scapula

Easy to Remember: To remember the muscles of the rotator cuff, think "SITS"! This stands for:
Supraspinatus
Infraspinatus
Teres Minor
Subscapularis

Origin: Lateral/Axillary Border of Scapula
Insertion: Greater Tubercle of Humerus
Action(s): Lateral Rotation, Horizontal Abduction of Shoulder
Innervation: Axillary Nerve
Synergist: Infraspinatus
Antagonist: Pectoralis Major

Trapezius

Trapezius is a large muscle of the back, named after its shape(trapezoid). Trapezius is the most superficial muscle of the back.

Trapezius originates on the external occipital protuberance of the occipital bone, and the spinous processes of T1-T12. Trapezius inserts on the acromion process, the spine of the scapula, and the lateral 1/3 of the clavicle.

The trapezius can be divided into three sections: upper trapezius, middle trapezius, and lower trapezius. When contracting, upper trapezius assists in elevation of the scapula. When contracting, middle trapezius assists in retraction/adduction of the scapula. When contracting, lower trapezius depresses the scapula.

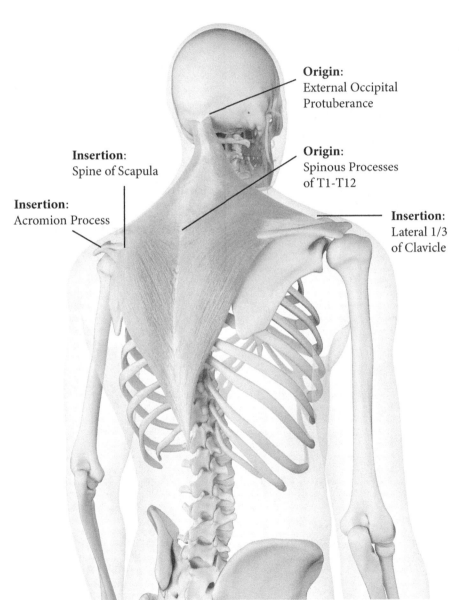

Origin:
External Occipital
Protuberance

Insertion:
Spine of Scapula

Insertion:
Acromion Process

Origin:
Spinous Processes
of T1-T12

Insertion:
Lateral 1/3
of Clavicle

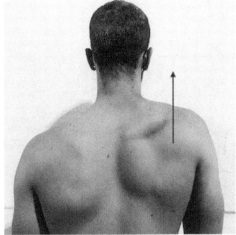

Scapula Elevation

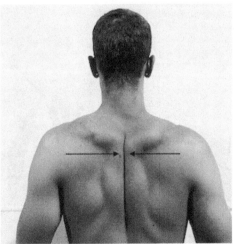

Scapula Retraction/Adduction

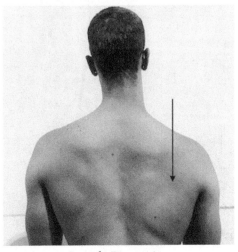

Scapula Depression

Origin: External Occipital Protuberance, Spinous Processes of T1-T12
Insertion: Lateral 1/3 of Clavicle, Acromion Process, Spine of Scapula
Action(s): Elevation, Retraction/Adduction, Depression of Scapula
Innervation: Accessory Nerve, Cervical Nerves C3 and C4
Synergist: Levator Scapulae(elevation), Rhomboids(retraction), Serratus Anterior(depression)
Antagonist: Serratus Anterior(elevation), Pectoralis Minor(retraction), Levator Scapulae(depression)

Muscles of the Chest

Muscles to Know:
Pectoralis Major
Pectoralis Minor
Serratus Anterior

Terms to Know:
Serratus: Finely Notched Edge
pector/o: Chest

Actions to Know:
Shoulder Flexion
Shoulder Extension
Shoulder Horizontal Adduction
Shoulder Medial Rotation
Scapula Protraction
Scapula Depression

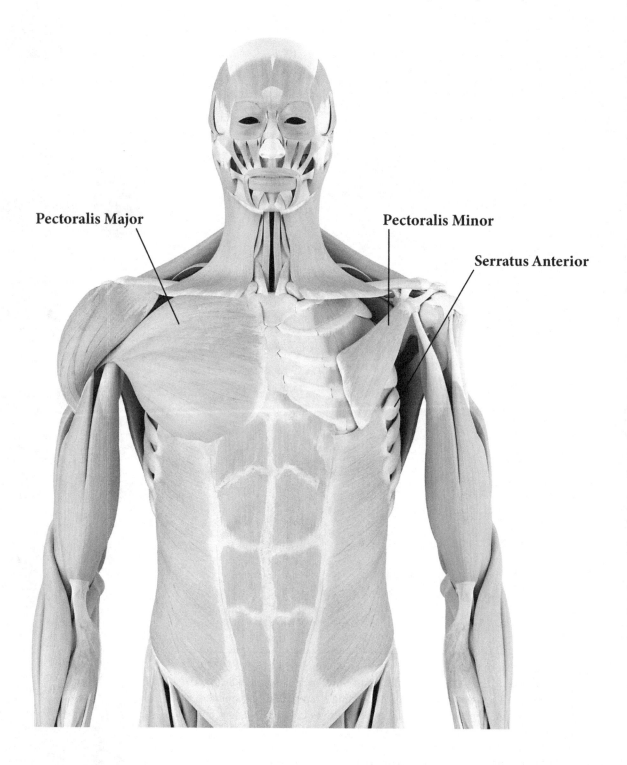

Pectoralis Major

Pectoralis Minor

Serratus Anterior

Pectoralis Major

Pectoralis major is a large muscle of the chest. The term "pector/o" means "breast" or "chest".

Pectoralis major originates on the medial half of the clavicle, the anterior surface of the sternum, and the costal cartilage of ribs 1-6. Pectoralis major inserts onto the lateral lip of the intertubercular groove.

When contracting, the pectoralis major has multiple actions: flexion, medial rotation, and horizontal adduction of the shoulder. Pectoralis major also performs extension of the shoulder when the shoulder is already flexed, making it an antagonist to itself.

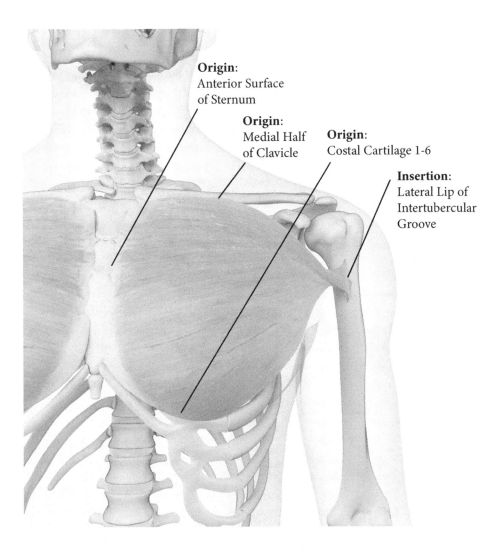

Origin:
Anterior Surface of Sternum

Origin:
Medial Half of Clavicle

Origin:
Costal Cartilage 1-6

Insertion:
Lateral Lip of Intertubercular Groove

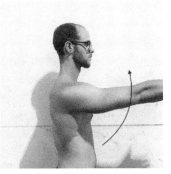

Shoulder Flexion

Shoulder Medial Rotation

Shoulder Extension

Shoulder Horizontal Adduction

Origin: Medial Half of Clavicle, Anterior Surface of Sternum, Costal Cartilage 1-6
Insertion: Lateral Lip of Intertubercular Groove
Action(s): Flexion, Medial Rotation, Horizontal Adduction, Extension of Shoulder
Innervation: Lateral and Medial Pectoral Nerves
Synergist: Coracobrachialis, Biceps Brachii, Anterior Deltoid
Antagonist: Latissimus Dorsi, Teres Major, Subscapularis, Posterior Deltoid

Pectoralis Minor

Pectoralis minor is a muscle of the chest, lying deep to the pectoralis major.

Pectoralis minor originates on the anterior surface of ribs 3-5. Pectoralis minor inserts onto the coracoid process.

When pectoralis minor contracts, it protracts/abducts the scapula. Along with serratus anterior, it is an antagonist to the rhomboids.

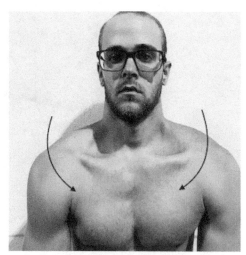

Scapula Protraction/Abduction

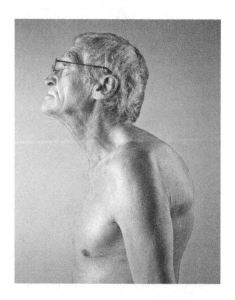

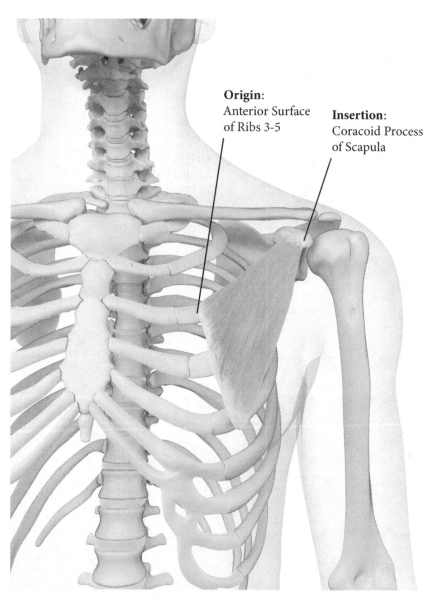

Origin:
Anterior Surface
of Ribs 3-5

Insertion:
Coracoid Process
of Scapula

DID YOU KNOW?

Pectoralis minor is often associated with Thoracic Outlet Syndrome. When hypertonic, pectoralis minor may compress the brachial plexus, subclavian artery, and subclavian nerve, which may cause a lack of sensation in the upper limb, or restrict blood supply. In addition, pectoralis minor is very commonly associated with kyphosis, a rounding of the back in the thoracic region of the vertebrae(hunch back), caused by pectoralis minor being hypertonic, pulling the scapulae anteriorly!

Origin: Anterior Surface of Ribs 3-5
Insertion: Coracoid Process of Scapula
Action(s): Protraction/Abduction of Scapula
Innervation: Medial Pectoral Nerve
Synergist: Serratus Anterior
Antagonist: Rhomboids

Serratus Anterior

Serratus anterior is a muscle of the chest, named after its appearance. "Serratus" means "finely notched edge", such as a serrated knife.

Serratus anterior originates on the anterior surface of ribs 1-8. Serratus anterior inserts onto the anterior surface of the medial/vertebral border of the scapula.

When serratus anterior contracts, it moves the scapula anteriorly, producing protraction/abduction. Serratus anterior also may assist in depression of the scapula.

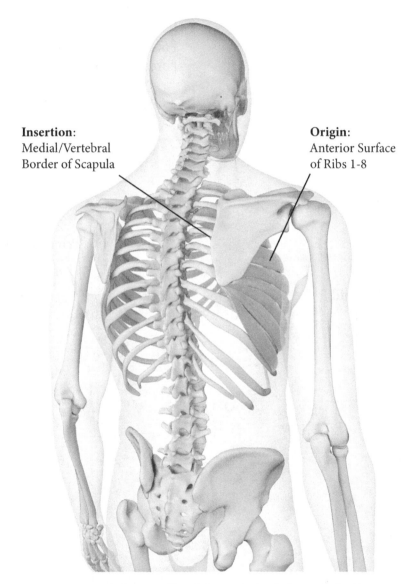

Insertion:
Medial/Vertebral
Border of Scapula

Origin:
Anterior Surface
of Ribs 1-8

Scapula Protraction/Abduction

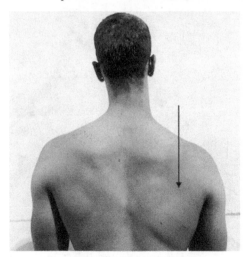

Scapula Depression

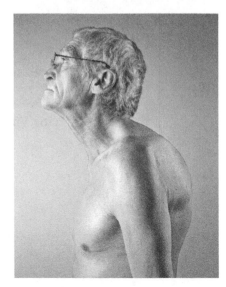

 DID YOU KNOW?

If serratus anterior is hypertonic, it may pull the scapulae too far into protraction/abduction, which would produce kyphosis, a rounding of the vertebrae in the thoracic region!

Origin: Anterior Surface of Ribs 1-8
Insertion: Medial/Vertebral Border of Scapula
Action(s): Protraction/Abduction, Depression of Scapula
Innervation: Long Thoracic Nerve
Synergist: Pectoralis Minor, Lower Trapezius
Antagonist: Rhomboids, Levator Scapulae

Muscles of the Arm

Muscles to Know:
Biceps Brachii
Brachialis
Coracobrachialis
Deltoid
Triceps Brachii

Terms to Know:
brachi/o: Arm
corac/o: Crow-like
bi-: Two
tri-: Three
-cep: Head

Actions to Know:
Shoulder Flexion
Shoulder Extension
Shoulder Horizontal Adduction
Shoulder Medial Rotation
Shoulder Lateral Rotation
Shoulder Abduction
Elbow Flexion
Elbow Extension
Forearm Supination
Forearm Pronation

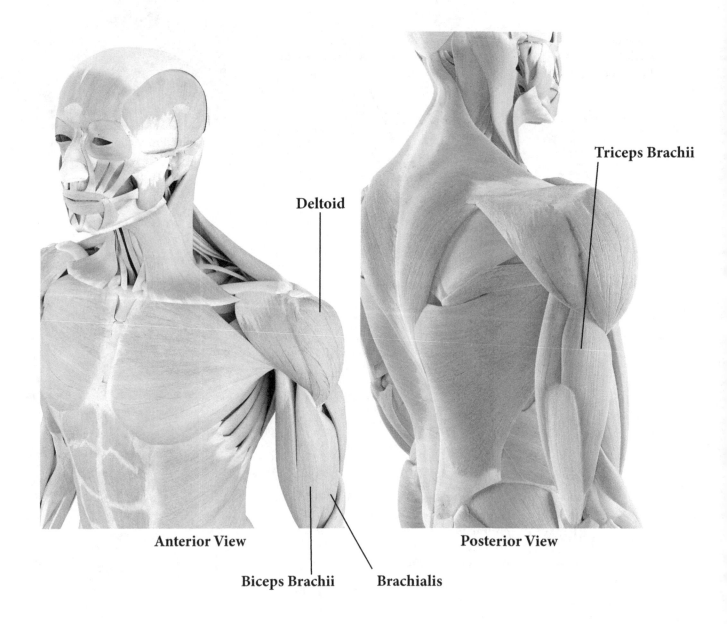

Deltoid

Triceps Brachii

Anterior View

Posterior View

Biceps Brachii

Brachialis

Not Pictured: Coracobrachialis

Biceps Brachii

Biceps brachii is a muscle of the arm. The term "biceps" means "two heads", and "brachii" refers to the arm. Biceps brachii has two heads.

The short head of the biceps brachii originates on the coracoid process. The long head of the biceps brachii originates on the supraglenoid tubercle. Both heads join together in the arm, and together insert onto the radial tuberosity.

When biceps brachii contracts, it helps produce flexion of the shoulder, flexion of the elbow, and supination of the forearm. Biceps brachii is the prime mover of supination.

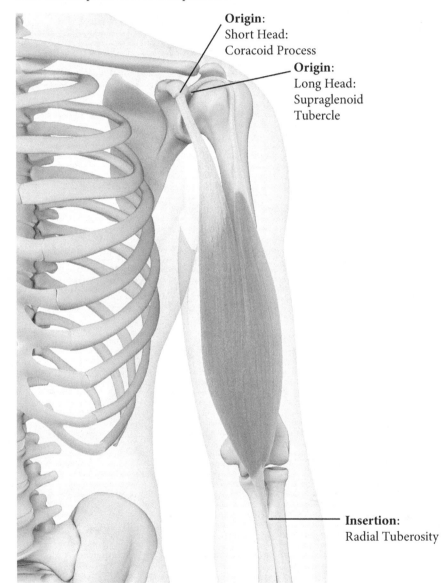

Origin:
Short Head:
Coracoid Process

Origin:
Long Head:
Supraglenoid
Tubercle

Insertion:
Radial Tuberosity

Shoulder Flexion

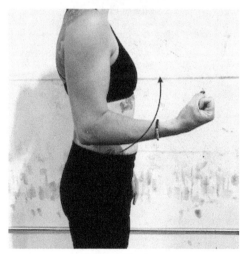

Elbow Flexion

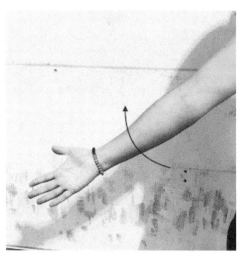

Forearm Supination

Origin: Long Head: Supraglenoid Tubercle; Short Head: Coracoid Process
Insertion: Radial Tuberosity
Action(s): Flexion of Shoulder, Flexion of Elbow, Supination of Forearm
Innervation: Musculocutaneous Nerve
Synergist: Pectoralis Major, Brachialis, Supinator
Antagonist: Triceps Brachii, Pronator Teres

Brachialis

Brachialis is a muscle of the arm. It is named after it's location, the "brachial" region.

Brachialis originates on the anterior distal shaft of the humerus, and inserts onto both the coronoid process of the ulna, and the ulnar tuberosity.

Brachialis is a powerful muscle. It is the prime mover of elbow flexion. It is located deep to the biceps brachii. When brachialis contracts, it pushes the biceps brachii up, allowing biceps brachii to be more visible during this action.

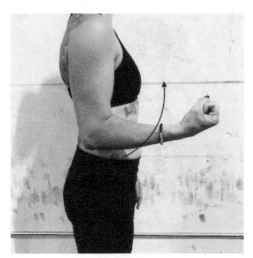

Elbow Flexion

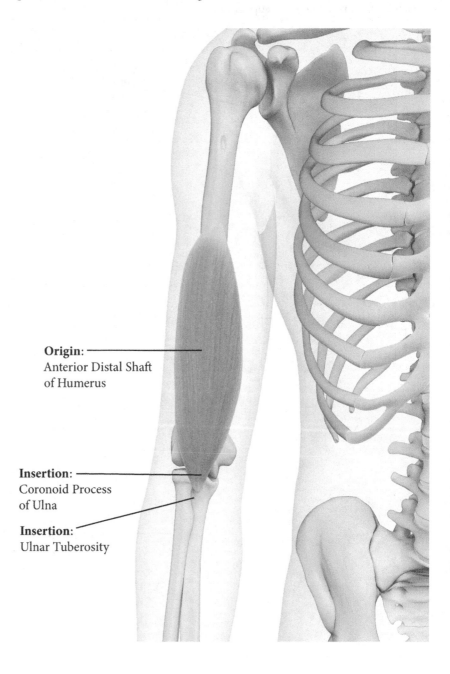

Origin:
Anterior Distal Shaft
of Humerus

Insertion:
Coronoid Process
of Ulna

Insertion:
Ulnar Tuberosity

Origin: Anterior Distal Shaft of Humerus
Insertion: Coronoid Process and Ulnar Tuberosity
Action(s): Flexion of Elbow
Innervation: Musculocutaneous Nerve
Synergist: Biceps Brachii
Antagonist: Triceps Brachii

Coracobrachialis

Coracobrachialis is a muscle of the arm, named after it's origin and location.

Coracobrachialis originates on the coracoid process, and inserts onto the medial proximal shaft of the humerus.

Coracobrachialis is primarily a synergist to pectoralis major. When coracobrachialis contracts, it flexes and horizontally adducts the shoulder.

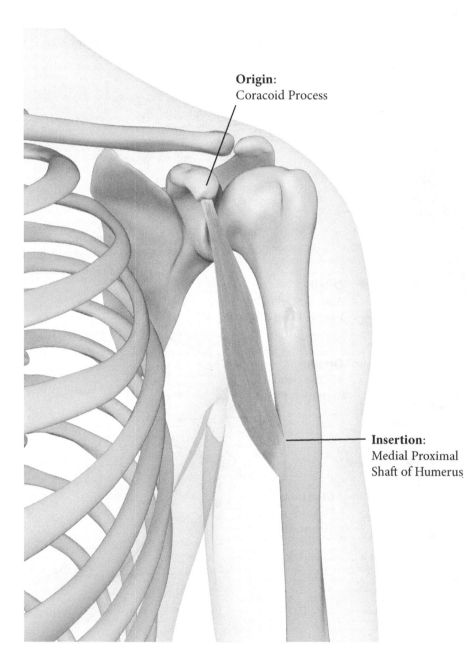

Origin:
Coracoid Process

Insertion:
Medial Proximal
Shaft of Humerus

Shoulder Flexion

Shoulder Horizontal Adduction

Origin: Coracoid Process
Insertion: Medial Proximal Shaft of Humerus
Action(s): Flexion, Horizontal Adduction of Shoulder
Innervation: Musculocutaneous Nerve
Synergist: Pectoralis Major, Biceps Brachii
Antagonist: Infraspinatus, Teres Minor

Deltoid

Deltoid is a muscle of the arm/shoulder, named after the Greek letter "delta", which is shaped like an equilateral triangle(all sides are the same length). Deltoid has three different portions that make up the muscle: anterior deltoid, middle deltoid, and posterior deltoid. All three combined create the deltoid muscle.

Anterior deltoid originates on the lateral third of the clavicle. Middle deltoid originates on the acromion process. Posterior deltoid originates on the spine of the scapula. All three join together distally and insert onto the deltoid tuberosity.

The deltoid has many different actions, depending on which fibers of the muscle are contracting. Anterior deltoid assists in flexion, horizontal adduction, and medial rotation of the shoulder. Posterior deltoid assists in extension, horizontal abduction, and lateral rotation of the shoulder. Middle deltoid, in conjunction with the two other deltoid fibers, abducts the shoulder.

Shoulder Abduction

Shoulder Horizontal Abduction

Shoulder Medial Rotation

Shoulder Flexion

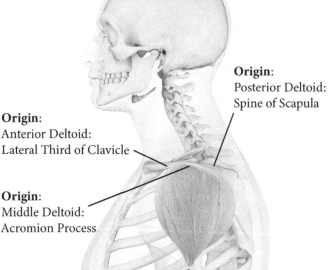

Origin:
Posterior Deltoid:
Spine of Scapula

Origin:
Anterior Deltoid:
Lateral Third of Clavicle

Origin:
Middle Deltoid:
Acromion Process

Insertion:
Deltoid
Tuberosity

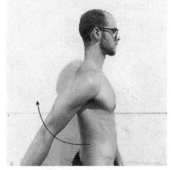

Shoulder Lateral Rotation

Shoulder Extension

Shoulder Horizontal Adduction

Origin: Anterior Deltoid: Lateral Third of Clavicle;
Middle Deltoid: Acromion Process; Posterior Deltoid: Spine of Scapula
Insertion: Deltoid Tuberosity
Action(s): Abduction, Medial Rotation, Lateral Rotation, Horizontal Adduction, Horizontal Abduction, Flexion, Extension of Shoulder
Innervation: Axillary Nerve
Synergist: Supraspinatus, Pectoralis Major, Infraspinatus
Antagonist: Latissimus Dorsi, Infraspinatus, Pectoralis Major

Triceps Brachii

Triceps brachii is a muscle of the posterior arm. The name "triceps" means "three heads", and "brachii" refers to the arm. Triceps brachii has three heads.

The long head originates on the infraglenoid tubercle of the scapula. The medial head originates on the posterior shaft of the humerus, on the medial side. The lateral head originates on the posterior shaft of the humerus, on the lateral side. All three heads join together and insert on the olecranon process.

When triceps brachii contracts, it extends the shoulder and extends the elbow.

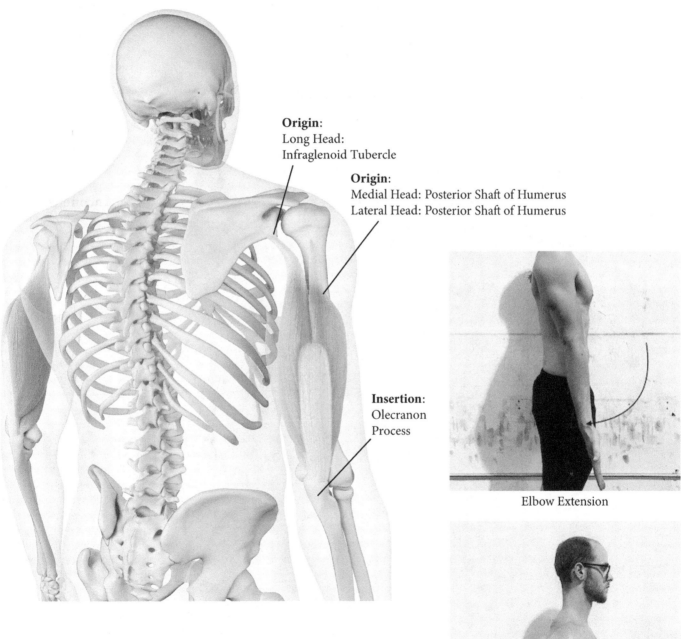

Origin:
Long Head:
Infraglenoid Tubercle

Origin:
Medial Head: Posterior Shaft of Humerus
Lateral Head: Posterior Shaft of Humerus

Insertion:
Olecranon
Process

Elbow Extension

Shoulder Extension

Origin: Long Head: Infraglenoid Tubercle;
Medial Head: Posterior Shaft of Humerus;
Lateral Head: Posterior Shaft of Humerus
Insertion: Olecranon Process
Action(s): Extension of Shoulder, Extension of Elbow
Innervation: Radial Nerve
Synergist: Latissimus Dorsi, Anconeus
Antagonist: Pectoralis Major, Biceps Brachii

Muscles of the Forearm

Muscles to Know:
Anconeus
Brachioradialis
Pronator Teres

Terms to Know:
Agkon: Elbow
Teres: Round and Long
brachi/o: Arm

Actions to Know:
Elbow Extension
Elbow Flexion
Forearm Pronation

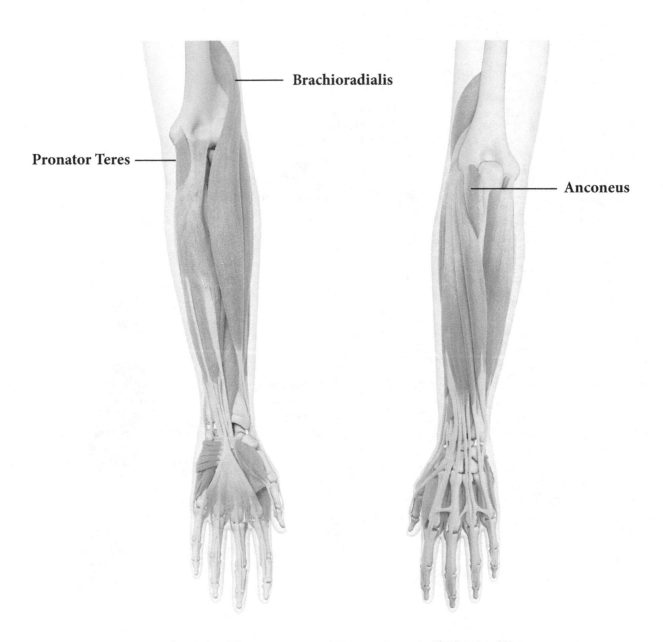

Brachioradialis

Pronator Teres

Anconeus

Anterior View   **Posterior View**

Anconeus

Anconeus is a muscle of the forearm. Its name derives from the Greek "agkon", which means "elbow".

Anconeus originates on the lateral epicondyle of the humerus, and inserts onto the olecranon process.

Anconeus is primarily only a synergist to the triceps brachii, assisting to perform elbow extension.

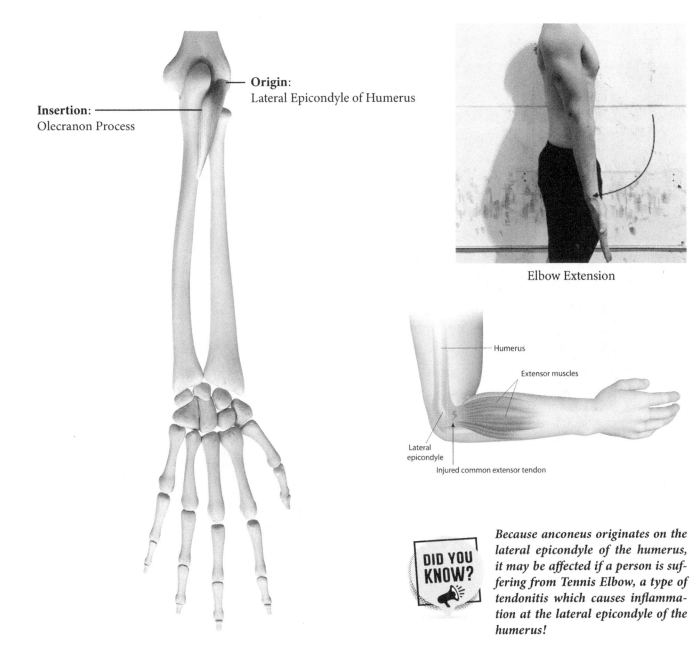

Origin:
Lateral Epicondyle of Humerus

Insertion: ——
Olecranon Process

Elbow Extension

Humerus

Extensor muscles

Lateral epicondyle

Injured common extensor tendon

DID YOU KNOW?

Because anconeus originates on the lateral epicondyle of the humerus, it may be affected if a person is suffering from Tennis Elbow, a type of tendonitis which causes inflammation at the lateral epicondyle of the humerus!

Origin: Lateral Epicondyle of Humerus
Insertion: Olecranon Process
Action(s): Extension of Elbow
Innervation: Radial Nerve
Synergist: Triceps Brachii
Antagonist: Brachialis

Brachioradialis

Brachioradialis is a muscle of the forearm, named after its location and insertion. "Brachio" refers to the arm, and "radialis" refers to the radius.

Brachioradialis originates on the lateral supracondylar ridge of the humerus, the ridge just superior to the lateral epicondyle. Brachioradialis inserts onto the styloid process of the radius.

Brachioradialis primarily performs flexion of the elbow with the hand in the neutral position(neither in pronation or supination).

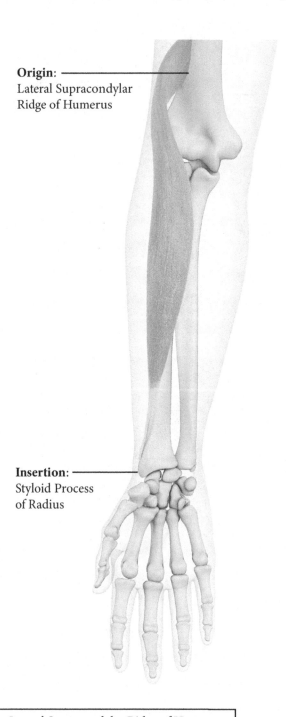

Origin:
Lateral Supracondylar
Ridge of Humerus

Insertion:
Styloid Process
of Radius

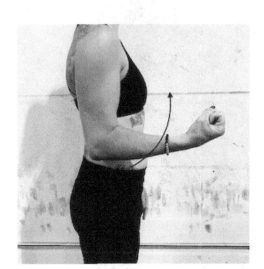

Elbow Flexion

Origin: Lateral Supracondylar Ridge of Humerus
Insertion: Styloid Process of Radius
Action(s): Flexion of Elbow
Innervation: Radial Nerve
Synergist: Biceps Brachii
Antagonist: Triceps Brachii

Pronator Teres

Pronator teres is a muscle of the forearm, named for its action and shape("Teres" means "round and long". Pronator teres has a long, round shape).

Pronator teres originates on the medial epicondyle of the humerus and the coronoid process of the ulna. Pronator teres inserts onto the middle of the lateral surface of the radius.

Pronator teres is the strongest pronator of the forearm. Because pronator teres crosses the elbow joint, it also assists in flexion of the elbow.

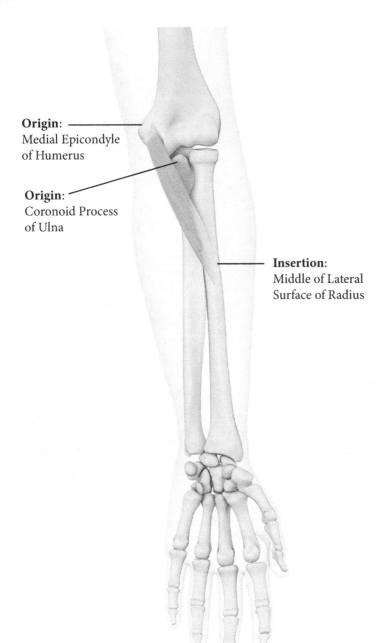

Origin:
Medial Epicondyle
of Humerus

Origin:
Coronoid Process
of Ulna

Insertion:
Middle of Lateral
Surface of Radius

Elbow Flexion

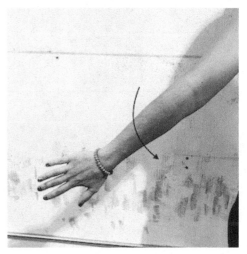

Forearm Pronation

Origin: Medial Epicondyle of Humerus, Coronoid Process of Ulna
Insertion: Middle of Lateral Surface of Radius
Action(s): Pronation of Forearm, Flexion of Elbow
Innervation: Median Nerve
Synergist: Pronator Quadratus, Brachialis
Antagonist: Biceps Brachii, Triceps Brachii

Muscles of the Abdomen

Muscles to Know:
Diaphragm
Rectus Abdominis

Terms to Know:
Diaphragma: Barrier
Rectus: Straight

Actions to Know:
Inhalation
Trunk Flexion

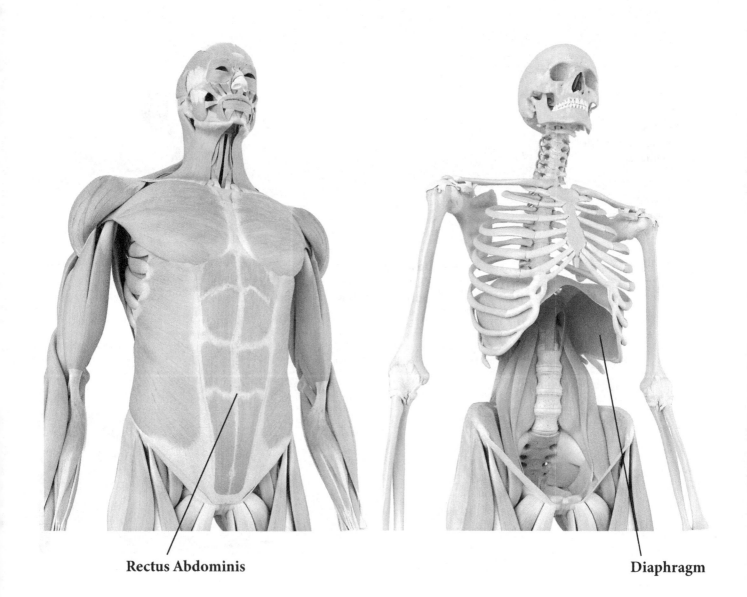

Rectus Abdominis

Diaphragm

Diaphragm

The diaphragm is a muscle of the abdomen, named after one of its actions("diaphragma" means "barrier" in Greek). The diaphragm is located between the abdomen and thorax, separating the two body cavities.

The diaphragm originates on the sternum, xiphoid process, inferior six ribs, and L1-L3. The diaphragm inserts onto a broad sheet of tendon known as the central tendon. The diaphragm is responsible for inhalation.

When the diaphragm contracts, it moves inferiorly, which creates a vacuum in the thorax, allowing air to move into the lungs. When the diaphragm relaxes, the muscle moves superiorly into the chest, pushing air out of the lungs. The central tendon anchors the diaphragm in place while breathing.

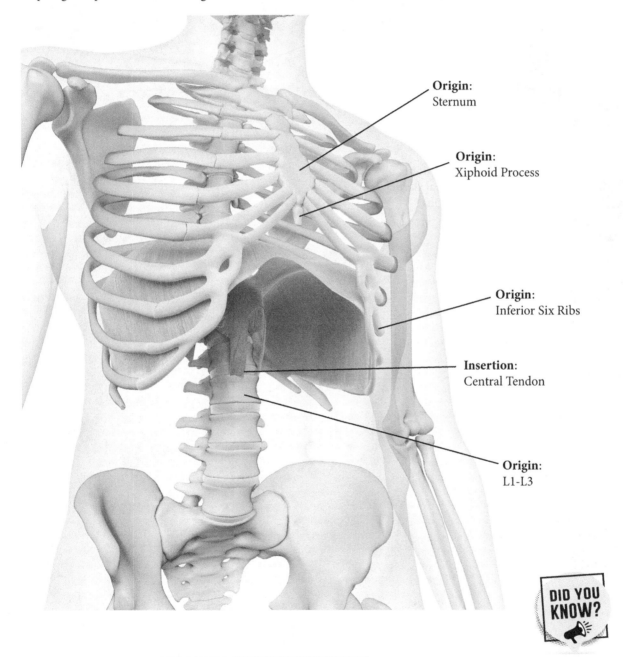

Origin:
Sternum

Origin:
Xiphoid Process

Origin:
Inferior Six Ribs

Insertion:
Central Tendon

Origin:
L1-L3

DID YOU KNOW?

Origin: Sternum, Xiphoid Process, Inferior Six Ribs, L1-L3
Insertion: Central Tendon
Action(s): Inhalation
Innervation: Phrenic Nerve
Synergist: External Intercostals
Antagonist: Internal Intercostals

Several structures actually pass through the diaphragm, including the esophagus, inferior vena cava, thoracic duct, and aorta. Because of these openings, the diaphragm is prone to herniation. For example, a hiatal hernia is when part of the stomach ascends upwards through the opening of the diaphragm the esophagus passes through!

Rectus Abdominis

Rectus abdominis is a muscle of the abdomen. Rectus abdominis is the most superficial muscle of the abdomen.

Rectus abdominis originates on the pubic symphysis and the pubic crest. Rectus abdominis inserts onto the xiphoid process of the sternum and the costal cartilage of ribs 5-7.

When rectus abdominis contracts, is allows the trunk to flex.

Trunk Flexion

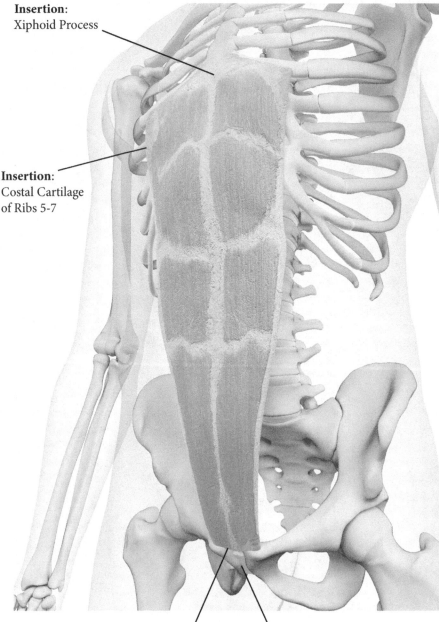

Insertion:
Xiphoid Process

Insertion:
Costal Cartilage
of Ribs 5-7

Origin:
Pubic Crest

Origin:
Pubic Symphysis

DID YOU KNOW?

If rectus abdominis is too weak, it may lead to a condition known as lordosis, or swayback. This causes an increased anterior tilt to the pelvis and lumbar vertebrae. Strengthening of the rectus abdominis may help return the pelvis and vertebrae to their natural state!

Origin: Pubic Symphysis, Pubic Crest
Insertion: Xiphoid Process, Costal Cartilage of Ribs 5-7
Action(s): Flexion of Trunk
Innervation: Anterior Primary Rami T7-T12
Synergist: External Obliques, Internal Obliques
Antagonist: Spinalis, Longissimus

Muscles of the Pelvis

Muscles to Know:
Gluteus Maximus
Iliacus
Piriformis
Psoas Major

Terms to Know:
Iliac: Ilium
Pirum: Pear
Psoa: Loin Region

Actions to Know:
Hip Extension
Hip Flexion
Hip Abduction
Hip Lateral Rotation
Trunk Flexion

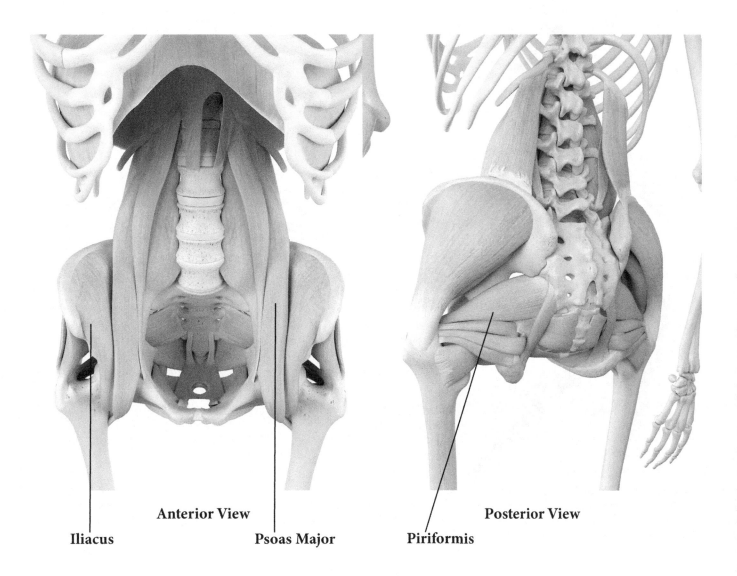

Anterior View

Iliacus   Psoas Major

Posterior View

Piriformis

Not Pictured: Gluteus Maximus

Gluteus Maximus

Gluteus maximus is a muscle of the pelvis, named for its location and size. Gluteus maximus is the most superficial of the gluteus muscle group.

Gluteus maximus originates on the posterior iliac crest, the posterior sacrum and coccyx, and the sacrotuberous ligament. Gluteus maximus inserts partially onto the gluteal tuberosity, and into the iliotibial band.

Gluteus maximus is primarily responsible for assisting in extension of the hip, and abduction of the hip.

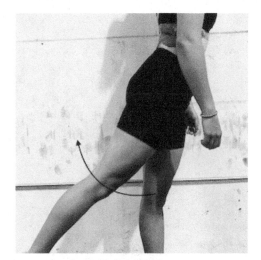

Hip Extension

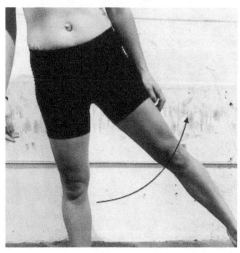

Hip Abduction

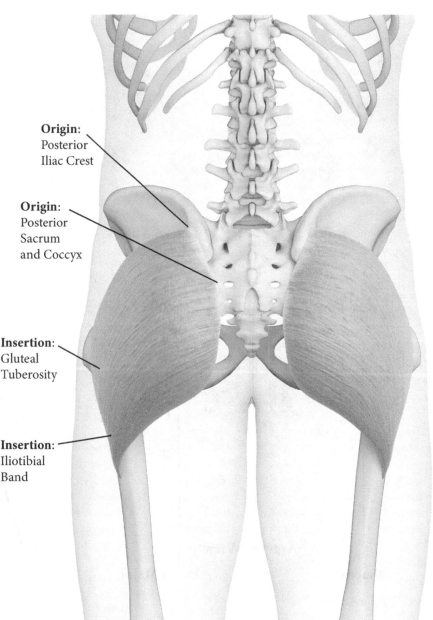

Origin: Posterior Iliac Crest

Origin: Posterior Sacrum and Coccyx

Insertion: Gluteal Tuberosity

Insertion: Iliotibial Band

DID YOU KNOW?

Gluteus maximus is the largest muscle in the body!

Origin: Posterior Iliac Crest, Posterior Sacrum and Coccyx, Sacrotuberous Ligament
Insertion: Gluteal Tuberosity, Iliotibial Band
Action(s): Extension, Abduction of Hip
Innervation: Inferior Gluteal Nerve
Synergist: Hamstrings, Piriformis
Antagonist: Rectus Femoris, Adductor Magnus

Iliacus

Iliacus is a muscle of the pelvis, named for its origin. It is often joined with the psoas major to make a single muscle named the iliopsoas.

Iliacus originates in the iliac fossa, and crosses the hip joint to insert onto the lesser trochanter.

Iliacus is one of the prime movers of hip flexion, working in conjunction with psoas major to perform the action.

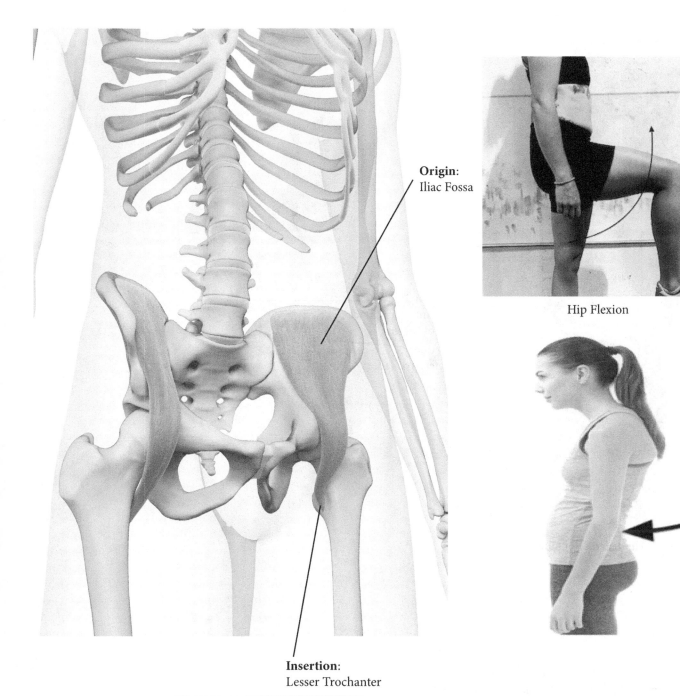

Origin:
Iliac Fossa

Hip Flexion

Insertion:
Lesser Trochanter

Origin: Iliac Fossa
Insertion: Lesser Trochanter
Action(s): Flexion of Hip
Innervation: Femoral Nerve
Synergist: Psoas Major
Antagonist: Hamstrings

DID YOU KNOW?

If the iliacus is hypertonic, it may pull the pelvis anteriorly. This shift of the pelvis results in a hypercurvature in the lumbar vertebrae, a condition known as lordosis(swayback)!

Piriformis

Piriformis is a muscle of the pelvis, named for its shape("piri" refers to "pirum", which means "pear" in Latin. Piriformis is shaped like a pear). Piriformis is part of the deep six muscle group.

Piriformis originates on the anterior surface of the sacrum, and inserts onto the greater trochanter.

Piriformis works with the gluteus maximus to perform abduction and lateral rotation of the hip.

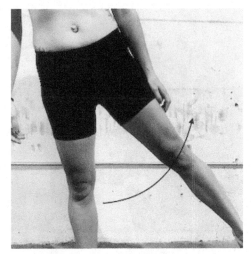

Hip Abduction

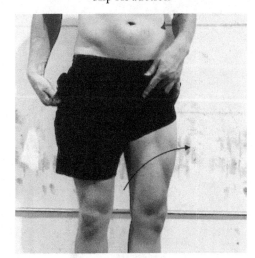

Hip Lateral Rotation

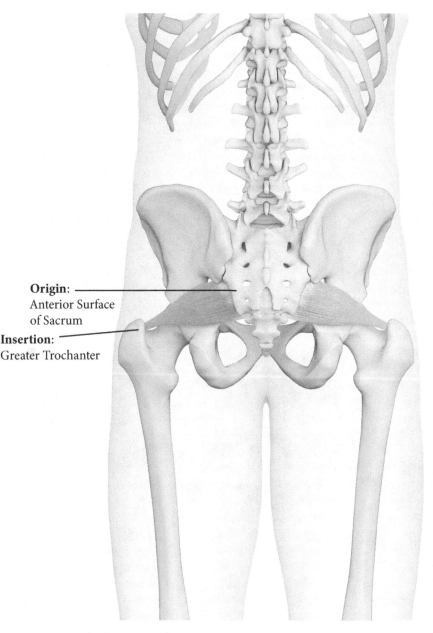

Origin: Anterior Surface of Sacrum

Insertion: Greater Trochanter

DID YOU KNOW?

When hypertonic, piriformis may place substantial pressure on the sciatic nerve, which passes by, and sometimes through, the muscle itself. This is known as piriformis syndrome. This can result in pain in the hip, posterior thigh, posterior leg, and plantar surface of the foot!

Origin: Anterior Surface of Sacrum
Insertion: Greater Trochanter
Action(s): Abduction, Lateral Rotation of Hip
Innervation: Piriformis Nerve
Synergist: Gluteus Maximus, Sartorius
Antagonist: Adductor Magnus, Pectineus

Psoas Major

Psoas major is a muscle of the abdomen and pelvis, named for its location("psoas" comes from the Greek word "psoa", which means "loin region") and size. Psoas major often joins with iliacus to form one muscle known as the iliopsoas.

Psoas major originates on the anterior surface of the lumbar vertebrae. Psoas major inserts onto the lesser trochanter.

Psoas major is responsible for flexion of the hip, along with iliacus.

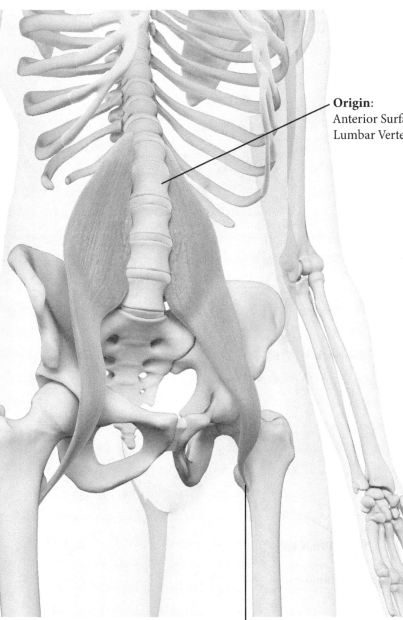

Origin:
Anterior Surface of
Lumbar Vertebrae

Insertion:
Lesser Trochanter

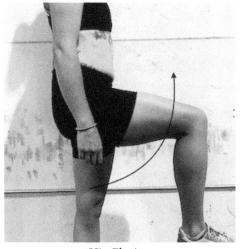

Hip Flexion

Trunk Flexion

Origin: Anterior Surface of Lumbar Vertebrae
Insertion: Lesser Trochanter
Action(s): Flexion of Hip, Flexion of Trunk
Innervation: Lumbar Plexus
Synergist: Iliacus, Rectus Abdominis
Antagonist: Hamstrings, Spinalis

DID YOU KNOW?

If the psoas major is hypertonic, it pulls the lumbar vertebrae anteriorly, which may also force the pelvis anteriorly. This is a condition known as lordosis(swayback)!

Muscles of the Thigh

Muscles to Know:
Adductor Magnus
Biceps Femoris
Gracilis
Rectus Femoris
Sartorius
Semimembranosus
Semitendinosus
Tensor Fasciae Latae

Terms to Know:
Fasciae: Band
Gracilis: Slender
Latae: Side
Magnus: Great
Membranosus: Skin
Rectus: Straight
Sartor: Tailor
Tendere: To Stretch
bi-: Two
semi-: Half
-cep: Head

Actions to Know:
Hip Adduction
Hip Abduction
Hip Flexion
Hip Extension
Hip Lateral Rotation
Knee Flexion
Knee Extension

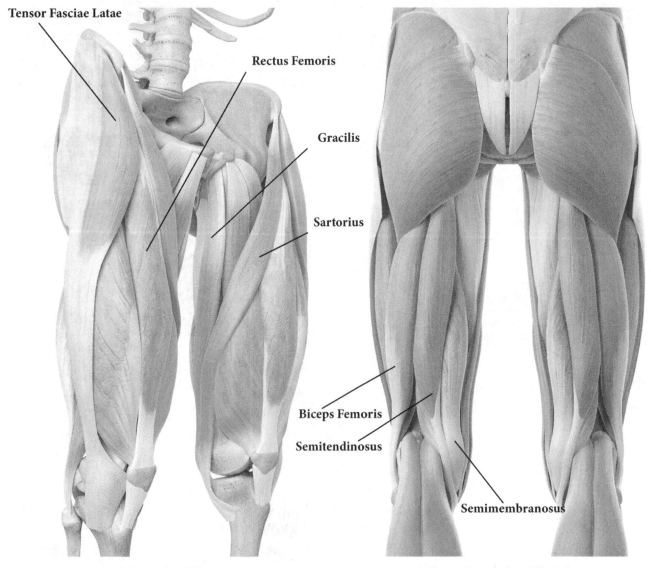

Tensor Fasciae Latae

Rectus Femoris

Gracilis

Sartorius

Biceps Femoris

Semitendinosus

Semimembranosus

Anterior View   **Posterior View**

Not Pictured: Adductor Magnus

Adductor Magnus

Adductor magnus is a muscle of the thigh, named after its action(adduction) and size("magnus" means "great" in Latin). Adductor magnus is the largest muscle of the adductor muscle group, which also consists of adductor longus, adductor brevis, gracilis, and pectineus.

Adductor magnus has multiple origins and insertions. Adductor magnus originates on the inferior ramus of the pubis and ischial tuberosity and inserts onto the medial lip of the linea aspera, and the adductor tubercle.

Adductor magnus is an antagonist to itself. It can adduct, flex, and extend the hip.

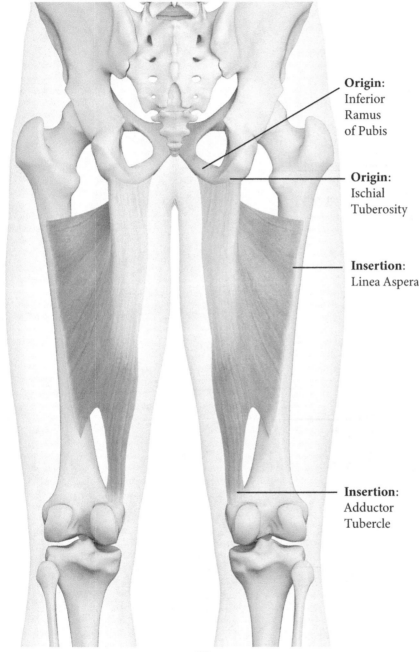

Origin: Inferior Ramus of Pubis

Origin: Ischial Tuberosity

Insertion: Linea Aspera

Insertion: Adductor Tubercle

Posterior View

Origin: Inferior Ramus of Pubis, Ischial Tuberosity
Insertion: Linea Aspera, Adductor Tubercle
Action(s): Adduction, Flexion, Extension of Hip
Innervation: Obturator Nerve, Sciatic Nerve(Tibial branch)
Synergist: Adductor Longus, Iliacus, Gluteus Maximus
Antagonist: Piriformis, Hamstrings, Rectus Femoris

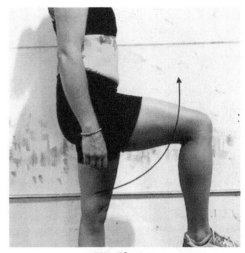

Hip Flexion

Hip Extension

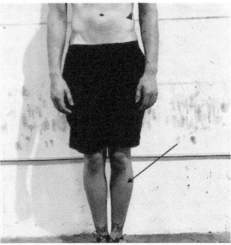

Hip Adduction

Biceps Femoris

Biceps femoris is a muscle of the posterior thigh, named after the number of heads it has("biceps" means "two heads") and its location(femur). Biceps femoris is a member of the hamstrings muscle group. It is the most lateral hamstring muscle, the only hamstring muscle that attaches to the fibula.

Biceps femoris has two origins: the long head of biceps femoris originates on the ischial tuberosity. The short head of biceps femoris originates on the lateral lip of the linea aspera, on the distal end of the femur. Biceps femoris inserts onto the head of the fibula.

Biceps femoris crosses the hip and the knee. When it contracts, it extends the hip, and flexes the knee.

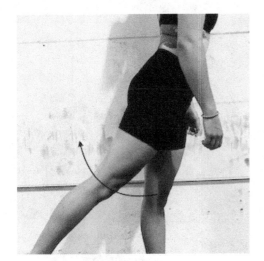

Hip Extension

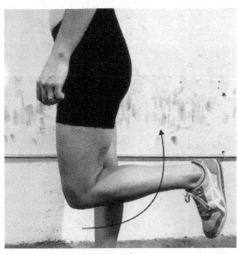

Knee Flexion

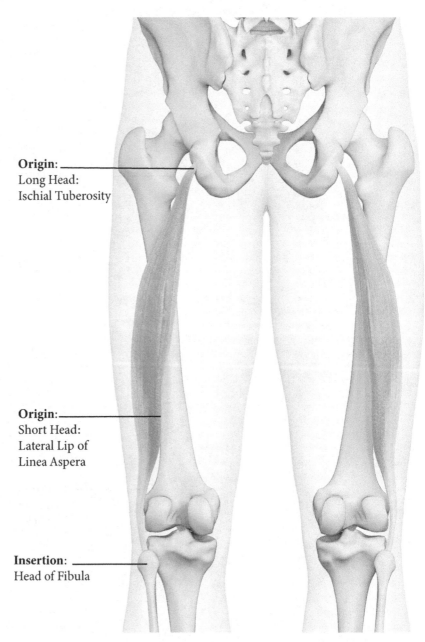

Origin:
Long Head:
Ischial Tuberosity

Origin:
Short Head:
Lateral Lip of
Linea Aspera

Insertion:
Head of Fibula

Origin: Long Head: Ischial Tuberosity;
Short Head: Lateral Lip of Linea Aspera
Insertion: Head of Fibula
Action(s): Extension of Hip, Flexion of Knee
Innervation: Sciatic Nerve(Tibial branch)
Synergist: Semimembranosus, Semitendinosus
Antagonist: Rectus Femoris

Gracilis

Gracilis is a muscle of the medial thigh. The word "gracilis" means "slender" in Latin. The gracilis is a thin, slender, long muscle. Gracilis is a member of the adductor muscle group, and is the most medial muscle of the group. The gracilis is the only adductor muscle that crosses two joints. All the other adductor muscles(adductor magnus, adductor longus, adductor brevis, pectineus) only cross the hip.

Gracilis originates on the inferior ramus of the pubis, along with adductor magnus. Gracilis inserts onto the pes anserinus, located on the medial proximal shaft of the tibia, just medial to the tibial tuberosity.

Gracilis performs adduction and flexion of the hip. Gracilis also crosses the knee, and will assist in flexion of the knee.

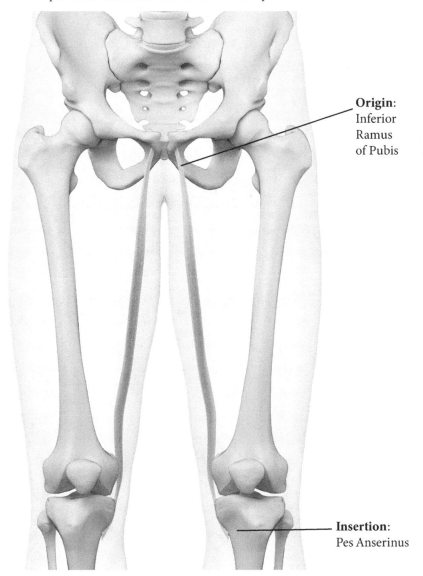

Origin:
Inferior
Ramus
of Pubis

Insertion:
Pes Anserinus

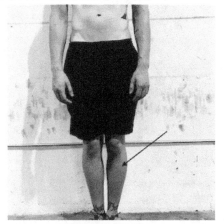

Hip Adduction

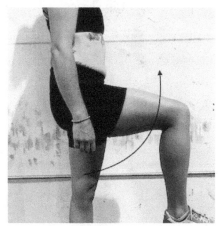

Hip Flexion

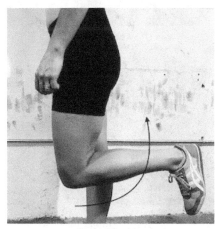

Knee Flexion

 Easy to Remember: To remember the three muscles that attach to the pes anserinus, just remember "SGT Goosefoot"! S for Sartorius, G for Gracilis, T for SemiTendinosus!

Origin: Inferior Ramus of Pubis
Insertion: Pes Anserinus
Action(s): Adduction, Flexion of Hip, Flexion of Knee
Innervation: Obturator Nerve
Synergist: Adductor Magnus, Gastrocnemius
Antagonist: Gluteus Maximus, Hamstrings, Rectus Femoris

Rectus Femoris

Rectus femoris is a muscle of the thigh, named after its function("rectus" in Latin means "straight", referring to ones ability to stand straight) and location. Rectus femoris is the most anterior muscle of the quadriceps muscle group, and is the only quadriceps muscle that crosses two joints(hip and knee). The rest of the quadriceps muscles only cross the knee.

Rectus femoris originates on the anterior inferior iliac spine(AIIS), and inserts onto the tibial tuberosity.

Rectus femoris is the prime mover of both hip flexion and knee extension.

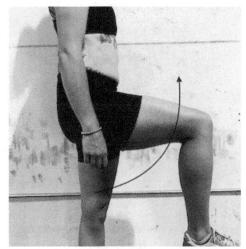

Hip Flexion

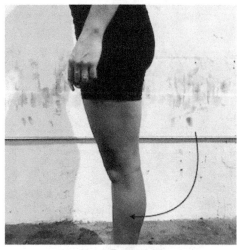

Knee Extension

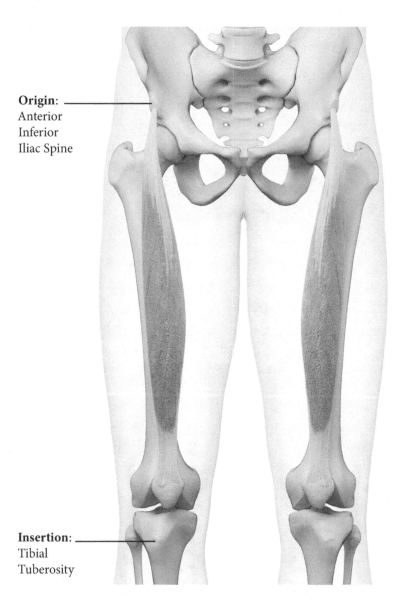

Origin: Anterior Inferior Iliac Spine

Insertion: Tibial Tuberosity

During adolescence, if the rectus femoris becomes hypertonic, it can pull on the insertion at the tibial tuberosity, causing an increase of bone growth in the area. This is known as Osgood-Schlatter Disease!

Origin: Anterior Inferior Iliac Spine
Insertion: Tibial Tuberosity
Action(s): Flexion of Hip, Extension of Knee
Innervation: Femoral Nerve
Synergist: Sartorius, Vastus Lateralis
Antagonist: Hamstrings

Sartorius

Sartorius is a muscle of the thigh, named for its action("sartor" is Latin for "tailor". It is named as such due to the actions of the muscle, which are the position a tailor places their leg into while working).

Sartorius originates on the anterior superior iliac spine(ASIS), and inserts onto the pes anserinus, located just medial to the tibial tuberosity. Sartorius is responsible for flexion and lateral rotation of the hip, and flexion of the knee.

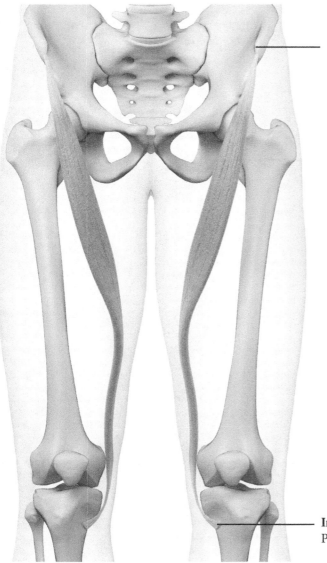

Origin:
Anterior
Superior
Iliac Spine

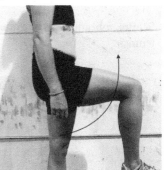
Hip Flexion

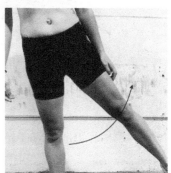
Hip Abduction

Knee Flexion

Insertion:
Pes Anserinus

Easy to Remember: To remember the three muscles that attach to the pes anserinus, just remember "SGT Goosefoot"! S for Sartorius, G for Gracilis, T for SemiTendinosus!

DID YOU KNOW?

Sartorius is the longest muscle in the human body!

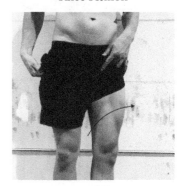
Hip Lateral Rotation

Origin: Anterior Superior Iliac Spine
Insertion: Pes Anserinus
Action(s): Flexion, Abduction, Lateral Rotation of Hip, Flexion of Knee
Innervation: Femoral Nerve
Synergist: Rectus Femoris, Gluteus Maximus, Piriformis, Gastrocnemius
Antagonist: Biceps Femoris, Adductor Magnus, Pectineus, Rectus Femoris

Semimembranosus

Semimembranosus is a member of the hamstring muscle group, located on the posterior thigh, named after its appearance("semi" means "half", "membranosus" means "skin". Semimembranosus is about half muscle, half membranous tendon). Semimembranosus is the most medial of the hamstring muscles.

Semimembranosus originates on the ischial tuberosity, and inserts onto the posterior medial condyle of the tibia.

Semimembranosus is one muscle responsible for extension of the hip, and flexion of the knee, along with semitendinosus and biceps femoris.

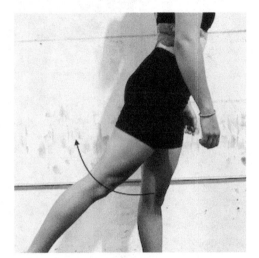

Hip Extension

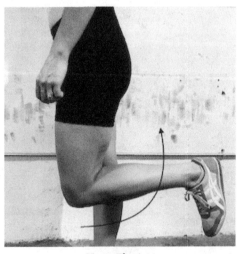

Knee Flexion

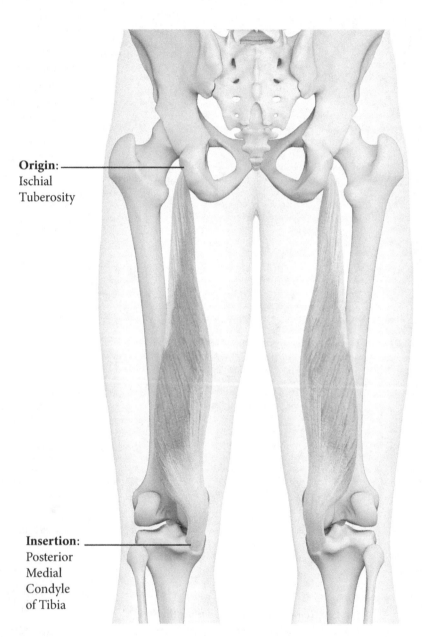

Origin: Ischial Tuberosity

Insertion: Posterior Medial Condyle of Tibia

Origin: Ischial Tuberosity
Insertion: Posterior Medial Condyle of Tibia
Action(s): Extension of Hip, Flexion of Knee
Innervation: Sciatic Nerve(Peroneal branch)
Synergist: Semitendinosus
Antagonist: Rectus Femoris

Semitendinosus

Semitendinosus is a member of the hamstring muscle group, located on the posterior thigh, named for its appearance("semi" means "half", "tendinosus" refers to the Latin word "tendere", which means "to stretch"). Semitendinosus sits atop semimembranosus, and is the intermediate hamstring muscle.

Semitendinosus originates on the ischial tuberosity, and inserts onto the pes anserinus, located just medial to the tibial tuberosity.

Semitendinosus is one muscle responsible for extending the hip and flexing the knee, along with semimembranosus and biceps femoris.

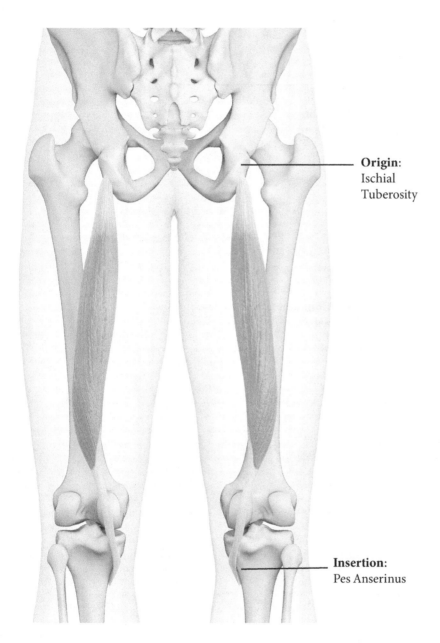

Origin:
Ischial
Tuberosity

Insertion:
Pes Anserinus

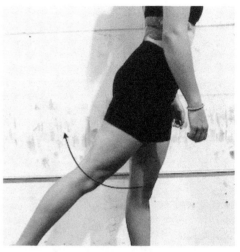

Hip Extension

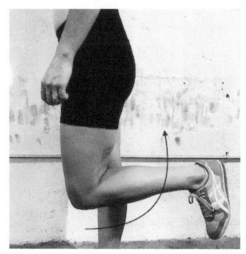

Knee Flexion

Origin: Ischial Tuberosity
Insertion: Pes Anserinus
Action(s): Extension of Hip, Flexion of Knee
Innervation: Sciatic Nerve(Peroneal branch)
Synergist: Biceps Femoris
Antagonist: Rectus Femoris

Easy to Remember: To remember the three muscles that attach to the pes anserinus, just remember "SGT Goosefoot"! S for Sartorius, G for Gracilis, T for SemiTendinosus!

Tensor Fasciae Latae

Tensor fasciae latae is a muscle of the thigh, named after its appearance("tensor" comes from the Latin "tensere", which means "to stretch". "Fasciae" is Latin for "band". "Latae" is Latin for "side", such as the term "lateral").

Tensor fasciae latae originates on the anterior superior iliac spine(ASIS) and the iliac crest. Tensor fasciae latae inserts into the iliotibial tract(also known as the IT band).

Tensor fasciae latae is a synergist in hip flexion.

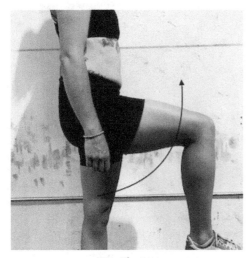

Hip Flexion

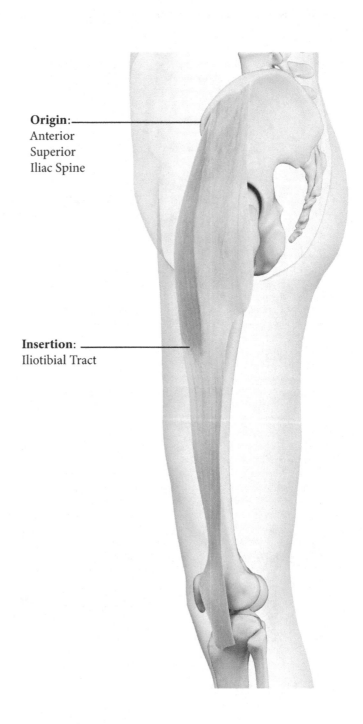

Origin: Anterior Superior Iliac Spine

Insertion: Iliotibial Tract

Origin: Anterior Superior Iliac Spine, Iliac Crest
Insertion: Iliotibial Tract
Action(s): Flexion of Hip
Innervation: Superior Gluteal Nerve
Synergist: Rectus Femoris
Antagonist: Hamstrings

Muscles of the Leg

Muscles to Know:
Gastrocnemius
Peroneus Longus
Plantaris
Soleus
Tibialis Anterior
Tibialis Posterior

Terms to Know:
Kneme: Leg
Longus: Long
gastr/o: Stomach

Actions to Know:
Knee Flexion
Plantarflexion
Dorsiflexion
Foot Inversion
Foot Eversion

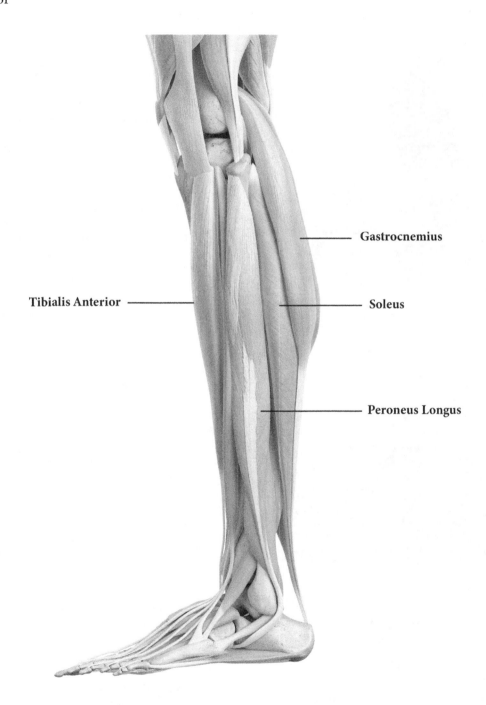

Gastrocnemius

Tibialis Anterior

Soleus

Peroneus Longus

Lateral View

Not Pictured: Plantaris, Tibialis Posterior

Gastrocnemius

Gastrocnemius is a muscle of the posterior leg. Its name means stomach(gastro) of the leg(kneme), from Greek origin.

Gastrocnemius originates on the medial and lateral epicondyles of the femur on the posterior side. The two muscle bellies join together at the calcaneal tendon, and insert at the calcaneus. Another name for the calcaneal tendon is "Achilles tendon", so named after the Greek legend of Achilles.

Gastrocnemius, when contracted, assists the hamstrings in performing flexion of the knee. Gastrocnemius is the prime mover of plantarflexion. A primary synergist to gastrocnemius is the soleus, the muscle deep to the gastrocnemius. Soleus joins with the gastrocnemius at the calcaneal tendon, and assists in plantarflexion.

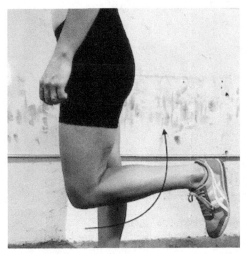

Knee Flexion

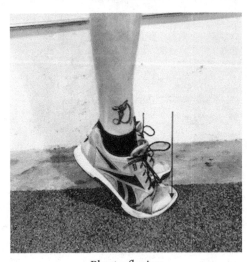

Plantarflexion

The calcaneal tendon is the strongest tendon in the body!

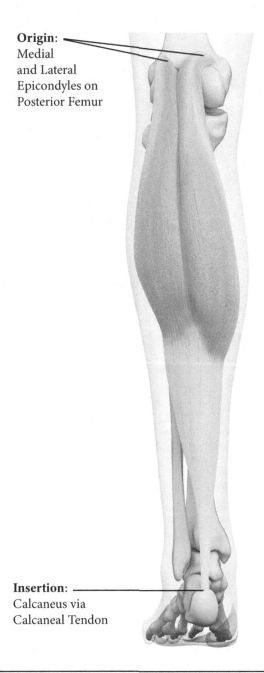

Origin:
Medial
and Lateral
Epicondyles on
Posterior Femur

Insertion:
Calcaneus via
Calcaneal Tendon

Origin: Medial and Lateral Epicondyles on Posterior Femur
Insertion: Calcaneus via Calcaneal Tendon
Action(s): Flexion of Knee, Plantarflexion
Innervation: Tibial Nerve
Synergist: Hamstrings, Soleus
Antagonist: Rectus Femoris, Tibialis Anterior

Peroneus Longus

Peroneus longus is a muscle of the lateral leg, named after its origin("perone" means "fibula" and the two are interchangable) and length.

Peroneus longus originates on the proximal lateral shaft of the fibula, and the head of the fibula. It wraps beneath the lateral malleolus and onto the plantar surface of the foot, inserting onto the base of the 1st metatarsal and cuneiform I(also known as the medial cuneiform).

When peroneus longus contracts, is is the prime mover of eversion/pronation of the foot. It also assists the gastrocnemius and soleus in performing plantarflexion.

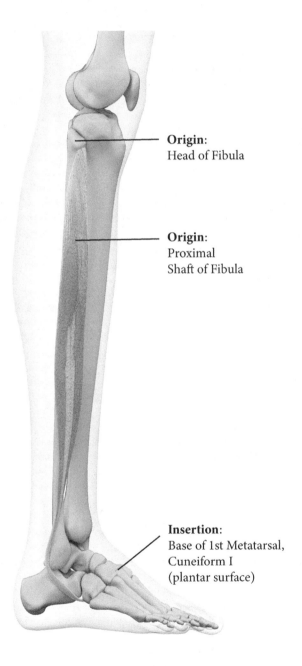

Origin:
Head of Fibula

Origin:
Proximal
Shaft of Fibula

Insertion:
Base of 1st Metatarsal,
Cuneiform I
(plantar surface)

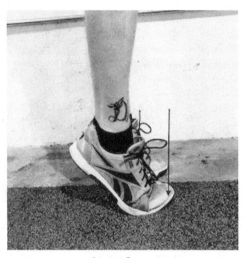

Plantarflexion

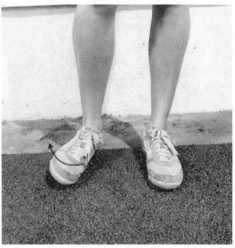

Foot Eversion

Origin: Head of Fibula, Proximal Shaft of Fibula
Insertion: Base of 1st Metatarsal, Cuneiform I
Action(s): Plantarflexion, Eversion/Pronation of Foot
Innervation: Superficial Peroneal Nerve
Synergist: Peroneus Brevis
Antagonist: Tibialis Anterior

Plantaris

Plantaris is a muscle of the posterior leg, named after its action(plantarflexion).

Plantaris originates on the lateral supracondylar ridge of the femur, just above the lateral epicondyle. It crosses the knee and ankle, inserting onto the calcaneus. The longest tendon in the body connects the plantaris to the calcaneus.

Plantaris is a synergist in all of its actions. At the knee, it assists the hamstrings and gastrocnemius in flexion. At the ankle, it assists gastrocnemius and soleus in plantarflexion.

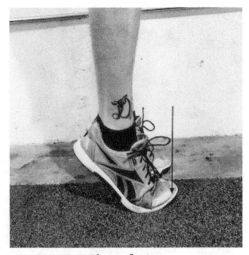

Plantarflexion

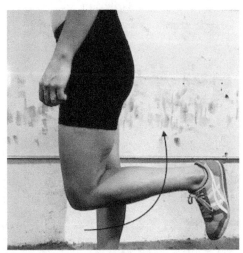

Knee Flexion

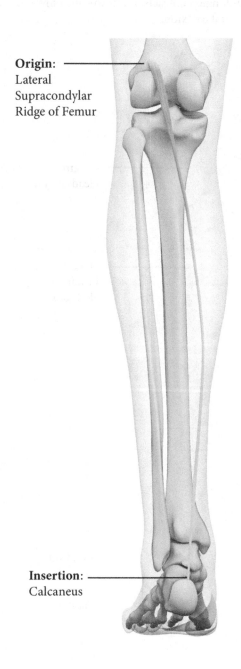

Origin: Lateral Supracondylar Ridge of Femur

Insertion: Calcaneus

If a person injures the plantaris, they may be diagnosed with a condition known as Tennis Leg, a straining of not just the plantaris, but the other calf muscles!

Origin: Lateral Supracondylar Ridge of Femur
Insertion: Calcaneus
Action(s): Flexion of Knee, Plantarflexion
Innervation: Tibial Nerve
Synergist: Gastrocnemius
Antagonist: Tibialis Anterior

Soleus

Soleus is a muscle of the posterior leg, named after its appearance(resembles a sole fish in shape).

Soleus originates on the soleal line, a ridge located on the posterior proximal surface of the tibia, and the head of the fibula. Soleus joins with the gastrocnemius at the calcaneal tendon, inserting onto the calcaneus.

Soleus is primarily a synergist to the gastrocnemius, performing plantarflexion.

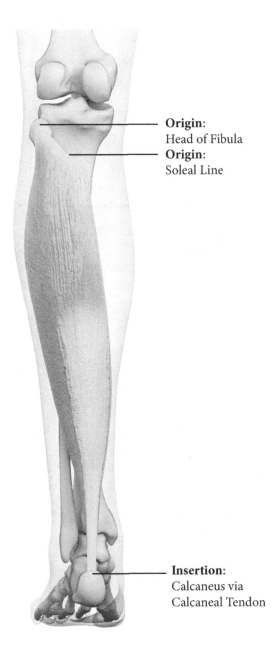

Origin:
Head of Fibula
Origin:
Soleal Line

Insertion:
Calcaneus via
Calcaneal Tendon

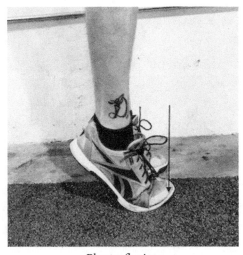

Plantarflexion

Origin: Soleal Line, Head of Fibula
Insertion: Calcaneus via Calcaneal Tendon
Action(s): Plantarflexion
Innervation: Tibial Nerve
Synergist: Gastrocnemius
Antagonist: Tibialis Anterior

Tibialis Anterior

Tibialis anterior is a muscle of the anterior leg, named after its origin(tibia) and location(anterior).

Tibialis anterior originates on the lateral proximal shaft of the tibia, beside the fibula. Tibialis anterior wraps onto the medial plantar surface of the foot, inserting onto the base of the 1st metatarsal, and cuneiform I(also known as the medial cuneiform). It shares its insertion with peroneus longus, its direct antagonist.

Tibialis anterior is the prime mover of inversion/supination of the foot, pulling the soles of the feet in towards the midline when the muscle contracts. It is also the prime mover of dorsiflexion, pulling the foot up.

Foot Inversion

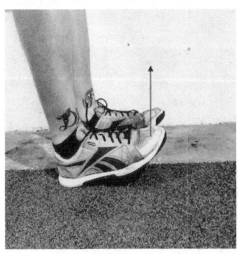

Dorsiflexion

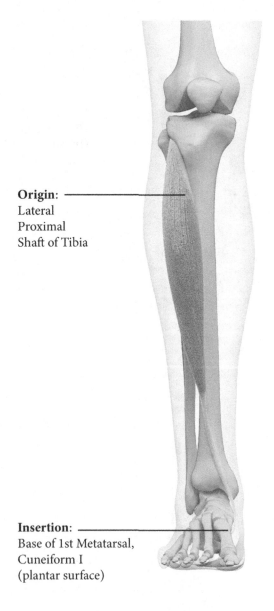

Origin:
Lateral
Proximal
Shaft of Tibia

Insertion:
Base of 1st Metatarsal,
Cuneiform I
(plantar surface)

DID YOU KNOW?

If a person is affected by paralysis in the deep peroneal nerve, the tibialis anterior is severely weakened. This results in inability to dorsiflex, a condition known as drop foot!

Origin: Lateral Proximal Shaft of Tibia
Insertion: Base of 1st Metatarsal, Cuneiform I
Action(s): Dorsiflexion, Inversion/Supination of Foot
Innervation: Deep Peroneal Nerve
Synergist: Extensor Digitorum Longus, Tibialis Posterior
Antagonist: Peroneus Longus

Tibialis Posterior

Tibialis posterior is a muscle of the posterior leg, named after its location(on the posterior tibia).

Tibialis posterior originates on the posterior proximal shaft of the tibia and fibula. It crosses the ankle and runs into the plantar surface of the foot, inserting onto the navicular, cuneiform I(also called the medial cuneiform), and metatarsals 2-4.

Tibialis posterior is primarily a synergist, assisting tibialis anterior in inversion/supination of the foot, and assisting gastrocnemius and soleus in plantarflexing the ankle.

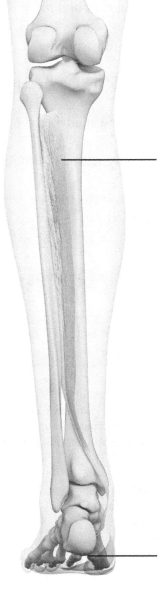

Origin: Posterior Proximal Shaft of Tibia and Fibula

Insertion: Navicular, Cuneiform I, Metatarsals 2-4 (plantar surface)

Foot Inversion

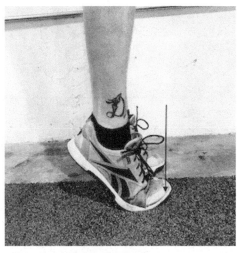

Plantarflexion

Origin: Posterior Proximal Shaft of Tibia and Fibula
Insertion: Navicular, Cuneiform I, Metatarsals 2-4
Action(s): Inversion of Foot, Plantarflexion
Innervation: Tibial Nerve
Synergist: Tibialis Anterior, Gastrocnemius
Antagonist: Peroneus Longus, Extensor Digitorum Longus

Kinesiology Matching

_____: Action performed by Brachialis

_____: Insertion of Brachioradialis

_____: Muscle that inserts on the Mastoid Process of the Temporal Bone

_____: Plane that elbow flexion moves in

_____: Origin of Temporalis

_____: Action shared by Tibialis Anterior and Tibialis Posterior

_____: Muscle inserting onto the Radial Tuberosity

_____: Prime mover of shoulder abduction

_____: Insertion of Rectus Abdominis

_____: Muscle inserting onto the Pes Anserinus

_____: Origin of Sartorius

_____: Insertion of Gracilis

_____: Muscles responsible for retracting/adducting the scapula

_____: Action performed by the Biceps Brachii, in which it is the prime mover

_____: Plane that vertebral rotation moves in

_____: Origin of Infraspinatus

_____: Insertion of the Quadriceps

_____: Action performed by the Latissimus Dorsi

_____: Muscle originating in the Supraspinous Fossa

_____: Primary action performed by the Pectoralis Major

_____: Action of the Hamstrings and Gastrocnemius

_____: Bipennate muscle that crosses the hip and knee on the anterior thigh

A: Biceps Brachii
B: Anterior Superior Iliac Spine
C: Elbow Flexion
D: Supraspinatus
E: Deltoid
F: Sagittal Plane
G: Knee Flexion
H: Shoulder Adduction
I: Rectus Femoris
J: Tibial Tuberosity
K: Sartorius

L: Styloid Process of Radius
M: Horizontal/Transverse Plane
N: Sternocleidomastoid
O: Horizontal Adduction of the Shoulder
P: Rhomboids
Q: Infraspinous Fossa
R: Xiphoid Process
S: Forearm Supination
T: Inversion
U: Pes Anserinus
V: Temporal Fossa

Answer Key on Page 308

Kinesiology Crossword

Across

3. The longest adductor muscle
6. Muscle responsible for hip flexion
8. Muscle responsible for plantarflexion and eversion
10. The longest tendon in the body connects to this muscle
13. Muscle responsible for elbow flexion
14. Muscle responsible for scapular protraction
16. Quadriceps muscle that crosses the hip and knee
17. Synergist in performing elbow extension
18. Origin of rectus femoris, abbv.

Down

1. Muscle responsible for dorsiflexion and inversion
2. Muscle group originating on the ischial tuberosity
4. Muscle responsible for shoulder extension and elbow extension
5. Origin of infraspinatus
7. Strongest tendon in the body, attaches to gastrocnemius and soleus
9. Action the hamstrings perform on the hip
11. Longest muscle in the body
12. Origin of sartorius, abbv.
15. Muscle responsible for shoulder abduction

Answer Key on Page 310

Muscle Labeling

Identify the numbered muscles. Write your answers on a separate piece of paper to allow yourself the ability to take this assignment multiple times!

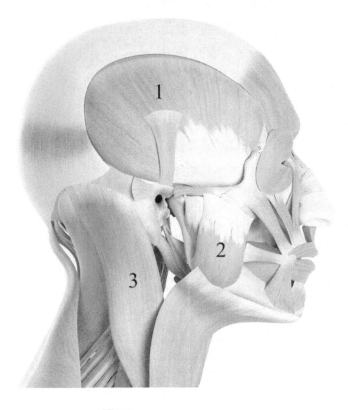

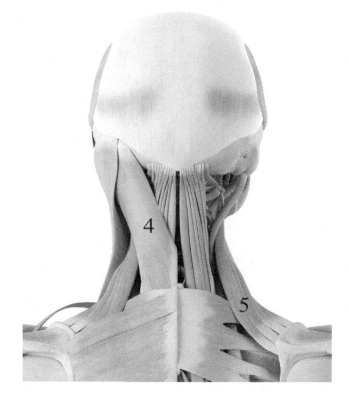

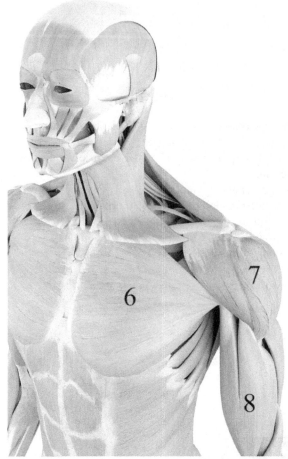

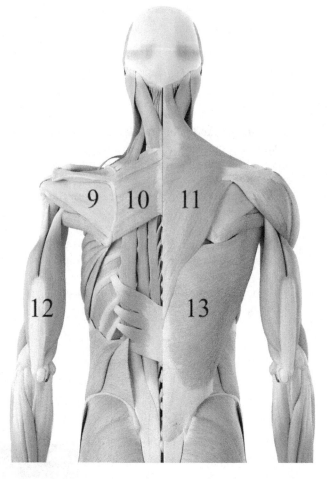

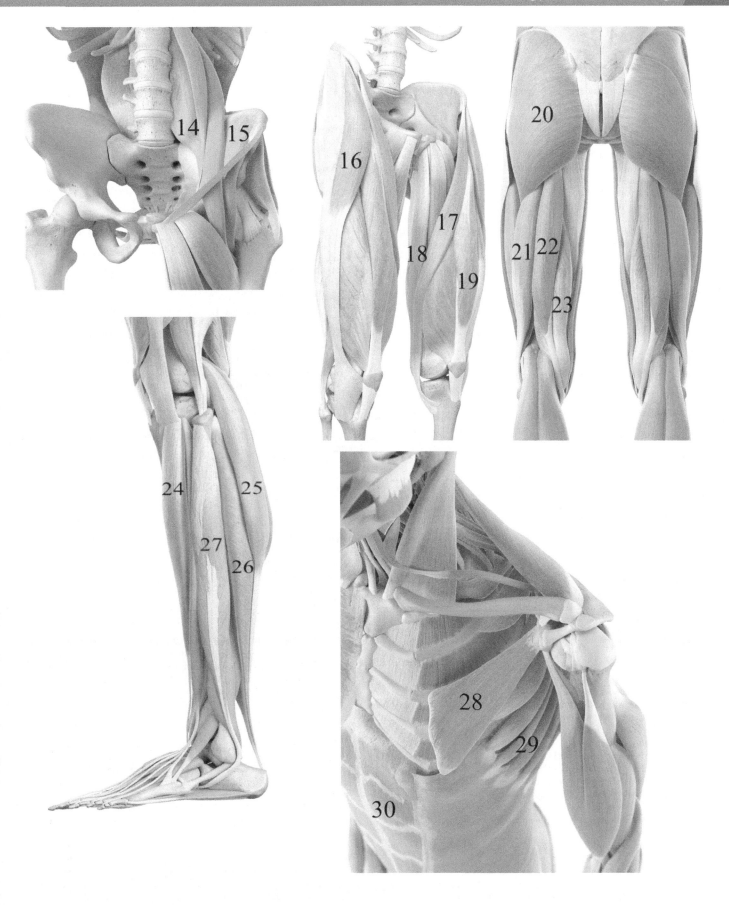

Answer Key on Page 310

Kinesiology Practice Test

1. Which three muscles attach to the coracoid process
A. Brachialis, coracobrachialis, brachioradialis
B. Long head of biceps brachii, pectoralis major, supraspinatus
C. Short head of biceps brachii, coracobrachialis, pectoralis minor
D. Trapezius, serratus anterior, coracobrachialis

2. A massage therapist recommends a client stretch their hamstrings to help the pelvis return to a normal tilt when in a posterior tilt. What two positions would the client need to place their body in order to stretch the hamstrings
A. Knee flexion and hip extension
B. Hip medial rotation and hip abduction
C. Hip adduction and knee flexion
D. Knee extension and hip flexion

3. A client states they have begun a weight-lifting program, with the goal of increasing the overall size of the pectoralis major muscles. All of the following are actions the client performs to help strengthen the pectoralis major except
A. Shoulder abduction
B. Shoulder horizontal adduction
C. Shoulder medial rotation
D. Shoulder flexion

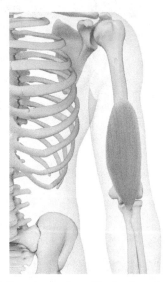

4. Identify the action performed by the pictured muscle
A. Elbow extension
B. Forearm supination
C. Elbow flexion
D. Forearm pronation

5. A client details on an intake form that they work at a desk all day and use a computer the majority of the time. The therapist performs a visual assessment, and determines the client's shoulders both appear to be in an elevated position. Which of the following would not likely be a contributing factor to the client's overly-elevated scapulae
A. There may be a weakness of the latissimus dorsi muscles
B. There may be hypertonicity of the levator scapulae muscles
C. There may be weakness of the serratus anterior muscles
D. There may be hypertonicity of the upper fibers of the trapezius

6. Which of the following is not an action performed by biceps brachii
A. Shoulder flexion
B. Elbow flexion
C. Forearm supination
D. Shoulder lateral rotation

7. The longest tendon in the body attaches which muscle to which bone
A. Biceps brachii and radius
B. Plantaris and calcaneus
C. Tibialis anterior and medial cuneiform
D. Sartorius and tibia

8. If a person were to perform flexion of the knee, what plane would the action be performed in
A. Midsagittal plane
B. Coronal plane
C. Sagittal plane
D. Horizontal plane

9. All of the following are muscles that perform plantarflexion except
A. Peroneus longus
B. Tibialis posterior
C. Soleus
D. Extensor digitorum longus

10. A concentric contraction of the upper fibers of trapezius would produce what action
A. Shoulder flexion
B. Head extension
C. Scapular elevation
D. Trunk rotation

11. Upon visual assessment, a therapist notes that the client is experiencing an excessive curvature in the lumbar vertebrae. The client explains to the therapist that they experience pain in the low back. What muscles are likely to be causing the excessive curvature and pain the client is experiencing
A. Iliocostalis, longissimus thoracis, rotatores
B. Rectus femoris, iliopsoas, sartorius
C. Gluteus maximus, piriformis, semimembranosus
D. Adductor magnus, multifidus, spinalis

12. The lateral supracondylar ridge of the humerus is the origination site of which muscle
A. Brachioradialis
B. Biceps femoris
C. Biceps brachii
D. Coracobrachialis

13. A client notes that they experience drop foot on the right side of the body. Drop foot is associated with an issue with the deep peroneal nerve, preventing dorsiflexion from taking place. Which of the following muscles would be directly inhibited by drop foot
A. Soleus
B. Tibialis anterior
C. Plantaris
D. Peroneus longus

14. A client explains to a massage therapist in a pre-massage interview that they experience headaches and often feel off-balance as if their head is turned or tilted to one side. The massage therapist performs a visual assessment and concludes that the client's head is indeed tilted slightly to one side. Which muscle is the primary cause of this issue
A. Platysma
B. Trapezius
C. Omohyoid
D. Sternocleidomastoid

15. If a massage therapist were to palpate the origin of the longest muscle in the body, which structure would they be touching
A. Ischial tuberosity
B. Coracoid process
C. Anterior superior iliac spine
D. Acromion process

16. A person is preparing for a strength competition and has been working extensively on increasing the weight they can squat. After several consecutive days of adding weight to squats, the client is experiencing delayed onset muscle soreness and decides to take a break to allow their body to recover. Which muscle is most likely involved in the client's pain
A. Rectus femoris
B. Latissimus dorsi
C. Gastrocnemius
D. Adductor magnus

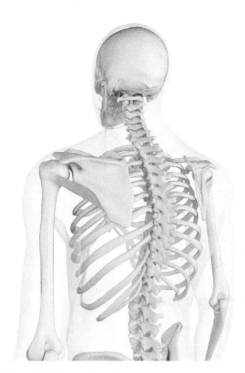

22. If a person experiences impingement of the musculocutaneous nerve, which of the following actions may be affected
A. Elbow flexion
B. Trunk extension
C. Hip adduction
D. Ankle plantarflexion

23. A concentric contraction of the serratus anterior performs which of the following actions on the scapula
A. Retraction
B. Adduction
C. Flexion
D. Depression

24. A client explains to a therapist that they experience pain when they begin walking after standing, but feel fine when they are only standing. The therapist asks where the client feels pain, and the client says it occurs in the hip. Which of the following muscles is most likely producing pain when the client initiates walking
A. Biceps femoris
B. Iliopsoas
C. Gracilis
D. Gluteus maximus

17. Identify the pictured muscle
A. Subscapularis
B. Infraspinatus
C. Teres major
D. Teres minor

18. A client informs a massage therapist that they are experiencing pain in the shoulder. The therapist asks the client to abduct the shoulder to test range-of-motion. The client performs the action and says they do feel slight discomfort, but the pain is more pronounced when they bring their shoulder forward. When the client performs abduction of the shoulder, which plane is the action taking place in
A. Frontal plane
B. Transverse plane
C. Midsagittal plane
D. Sagittal plane

19. A client explains to a massage therapist that they run marathons for fun twice a year, and are constantly training. The client states that they experience pain when pushing off with the right foot. The therapist asks where the pain is felt, and the client states the side of the leg. The therapist asks to view the soles of the client's shoes, and notices wear on the inner sole of the shoe. Based on this information, which is the most likely explanation for the client's pain
A. The client is experiencing a weakened gastrocnemius causing pain while performing dorsiflexion
B. The client is experiencing an overly-everted foot caused by tightness in the peroneus longus
C. The client is experiencing a strain in the tibialis anterior causing pain when placing the foot into eversion
D. The client is experiencing a straining of the pes anserinus, affecting the actions of sartorius, gracilis, and semitendinosus

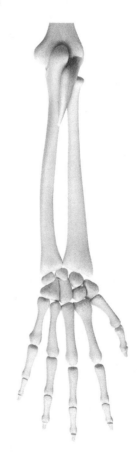

20. If a person were to suffer a third degree sprain of the anterior cruciate ligament resulting from a car accident, which actions would be affected
A. Forearm supination and pronation
B. Shoulder medial rotation and lateral rotation
C. Knee flexion and extension
D. Hip adduction and abduction

21. A synergist to the triceps brachii while performing extension of the elbow
A. Teres minor
B. Latissimus dorsi
C. Brachioradialis
D. Anconeus

25. When the pictured muscle performs a concentric contraction, which plane is the action taking place in
A. Midsagittal plane
B. Horizontal plane
C. Sagittal plane
D. Frontal plane

Answer Key on Page 322

All successes begin with self-discipline. It starts with you.

- Dwayne Johnson

Critical Thinking and Applied Knowledge

Critical thinking is an extremely important aspect of the MBLEx. This entire section is designed to help you think outside the box, and understand how much information can be hidden in one small piece of text.

Many of the questions on the MBLEx are designed for you to apply your knowledge in situations you could experience in a real-world massage setting. This may be tricky at first, but with practice, you can become extremly adept at it. Let me show you how I personally handle questions like these that require applied knowledge.

Here is a question requiring applied knowledge. We'll break it down one sentence at a time to see where my personal thought process leads:

Part 1. A massage therapist sees a client who explains they participate in a weekend flag football league, and they are sore from the previous game.

I immediately think of the sport of football and all of the muscle actions that are performed while playing. Obviously there are a lot of movements involved, but it especially involves a ton of running. Could it be running involved? The question also states that it is a flag football league, so people aren't being tackled, and the chances of someone who isn't playing quarterback being sore anywhere above the waist is slim.

Part 2. The client states that when they are walking, they experience a dull ache while pushing off with the foot and in the hip when they begin walking.

Now the question has given us exact muscle actions. Now that I have specific actions, "pushing off with the foot" and "in the hip when they begin walking", I can start figuring out what muscles are involved. Think about the position someone's foot is in when they are "pushing off". When the foot pushes against the ground and allows us to lean forward, the heel moves up while the toes stay on the ground. What action is this? Right, it's plantarflexion! Now let's identify muscles involved with "in the hip when they begin walking". Imagine yourself standing still, and then you begin to take a step. How does the hip move when you are walking forward? The initial phase of walking is hip flexion! So the two actions we know we're being asked about are plantarflexion and hip flexion.

From there, we need to identify the muscles that perform each of these actions. All of the important actions and muscles you should know that perform these actions are listed in the Muscle Actions section of this study guide. What three muscles perform plantarflexion? Right, it's gastrocnemius, soleus, and peroneus longus! Let's do the same for hip flexion. What are the four muscles you should know that perform hip flexion? If you said rectus femoris, sartorius, iliacus, and psoas major, you're correct! From this point, we've identified our main muscles involved in the question. Let's move on to the third part of the question.

Part 3. The client requests these areas specifically be stretched. In which way would the client's body need to be moved in order to stretch the affected areas?

Finally, we get to the REAL question! How do we stretch the areas that are sore? We know the actions involved are plantarflexion and hip flexion. How do we stretch a muscle? By moving the muscle in the opposite position of its action! What is the opposite of plantarflexion? Dorsiflexion! What is the opposite of hip flexion? Hip extension! You can take this a step further and do the same thing we did above and identify the muscles that perform these actions. Dorsiflexion is performed by tibialis anterior, and hip extension is performed by the hamstrings and gluteus maximus! Guess what we also just did? We also identified the antagonists of our original muscles! Now let's look at the entire question with a list of answers, and see if we can find the correct answer!

Q. A massage therapist sees a client who explains they participate in a weekend flag football league, and they are sore from the previous game. The client states that when they are walking, they experience a dull ache while pushing off with the foot and in the hip when they begin walking. The client requests these areas specifically be stretched. In which way would the client's body need to be moved in order to stretch the affected areas?
A. The massage therapist should move the hip into flexion and the ankle into dorsiflexion
B. The massage therapist should move the hip into extension and the ankle into dorsiflexion
C. The massage therapist should move the hip into flexion and the ankle into plantarflexion
D. The massage therapist should move the hip into extension and the ankle into plantarflexion

What is the answer?

B!

This is how I personally break down a question and apply the knowledge I've learned. That is what this entire section is about. Practice your critical thinking, use logic, and apply your knowledge. Take it one sentence at a time, identify key words, stop and actually think about what you're reading, and don't rush through the question or answers. You can do it!

1. Mrs Clean?

Katie is a newly licensed massage therapist, working in a day spa. Today, she is seeing a client for a basic Swedish massage. The client, a regular at the spa, is very nice and polite, respectful of the rules and regulations set forth not just from the spa, but from Katie herself.

The massage goes off without a hitch. Katie works on all of the client's trouble spots, performs some stretches, explains the reasons for her techniques as she goes through the massage whenever the client has a question.

Katie finishes the massage by working on the client's face. The session ends, and the client is extremely happy with Katie's massage. After giving the client instructions for getting off the table and where to go afterwards, Katie opens the door and leaves the room. Katie immediately goes to the rest room and washes her hands. Katie grabs a small cup of water to offer to her client. The client emerges from the massage room, drinks the water, and thanks Katie for the fantastic massage.

After dropping off the client in the changing area, Katie returns to her massage room. She takes the sheets off the table, sprays the table, bolsters, and head rest with a soap and water mixture. After wiping the table off, she then sprays the table with isopropyl alcohol to make sure everything is clean and ready for the next client. Katie gathers the dirty linens. Katie opens the door, disposes of the dirty linens, and is ready for her next client.

Katie meets her next client in the spa waiting area, greets the client, and shakes the client's hand. Katie takes the client in to the massage room to begin the session.

What did Katie do wrong?

2. Extremely Confident(ial)

Brandon is a long-time massage therapist, owning his own massage establishment for over ten years. Brandon has seen hundreds of different clients, but has a solid regular client base. He is usually booked all week, with only one or two available appointments every week.

A regular client of Brandon's, named Stan, comes in for his weekly massage appointment. The massage is the same massage Brandon always does for Stan, working on all his areas of concern, paying extra attention to his hamstrings because he runs marathons and his thighs tighten up quite a bit during training. He even lets Brandon know he is running a marathon later that week! The session ends, and Stan leaves as happy as ever, feeling great.

Brandon works Tuesday through Saturday. It is now Saturday evening, and Brandon has just finished his last appointment for the week. To help himself relax, Brandon walks to a hole in the wall bar a couple blocks from his massage establishment. He takes a seat at the bar and orders a brewski. He looks to his right, and sees Stan sitting further down the bar with a couple friends.

Brandon grabs his beer and walks over to Stan, greeting him warmly. They shake hands, and Stan introduces Brandon to his friends. After greeting Stan's friends, Brandon turns to Stan and asks about the marathon Stan had just run. Stan tells him he finished in about three hours. Brandon asks how Stan's hamstrings are feeling, and if massage helped him feel better while running. Stan claims the massage did help.

What did Brandon do wrong?

3. Cracking Me Up

Johnny works in a chiropractic office as the only massage therapist on staff. He's been working here for over a year, and really enjoys the work. It's a steady job and pays well, and he really enjoys the clientele he gets to work with.

Johnny greets his next client with a very professional demeanor, shaking the client's hand and introducing himself. He brings the client back to the massage room, performs the pre-massage interview and assessment, and instructs the client how he'd like the client on the table. He leaves the room and the client gets on the table as instructed.

Johnny enters the room and begins the massage. While the client is prone, Johnny works on the back. The client enjoys the work on the back, as the client does a lot of manual labor and is constantly lifting heavy objects.

The client seems to be experiencing a small amount of discomfort whenever Johnny massages one specific area in the low back. Johnny asks if the client is all right, and the client says yes, just that it's a little uncomfortable in the area. The client states it feels as if a bone is out of place and needs to be popped back in.

Johnny thinks about this for a second, and remembers watching his boss perform spinal manipulation. Johnny offers to pop the client's back, thinking this could help alleviate the client's pain. The client agrees, and Johnny pushes on the client's back, trying to force the back to pop. He succeeds, and the back does pop. The client thanks Johnny for helping him with his pain. Johnny resumes the massage to completion.

What did Johnny do wrong?

4. New Boot Goofin'

Steph is a massage therapist working for a mountain resort. It is winter time, so it is extremely busy, and the ski slopes are packed. Steph sees many different clients, most of whom she never gets the opportunity to massage again.

A client comes in for a massage scheduled with Steph. Steph greets the client as usual and brings the client back to her massage room. Steph begins the massage, and the client seems to be enjoying it.

During the course of the massage, the client and Steph begin chatting. The client tells Steph that she is in town to ski, but forgot her ski boots at home, and does not want to buy a brand new pair just for this one trip. Steph remembers, she has a couple used pairs of ski boots she never uses any more that she'd be willing to part with. Steph offers to sell the client her used ski boots. The client becomes excited and agrees to buy the boots.

After the session ends, the client and Steph make arrangements to meet at the resort's coffee shop to make the transaction. Later that day they meet at the coffee shop, and the client pays Steph for her used ski boots.

What did Steph do wrong?

5. I Think I Love You

Amber, a massage therapist of six years, has built up a regular clientele base and typically sees the same people at least once every two weeks or so. There is one client in particular she enjoys working on, named James.

James is a good looking man, only a couple years older than Amber. Their personalities mesh, they always have great conversations when he comes in for a massage, and James never misses an appointment. They get along so well, in fact, Amber wonders what might happen if she asks James out on a date.

James comes in for his weekly appointment. Amber has been thinking about James a lot lately, and becomes flustered when she sees him. She brings him in to the massage room, he gets on the table, and the session begins.

The massage is perfectly professional, with no boundaries being crossed by either party. The conversation is delightful as usual. After the massage, Amber meets James outside the massage room with his standard cup of water. James pays for the massage, and books another appointment in one week.

Nervous, Amber stops James before he walks out the door. She states that they've been seeing each other for quite a while and have really gotten to know each other well. She continues, asking James if he'd be interested in going out to dinner with her later that week. James smiles and agrees, and they set up a date.

What did Amber do wrong?

6. Five Finger Discount

Jonah has just been hired as a massage therapist at a local membership-based massage establishment. It is his first massage job, and he's excited to begin his career.

Jonah meets all of his fellow co-workers, and feels right at home at his job. Anxiously, he walks to the waiting area and greets his client. He brings his client to the massage room, instructs the client on how he'd like them on the table, then he leaves. The client gets on the table.

Jonah forgets that he left his massage oil and holster in the break room. He walks down the hall to the employee break room, opens the door, and spots a fellow male co-worker looking in a female co-worker's purse. His co-worker looks up, sees Jonah, and immediately looks away from the purse. He makes quick small talk with Jonah, then leaves the break room, all without Jonah taking his eyes off of him. Jonah grabs his massage oil and holster and leaves the break room, heading back to perform his first massage.

Jonah suspects his co-worker of trying to steal from their other co-workers.

What should Jonah do?

7. Blurred Lines

Charlie is performing a massage on a female client he's never met before. She seems normal, and seems to receive massage quite often. The client complains to Charlie of pain in her low back and glute area.

During the massage, Charlie performs massage on the client, making sure to work on her lower back. The client states that Charlie can work lower, but Charlie states he is already working at the edge of the sheet and cannot work any lower than this.

In an effort to get Charlie to work lower, the client pulls the sheet down further, exposing more of her lower back, but also her underwear.

What should Charlie do?

8. The Bad Touch

Sasha brings a client in for a massage at the local day spa she works at. She has never met the man before, but he seems pleasant.

She begins the massage, working on his back. While working on the trapezius, the client begins making moaning sounds. This is a little strange to Sasha, but nothing she hasn't heard before. Suddenly, she feels the client's hand touch her thigh, and move up towards her buttocks.

What should Sasha do?

9. Flipping Out

Skylar is a young, active teenager involved in gymnastics. She recently had a big meet out of town and her mom booked an appointment for her to receive massage. When Skylar comes in her mom fills out the needed paperwork. The therapist notices that Skylar has some small pustular looking lesions on her skin around her mouth that have dried, forming a honey color crust. The therapist asks about the area and Skylar says it started recently and the area sometimes itches and even burns a little.

What pathologic condition may Skylar be experiencing?

What is it and what are the most common causes?

Is this condition contagious?

Is it safe for Skylar to receive a massage?

What considerations or protocols may the therapist need to make or follow?

10. Harder, Better, Faster, Stronger

Deshaun has decided to get into shape and start lifting weights. After consulting with a personal trainer and doing research on the internet, he determines which exercises to perform to build the muscles he'd like to be larger. During his first visit to the gym, he wants to impress all of the other gym patrons, so he grabs a 45 pound plate in one hand, and carries it across the gym and back. He switches hands, and repeats the process, holding the plate by his side and walking from one end to the gym and back. The next day, Deshaun experiences muscle soreness, and is not able to move certain areas as effectively as before. The next day, the pain has mostly subsided, and Deshaun is able to move the areas again.

What muscle or muscles is Deshaun likely experiencing pain in?

What action was being performed by the side holding the plate to keep it in place?

What type of muscle contraction was performed as Deshaun held the plate in place?

What medical condition has Deshaun suffered, and are there any precautions a massage therapist should take in regards to it?

11. You Were Cold As Ice

Tracey makes an appointment to get a massage for her birthday. She doesn't get them frequently and is seeing a massage therapist she has never seen before. When she arrives, she fills out the intake form and gives it to the therapist. She has checked off the box that indicates that she experiences numbness. The therapist asks Tracey where she experiences the numbness, how often, and if there is any associated pain. The therapist discovers that the numbness is in Tracey's hands. Tracey says her fingers will turn sort of white or lighter in color, then the numbness and pins and needle feeling starts, then they turn a grayish blue color which has a stinging or throbbing feeling, and then it turns back to normal color and sensation. Today, she is not experiencing any of those symptoms. Other than that, Tracey has indicated no other health concerns and just wants to relax for today's session.

What pathologic condition might Tracey be experiencing?

Is massage safe for Tracey?

What considerations may you need to make while Tracey is on the table?

What is the medical name for the white or lighter color called that Tracey experiences?

What is the medical term for "pins and needles"?

What is the medical name for the grayish-blue color that Tracey experiences?

12. A-OK

Dan is a car mechanic and is coming in to the clinic for a massage. His wife booked his massage appointment because he has been complaining of many aches and pains, and she thought it would help. His therapist asks questions about his areas of concern, and all sound like normal muscular issues. Dan does mention that he has been having pain at the base of his right thumb, which is his dominant hand. The pain always gets worse as his work day progresses and is fairly sore at the moment. The therapist asks Dan to grasp his thumb with his four fingers and adduct the wrist. There is a sharp, intense pain at the distal end of the radius at the thumb side of the wrist.

What condition is Dan likely experiencing?

Is massage indicated or contraindicated for this condition?

What is the therapist's next step?

13. Pain in the Neck

Paige comes in to seek massage therapy for the first time. She complains of pain in her neck and in between her scapulae. While she is filling out her intake form, her therapists takes note that she sits with an increased thoracic curve, protracted scapulae, internally rotated shoulders, and a forward head posture. In the interview process the therapist asks some basic questions and discovers that the pain has gotten worse over time and comes and goes. Paige is a student who often sits for long hours in front of a computer as well as works on a computer at her job. The pain comes and goes but is normally worse at the end of the day. Paige finally went to see her doctor and they recommended she seek the help of a massage therapist.

What condition is likely present?

Is it safe for Paige to receive a massage?

What muscles might the therapist find that are short and tight?

What muscles might the therapist find that are stretched and weak?

Is there anything that the therapist would need to be cautious of?

What self-care recommendations should the therapist recommend Paige do?

14. Bowl Me Over

Barold loves to bowl. However, it has been a while since he's bowled. He grabs his ball, shoes, and hits the town ready to destroy some pins. He arrives at the bowling alley and sets up shop on a lane with a couple budskis. Barold is pumped to be back at the alley with all his friends. It is finally Barold's turn to bowl, and he grabs his bowling ball, and steps up to the lane. He sends the ball rolling down the lane, and hits a perfect strike. He openly weeps and smiles, as he is so overcome with joy.

When Barold rolls the ball, what action is his shoulder performing?

What action are Barold's fingers performing while he is holding the ball?

What muscles are contracting when Barold rolls the ball down the lane?

What muscle is contracting when Barold smiles?

15. Step By Step

Natalie seeks out massage treatment for pain and discomfort in her feet. Both seem to hurt as of recently but she says the right side is slightly worse. Her therapist asks some basic questions and discovers Natalie started a new job about a month and a half ago where she is on her feet much more than she used to be. The pain had a fast onset about a week ago and seems to be a burning and aching pain in the arch of the foot and the worst pain is felt when she pushes off of her step, especially when walking up the stairs at her apartment. The pain is the most intense near the heel when she wakes up in the morning and starts walking. Natalie went to see her doctor and they recommended she seek the help of a massage therapist.

What condition is likely present?

Is receiving massage safe for Natalie?

What muscles would the therapist want to work on to treat the condition?

Is there anything the therapist needs to be cautious of?

What is a typical cause of this condition?

What self-care recommendations should the therapist recommend Natalie do at home?

16. The Wanderer

Shawn is a touring musician, traveling the country playing concerts almost every night. He plays the guitar and sings, and has been building a steady fan base since beginning producing music five years ago. He arrives for his latest concert, sets up his merch stand, and greets the concert-goers as they arrive. When each concert-goer approaches Shawn, he extends his hand out and firmly shakes their hand. Eventually, it is time for Shawn to begin his concert. He steps on stage, takes a seat on the stool, sets the guitar in his lap, and begins singing and playing.

What muscles are responsible for putting the hand and forearm into position to shake hands?

What action are Shawn's digits performing when he holds the guitar and places his fingers on the frets?

What is the structure responsible for helping Shawn produce the sound that lets him sing?

What bony landmark is Shawn sitting on while performing, and what muscle group originates on this landmark?

17. We Got a Little Ol' Convoy

Dave, a long distance truck driver, has had a lot of lower back discomfort recently. He visited his doctor and explained he has been experiencing pain and weakness in his lower back, especially when standing, and the doctor recommended Dave see a massage therapist to help with muscular discomfort. Dave makes an appointment and during the intake the therapist asks Dave to stand up to assess Dave's posture and gait. The therapist notices Dave's abdomen seems to be sticking out anteriorly, and his pelvis is tilted anteriorly as well.

What condition could Dave be experiencing?

What muscles may be short and tight?

What muscles may be stretched and weakened?

Is massage indicated or contraindicated?

What special considerations may the therapist need to make?

What self-care recommendations should the therapist suggest to Dave?

18. Pump Up The Jam

Amanda and her husband have gotten a baby sitter for the evening, and are going on a date. They have made plans to visit the nicest, fanciest, most luxurious French restaurant west of the Mississippi. Amanda's husband dresses in his best suit, complete with a red neck tie(power knotted, of course). Amanda applies makeup, throws on a lovely halter-style backless cocktail dress, and she looks absolutely stunning. The one thing missing from her ensemble, however, is her shoes. Amanda grabs a pair of four inch open toed pumps. Real fancy high heeled stuff. She puts the shoes on, looks herself over in a mirror, spritzes herself with her most expensive perfume, and is ready to go.

What position is Amanda's ankle in when she is standing in her high heel shoes?

What muscles are contracted that allow this action to be performed?

What muscle is being stretched while Amanda is wearing her high heel shoes?

Amanda's husband is wearing a neck tie. The tie is placed around which region of the vertebral column?

The tie is tied at the origin of which muscle? This muscle is responsible for turning the head to the opposite side, and flexion of the head.

19. Thumbs Down

Doug is a licensed massage therapist who has been in practice for nine years. Through the years he has noticed pain in his thumbs on and off. The pain has gotten much worse and more frequent over the past two years. Doug assumed it was just from over-use and ignored it. Doug received massage as often as he could for his normal body aches, and would ask for focus on his hands and forearms. Doug had increased his hours at work over the past few years, and he noticed the discomfort turned into pain and visible inflammation. Now, Doug often has trouble making it through a full day of work, and has had to drop down to four days of work a week instead of five. He is also considering taking less clients due to the pain he experiences in his thumb.

What condition is Doug likely experiencing?

Is massage indicated for this condition?

What are some things Doug should do to help manage the condition?

20. Two Steaks, Four Potatoes

Robert has been working all day at the local paint shop. He's exhausted, beat, pooped, whatever you want to call it. He did not receive a long enough lunch break during the day, so he is starving. He jumps in his truck and heads to a chain Texas themed restaurant for some delicious dinner. The hostess seats him, asks what he'd like to drink, and he says "Soda pop would be lovely, thank you." The waitress returns, and after skimming through the menu, Robert decides on what to eat. "Hey. I'll have... two steaks.. and four potatoes.. and a bucket of peanuts." Robert says, obviously exhausted. The waitress takes his order, and a few minutes later, she brings Robert his food. At this point, he is so tired, he is practically unconscious at the table. The delicious smell of the steaks and potatoes riles him awake, and he quickly devours the meal.

What muscles are responsible for helping Robert chew his food?

When Robert swallows the food, what structure stops food from entering the larynx, preventing choking?

Smooth muscle in the digestive tract helps to move food through the body. This process is known as what?

Steak is made of muscle. What is the contractile unit of a muscle known as?

21. World Class Athlete

Ellie is an avid gym-goer, who loves exercise of all kinds. She loves to run, lift weights, and play sports. After a great session at the gym performing cardiovascular exercises, Ellie heads in to the locker room and jumps in the shower. This is typical, as Ellie doesn't particularly enjoy smelling like sweat and body odor after a workout. She finishes the shower, quickly dries as best she can, gets dressed, and leaves the gym. Several days pass, and while getting dressed in the morning, Ellie notices some redness and irritation between her toes. She examines further, and notices skin peeling in the area. The area slightly itches as well.

What medical condition has Ellie likely contracted, and what type of infection is it?

What kind of medication is used to combat this infection?

If the infection spreads to the nails, what is it called?

Running increases heart rate. What is an irregular heart rhythm?

Heat, such as hot water from a shower, has what affect on blood vessels?

22. Holiday Cancelled

Nick is a delivery man, who is used to carrying heavy loads of cargo. One cold and bitter evening, he places packages into his delivery satchel, and throws it over his back. Suddenly, Nick feels an intense pain in his low back. He sets his satchel on the ground to try and alleviate the pain, but the damage is already done. Nick's low back muscles begin to spasm. With such intense pain, Nick is forced to take the night off of work. The next day, Nick has difficulty moving his trunk, and is experiencing pain radiating down his posterior thigh and leg.

What medical condition may Nick have experienced?

How can this medical condition affect the spinal nerves emerging from the spinal cord?

Pain radiating down the posterior thigh and leg may be an indication of what condition?

What region of the vertebral column has experienced trauma?

Nick enjoys snacking on cookies and a whole milk during his breaks at work. What hormone stimulates the production of milk?

If Nick were to stay in the cold too long, his body temperature may drop to unsafe levels. What is this condition known as?

23. Give Me a Quarterback

Ross is a professional football player, who plays on the offensive line. Game day has arrived, and Ross is eagerly awaiting the start of the game. The game begins, he grabs his helmet, puts it on, and runs out onto the field for the first play. The quarterback calls out the play in the huddle, and they all line up for the play. The center snaps the ball to the quarterback, who hands it off to the running back. The play calls for Ross to make a key block on a linebacker to let the running back gain as many yards as possible. Ross finds the linebacker he's assigned to block and absolutely levels him, sending him flying backwards a few yards. The running back runs past the linebacker who is now flat on his back, and finds nothing but open field ahead of him. He runs the ball for a 75 yard touchdown! The team is excited, especially Ross, who runs down the field to celebrate with his running back and other teammates. Knowing that the running back would not have scored the touchdown without Ross, everyone hoists Ross onto their shoulders in celebration. Ross is the happiest offensive lineman in the world!

Helmets are used to protect the head and brain from injury. What injury can occur when there is a blow to the head that may result in loss of consciousness?

What bones in the skull produce a natural helmet for the body, providing protection for the brain?

The quarterback has to tell the other players what the play will be. What structure in the throat is responsible for producing sound used for speech?

After being blocked by Ross, the linebacker finds himself lying flat on his back. What body position is the linebacker in?

The running back sprints down the field as he approaches the end zone. What actions are the running back's ankles performing as he runs?

When celebrating, Ross sits on other players' shoulders. What is the scientific name of the shoulder joint, and what kind of synovial joint is it?

24. My Neck, My Back

Brianna is a student who is busy studying for the MBLEx. In conjunction with purchasing a brand new copy of the MBLEx Test Prep study guide, she also uses all the resources in the MBLEx Test Prep app(available on smart phones now!). Brianna sits at her desk, with her laptop in front of her, clicking and typing away. She knows that if she studies hard, she'll do a great job on the exam and pass with flying colors. As the night wears on, she becomes more tired, and begins leaning forward in her chair closer to the computer. Her head and neck are more anterior than normal, and her shoulders become rounded. Eventually, she calls it a night and stops studying, opting for the comfort of her bed.

Which cranial nerve is responsible for sight?

Which bones in the fingers are used on the keys when typing?

What curvature does the cervical vertebrae have, and what can happen to this curvature if Brianna does not correct this posture?

Rounding of the shoulders may result in which condition?

Which hormone regulates the body's circadian rhythm, also known as the wake/sleep cycle, and which gland produces it?

25. Tricky

Owen has grown up near the mountains, and always finds time to hit the slopes and get some snowboarding in when there is fresh snow. One morning, Owen heads to the ski resort, having packed all of his necessary equipment. He parks, grabs his stuff, and heads up the mountain on the ski lift. He reaches the top, and begins his descent down the mountain on his snowboard. Quickly he realizes that he has forgotten a layer of clothing to cover his face. He's hit with cold wind and snow as he works his way down the mountain. Once he reaches the bottom, his face stings from the sensation. He heads back to his car, finds his mask, and puts it on. To help warm himself further, he grabs a hot chocolate from a snack vendor and guzzles it.

If Owen's face were exposed to the cold for an extended period of time, what may form in the soft tissues of his face, and what is that condition known as?

Pain is detected by which sensory receptor?

What path does the hot chocolate take on its way through Owen's digestive tract, ending at the stomach?

Snowboarding is typically performed at higher altitudes. What does the body consume less of at higher altitudes, and what condition is this similar to in regards to systemic function?

26. The Compliant Gait

Harry likes being alone, and is an avid hiker. The time comes for his morning hike through the dark woods of the Pacific Northwest. Harry steps out of his abode located deep in the forest, and inhales the fresh morning air. He spots his typical walking trail, and makes his way towards it. He's walked this trail many times, and really enjoys how serene and quiet it is. After a mile or so, Harry notices footsteps behind him, maybe 50 yards or so. There usually aren't others on the trail, and this worries Harry slightly. Not willing to take any chances, Harry makes his way off the path and hides behind a tree. A few minutes pass, and two people walk by, examining Harry's footprints. They remark how large his footprints are, and seem extremely excited about them. Harry thinks this is rather odd, and remains hidden amongst the foliage. The people take photographs of Harry's footprints, and keep walking until they are out of sight and can no longer be heard. Harry is confused.

Assessing a person's walking pattern is known as what?

What muscle is responsible for inhalation?

Hip flexion plays an important role in walking. What are four muscles that perform flexion of the hip?

How many phalangeal bones are in each foot?

What type of protein produces hair?

27. Whip It Good

Carl has just left work and is ready to head home and see his beloved family. He hops in his car and hits the road. Carl is known to be a safe driver, obeying all traffic laws, being courteous on the road, and being as defensive as possible while behind the wheel. Unfortunately, this does not apply to others on the road! Carl approaches a red light and stops, waiting patiently for the light to change to green. Unbeknownst to him, another driver approaching the light is not paying attention to the road, instead fiddling with their cell phone in an attempt to start the next thrilling episode of the MBLEx Test Prep Podcast. The driver fails to see the red light until it's too late. The driver slams on the brakes, but there is not enough time to stop, and the car hits Carl's vehicle from behind. Because Carl was not anticipating the impact, he did not have time to brace himself for the collision. Carl's head is thrown back and then forward in a rapid motion. A few moments pass, and Carl assesses the situation, and climbs out of the car.

What injury did Carl likely sustain?

Is this injury a contraindication for massage, and if so, what kind of contraindication?

Traffic collisions and sports are the most common ways people tear the strongest ligament in the knee responsible for holding the tibia and femur together. What is this ligament?

A seatbelt is buckled near the hip joint. What is the scientific name of the hip joint, and what kind of synovial joint is it?

In a traffic collision, contusions may occur. What is a contusion, is a contusion contraindicated, and if so, what kind kind of contraindication is it?

28. Say Goodnight?

Colin has been working hard trying to balance his home life and his work life. Colin works in a high-stress environment, in which deadlines are firm and the bosses are uncompromising. After work, he's tasked with paying bills, cleaning the house, and tending to his children. The amount of stress Colin deals with on a daily basis is extensive, and Colin notices it taking an effect on his physical and mental well-being. At night, Colin is unable to get much sleep. What little sleep he gets isn't helpful in recovery, and he often wakes more tired than when he went to bed. He has begun increasing intake of carbohydrates and caffeine to increase his energy during the day. After an especially stressful day at work, Colin's wife suggests he receive a massage to help with the stress.

When the body is placed under stress, which division of the autonomic nervous system is activated?

What hormones specifically are released in a stress response, and what are effects of these hormones on the body?

What condition might Colin have that results in a lack of sleep?

Is this condition contraindicated for massage, and if so, what kind of contraindication is it? If not, what techniques and other elements should be utilized to help Colin?

Increased consumption of carbohydrates and caffeine may lead to which health complications?

29. A-Positive Development

Alucard's father loves a good cocktail here and there. His father is a big fan of Bloody Mary's. During a Halloween party, Alucard's father welcomes his guests in to his home and offers them a hand-made Bloody Mary. Alucard is not interested in the drink, but his father insists, saying it's where he gets his energy and good looks. Alucard's father drinks the Bloody Mary, feeling as refreshed as ever. He offers a Bloody Mary to Alucard once more as he heads towards the ingredients to make another. Alucard declines, and his father shrugs, reaching for the bottle of Bloody Mary mix. Alucard's father accidentally knocks the bottle over, and it shatters on the floor. A few moments pass, and the Bloody Mary mix begins to sort of congeal on the floor.

Blood consists of what four basic components?

Which component makes up the majority of blood, and what is its main function?

Coagulation of blood is performed by which blood cell?

What protein does oxygen and carbon dioxide attach to, allowing these molecules to be transported throughout the body?

If Alucard's father obtains too much "Bloody Mary mix" from another person, what condition may the person experience due to blood loss?

30. Quit Bugging Me

Pierre is a photographer in Montreal, who specializes in wedding photography. He also loves outdoor weddings, because it allows him to use natural lighting to capture the beauty of the occasion. Pierre arrives for his latest wedding shoot and photographs the ceremony perfectly. The ceremony finishes, and it's time for photographs in a more private setting with just the bride and groom. He takes them into a grassy field, which has a great natural golden tone to work with. Pierre asks his models to pose, and they oblige, and Pierre takes some amazing photos for their collection. The wedding reception goes just as well, and Pierre considers the day a success. Pierre heads home, removes his clothes to prepare for a shower, and notices a small insect burying itself into the skin near his ankle.

What insect is likely attached to Pierre?

What type of infection, and subsequent medical condition, can the insect spread to Pierre?

What kind of rash may a person experience around the bite location?

Certain people may be allergic to tall grass. What may the body produce in response to allergens, which cause blood vessels to dilate?

Sunlight exposure causes the skin to produce what nutrient?

31. A Vicious "Cycle"

Cathy is a huge fan of cycling, and makes sure she gets out and rides her bicycle every day or two. One morning, Cathy jumps on her bicycle and hits the road, heading to work. Cathy rides in the bicycle lane as much as possible, but once in a while she has to enter in to traffic. Cathy obeys traffic laws, and actually rides at a relatively high rate of speed, keeping pace with most cars on the road. Cathy approaches a stop light and stops behind a car, resting one leg on the asphalt. Cathy takes a deep breath, then reaches for her water bottle. She brings the water bottle to her mouth and squeezes it, sending water spraying out into her mouth. She takes another quick drink of water, and puts the water bottle back on her bicycle's body, just in time for the light to change colors. She begins riding again as traffic moves with her.

What are the primary actions performed by the hip when a person is riding a bicycle?

What are the primary actions performed by the knee when a person is riding a bicycle?

Riding a bicycle, along with many other exercises, can increase the production of what substance, used to decrease body temperature?

Exercise can temporarily increase blood pressure. In a blood pressure reading of 130/85, what does the higher number represent, and what is specifically being measured that determines the number given?

What number does water measure as on a pH scale?

32. Stop Wine-ing

Ashley is an outgoing woman who loves to go to the local watering hole with her friends. One night, she meets up with several of her friends, and they all take a seat around a large circular table. A waitress comes by to take their orders, and Ashley decides she's in the mood for a glass of Willamette Valley Vineyards Whole Cluster Pinot Noir(it's delicious, trust me). The drinks arrive, and Ashley pounds her glass of wine, pointing out how delicious it is to all her friends. She decides to order another, and she really pounds that one too! Ashley is feeling a little buzzed, but it's nothing she hasn't been able to handle before. She decides "YOLO" and orders ANOTHER glass of wine! Halfway through the third glass, Ashley begins feeling a headache starting. She polishes off the wine, and soon, the headache gets much, much worse. She has difficulty focusing on vision, light bothers her, sharp noises make the pain worse. She decides she has to leave and go home to recover. Her friends order her a ride-share, and she makes it home safely, but she feels even worse when she gets home than she did before she left. She makes it in to her house, turns off all the lights, jumps in bed, and tries to ride out whatever pain she's experiencing.

What medical condition is Ashley likely experiencing?

What are triggers that may contribute to this condition occurring?

What structures in the body are specifically causing Ashley to experience pain?

Wine contains alcohol, which increases the production of what substance in the body?

When a person is seated in a chair, what position are the hips in?

33. Lost at Sea

Julius slowly opens his eyes to the lapping of waves on the beach. He has no idea where he is, or how he got there. The last thing he remembers is being on an airplane somewhere over the Pacific ocean, and the oxygen masks suddenly dropping from the ceiling. Julius stands up and takes his surroundings into account. He appears to be on a deserted island, with nobody else in sight. The sun is beating down on Julius, so he removes his shirt and places it on his head to help himself cool down. He begins walking along the beach to search for anything, whether it be other people, a way off the island, or even just food and water. The island is small, there is a small amount of vegetation, and things aren't looking good for Julius.

The ocean contains a high concentration of which substance, an extremely important electrolyte in the body?

Excessive exposure to sunlight over a short period may result in what?

Excessive exposure to sunlight over a long period of time, in some cases years, may result in the development of what?

Medications that are designed to lower body temperature in cases such as fever are known as?

What are the three stages of "injury" a person may experience if their body temperature is too high for too long?

34. Found at Sea

Weeks pass, and Julius has found a way to survive. He's developed a way to catch rain fall, and has been eating nuts, roots, and insects he's found. He's even figured out how to catch fish! However, Julius is not willing to stay on the island his entire life, and is determined to find a way off and back to civilization. He builds himself a raft using a home-made hammer and tying pieces of driftwood together. Finally the day arrives where he plans on setting sail. He pushes the raft out into the water and climbs on. The wind blows the raft past the breakers, and Julius is now at sea, anxious to be rescued.

Two days go by, and Julius has begun running short on his supplies. Just as Julius begins feeling as if the end is near, he spots a shimmering light in the horizon. A ship! He signals to the ship using a piece of metal he found on the island, hoping they spot it. Luckily for Julius, they spot him, and turn towards him! Julius openly celebrates as the ship nears. His excitement can't be contained as the ship gets ever closer, and he jumps in the ocean and swims towards it. He's finally pulled aboard, and is saved!

Julius uses a hammer. What muscle is primarily responsible for performing the action of hammering?

What muscles perform extension of the hip, the primary action used when pushing an object?

What muscle is known as the "swimmer's muscle" due to its actions, which are performed when a person swims?

What specific actions do the "swimmer's muscle" perform?

35. Sorry 'Bout That One

Jenny works at as medical receptionist and is constantly on the telephone, often holding the phone to her ear with her shoulder. After several months of this, she decides enough is enough, and she needs to get a massage. She stops in to a chain massage establishment after work and books herself a massage for right then. She takes a seat in the waiting area, and the massage therapist, Becky, introduces herself and takes Jenny back to the massage room. Becky asks Jenny what brings her in for the appointment, and Jenny states that she has pain in her neck from her job. Becky asks Jenny to rotate and laterally flex her head/neck. After performing these brief exercises, Becky instructs Jenny to get on the table, under the top sheet. Jenny obliges after Becky leaves the room. Becky returns a moment later, and the massage begins. Becky asks Jenny if there were any areas she wants massaged specifically, and Jenny says she doesn't know, but she trusts Becky to do whatever because Becky knows what she's doing. Becky begins massaging the back, and Jenny lets out a deep sigh, then immediately apologizes, thinking her breathing has upset Becky in some way.

Becky assures Jenny that everything is fine. Jenny then apologizes for apologizing! Finally, Becky is able to get Jenny to relax and enjoy the massage.

Holding a phone with the shoulder and ear produces what type of muscle contraction to be performed?

What muscle, which is part of the anterior triangle of the neck, may be strained from performing this action excessively?

Becky asking Jenny to rotate and laterally flex her head/neck is part of what aspect of the massage session?

Jenny lies under the top sheet on the massage table. This is known as what, and what is the primary reason for this?

Jenny deferring to Becky on preferred areas to be massaged due to Becky's perceived expertise, and apologizing for coughing may be a sign of what occurring?

Answer Key on Page 311

Answer Keys

Matching Answer Keys

Massage Therapy		Assessment		Business		Ethics	
G	D	N	U	S	V	P	R
S	B	K	C	P	H	M	C
N	J	O	S	C	F	J	E
P	Q	F	J	U	E	O	F
A	E	L	I	Q	D	Q	S
M	R	R	H	N	T	U	H
C	L	P	T	L	I	N	V
I	F	A	G	J	M	B	K
V	H	V	B	G	B	T	G
O	U	Q	E	R	A	A	L
T	K	D	M	O	K	D	I

Word Roots		Prefixes		Suffixes		Anatomy and Physiology	
R	H	S	D	I	U	C	N
M	A	C	K	L	C	K	O
G	D	F	I	K	Q	E	A
J	E	B	O	S	V	T	H
K	V	U	E	O	J	U	S
L	S	A	H	A	D	D	J
P	I	J	N	P	F	M	F
Q	F	R	Q	H	T	L	G
U	O	T	L	B	E	B	I
B	N	G	V	G	N	Q	R
C	T	M	P	R	M	P	V

Pathology		Kinesiology	
D	R	C	U
P	I	L	P
G	V	N	S
U	M	F	M
A	L	V	Q
N	H	T	J
T	C	A	H
J	F	E	D
S	K	R	O
E	Q	K	G
O	B	B	I

Medical Terminology Breaking Down/Building

Breaking Down:
1. Artery/hard/condition
2. Renal pelvis/kidney/inflammation
3. Brain/inflammation
4. Lymph/swelling
5. Excessive/thyroid/condition
6. Bile/bladder/inflammation
7. Liver/inflammation
8. Vein/inflammation
9. Twisted/neck
10. Skin/plant/condition
11. Extremity/irregular enlargement
12. Muscle/heart/blood flow obstruction
13. Not/sleep
14. Nerve/pain
15. Tendon/synovial/inflammation

Building:
1. An/emia
2. Athero/scler/osis
3. Gastr/itis
4. Melan/oma
5. Fibro/my/algia
6. Osteo/arthr/itis
7. Cyst/itis
8. A/pnea
9. Onycho/myc/osis
10. Dermat/itis
11. Hyper/tension
12. Ar/rhythmia
13. Leuk/emia
14. Kyph/osis
15. Cellul/itis

Crossword Answer Keys

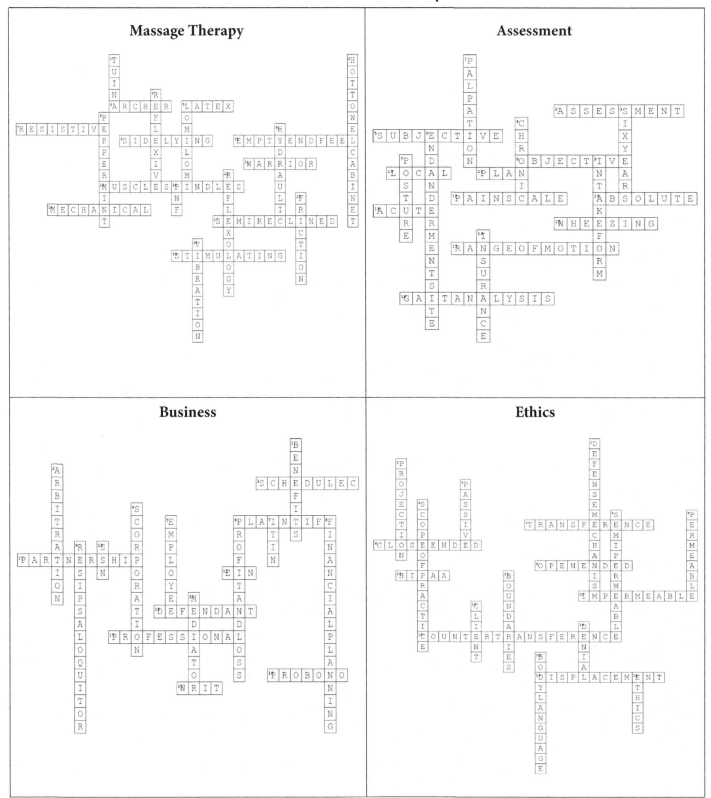

Massage Therapy

Assessment

Business

Ethics

Medical Terminology

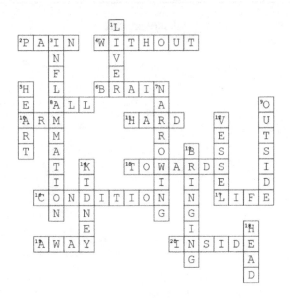

Anatomy and Physiology

Pathology

Kinesiology

Kinesiology Muscle Labeling

1. Temporalis
2. Masseter
3. Sternocleidomastoid
4. Splenius capitis
5. Levator scapulae
6. Pectoralis major
7. Deltoid
8. Biceps brachii
9. Infraspinatus
10. Rhomboids

11. Trapezius
12. Triceps brachii
13. Latissimus dorsi
14. Psoas major
15. Iliacus
16. Tensor fascia lata
17. Sartorius
18. Gracilis
19. Rectus femoris
20. Gluteus maximus

21. Biceps femoris
22. Semitendinosus
23. Semimembranosus
24. Tibialis anterior
25. Gastrocnemius
26. Soleus
27. Peroneus longus
28. Pectoralis minor
29. Serratus anterior
30. Rectus abdominis

Critical Thinking Answers

1. Katie forgot to clean the door handle! The client, who had not washed their hand, opened the door. This contaminated the door handle. Katie cleaned the table, bolsters, and head rest perfectly, but her hand became contaminated when she grabbed the door handle without cleaning it first. She then shook the hand of her next client, which resulted in cross-contamination. Make sure you clean anything the client touches!

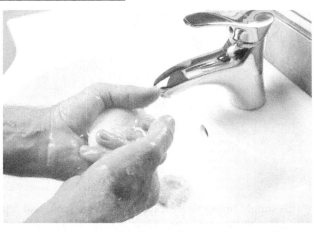

2. Brandon has violated confidentiality. Anything the client states during the massage is to be kept confidential, and should only be discussed with the client in a massage setting. By asking Stan about the marathon and the work on his hamstrings in a public setting, he has violated the confidentiality established with Stan.

3. Johnny has knowingly and intentionally performed chiropractic work, which is outside of his scope of practice. If this action had resulted in the client becoming hurt in any way, Brandon could be sued for malpractice and negligence. If a joint pops during the course of massage naturally, that is fine. But because Johnny knowingly attempted to perform work outside of his scope of practice, he could be held liable for damages. Do not work outside your scope of practice!

4. Steph has committed a violation of ethics. The client is seeing Steph for a massage, and nothing more. Attempting to solicit a client anything that is not directly massage related is a violation of ethics, and should not be done. Instead, Steph should have recommended the client go to a vendor that sells used ski boots.

5. Amber is crossing in to counter-transference and dual relationships. If a massage therapist begins feeling any sort of attraction towards a client, they should end the business relationship before it becomes a problem. If the therapist is working for someone, they should notify their employer of the situation so the client can be booked with another therapist. If the client wishes to date a client, the therapist needs to make sure they are no longer that therapist's client.

6. Jonah has likely witnessed a theft in progress. Jonah should report the potential theft to his employer. Jonah should not approach or confront the co-worker suspected of stealing. Doing so could create many issues between co-workers if there is no proof of any wrong doing, an altercation could ensue, etc. If any issue arises between co-workers, the issue should be brought to the attention of the employer.

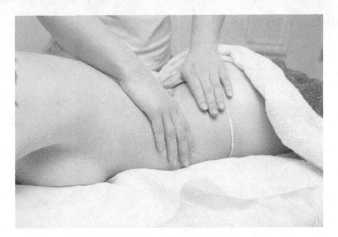

8. Sasha should immediately leave the massage room and report the incident to the employer. The client should be escorted off the property and barred from returning. This type of incident, in which a massage therapist is physically assaulted, can happen to anyone, and should never be tolerated. Side note, this exact circumstance happened to me once! Like I said, it can happen to anyone!

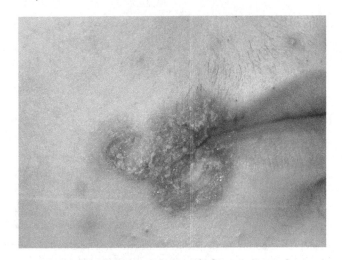

Is it safe for the therapist to give Skylar a massage?
No. It is a highly contagious infection therefore an absolute contraindication.

What recommendations could the therapist make to Skylar and her mother?
The therapist should recommend that she follow up with a doctor for diagnosis. If it is in fact impetigo, topical or oral antibiotics may be used to kill the bacteria. After the use of the antibiotic medication, Skylar should be able to return for her massage. Healing time should take about a week after the start of medication.

10. What muscle or muscles is Deshaun likely experiencing pain in?
Levator scapulae and upper fibers of the trapezius.

What action was being performed by the side holding the plate to keep it in place?
Scapular elevation.

What type of muscle contraction was performed as Deshaun held the plate in place?
Levator scapulae and upper fibers of the trapezius were performing an isometric contraction, in which there is tension in the muscle, but the length of the muscle remains constant.

7. The client has violated Charlie's boundaries. Boundaries set limitations on where the massage therapist works, and are set by both the therapist and client. When Charlie sets the drape, the boundary is established, and Charlie is non-verbally telling the client that there will be no massage past this point on the back. By pulling the sheet down, the client has violated Charlie's boundaries. Charlie should explain to the client that the sheet is setting the boundary, and needs to stay where it is. If the client insists on the sheet being lowered, Charlie may tell the client that the session will end.

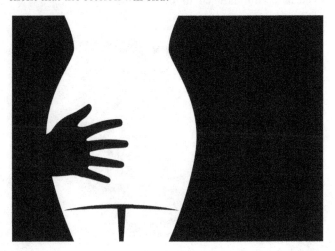

9. What pathologic condition may Skylar be experiencing?
Impetigo.

What is it and what are the most common causes?
Impetigo is a bacterial infection that is more common in children than adults. Most commonly the cause is staphylococci or streptococci bacteria.

Is this condition contagious?
Yes, it is highly contagious. It can be spread by direct contact with the client or through contaminated objects like the linens.

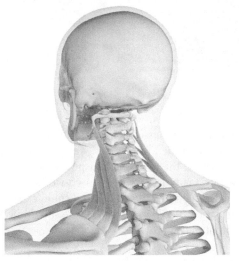

What medical condition has Deshaun suffered, and are there any precautions a massage therapist should take in regards to it?
Deshaun has suffered a grade 1 muscle strain, and is experiencing delayed onset muscle soreness. In the immediate acute stage, the massage therapist should avoid the area, but in the post-acute stage, massage may be performed to help speed healing by bringing more blood into the area.

11. What pathologic condition might Tracey be experiencing?
Raynaud's Disease.

Is massage safe for Tracey?
Yes. Between attacks or episodes massage is indicated and may help improve circulation. Be sure to have an extra blanket or table warmer if need be and keep her covered when possible.

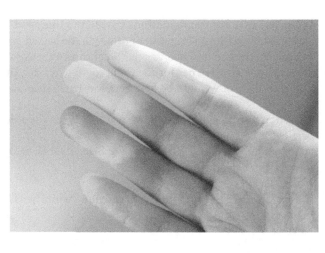

What considerations may you need to make while Tracey is on the table?
If she starts to have an attack or episode during the massage session, a warm towel may be applied if available.

Are there any contraindications to this pathological condition?
Cryotherapy.

What is the medical name for the white or lighter color called that Tracey experiences?
Pallor.

What is the medical term for "pins and needles"?
Paresthesia.

What is the medical name for the grayish blue color that Tracey experiences?
Cyanosis.

12. What condition is Dan likely experiencing?
De Quervain's Tenosynovitis.

Is massage indicated or contraindicated for this condition?
Massage is a local contraindication in the acute stage because it may increase inflammation and pain associated with this condition. Cryotherapy may be performed to decrease inflammation.

What is the therapist's next step?
The therapist should recommend Dan follow up with his doctor for diagnosis and treatment, and document this recommendation under the Plan section of SOAP notes.

13. What condition is likely present?
Kyphosis, a hyper-curvature of the thoracic vertebrae.

Is it safe for Paige to receive a massage?
As long as there is a doctor's clearance and Paige doesn't have an underlying condition that needs to be considered, massage is indicated.

What muscles might the therapist find that are short and tight?
Medial Rotation of the Shoulder: Pectoralis major, anterior deltoid, subscapularis, teres major, latissimus dorsi.
Protraction of Scapulae: Serratus anterior, pectoralis minor.
Forward Head Posture: Sternocleidomastoid, scalenes.
Upper Cervical Extension: Upper trapezius, levator scapulae.

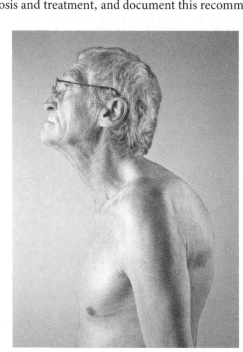

What muscles might the therapist find that are stretched and weak?
Medial rotation of the shoulder: Infraspinatus, posterior deltoid, teres minor.
Protraction of Scapula: Middle trapezius, rhomboid major.
Forward Head Posture: Longissimus capitis, longissimus cervicis.

Upper Cervical Extension: Suprahyoids, infrahyoids, thoracic erector spinae.

Is there anything that the therapist would need to be cautious of?
Endangerment sites in the neck and axilla, treatment duration and pressure, and positioning.

What self-care recommendations should the therapist recommend Paige do?
Demonstrate to the client proper posture in the seated position.
Encourage the client to take regular breaks from the computer and stretch and move around throughout the day.
Demonstrate all stretches for the client to do to stretch those short and tight muscles. Stretches should be slow and gentle and not be forced, and should be held between 15-30 seconds and done multiple times throughout the day.

14. When Barold rolls the ball, what action is his shoulder performing?
His shoulder first performs extension to bring the ball back, and then flexion to bring the ball forward.

What action are Barold's fingers performing while he is holding the ball?
Flexion.

What muscles are contracting when Barold rolls the ball down the lane?
When the shoulder is extended, the triceps brachii, latissimus dorsi, teres major, subscapularis, and posterior deltoid all contract. When the shoulder is flexed, biceps brachii, coracobrachialis, pectoralis major, and anterior deltoid all contract.

What muscle is contracting when Barold smiles?
Buccinator.

15. What condition is likely present?
Plantarfasciitis.

Is receiving massage safe for Natalie?
As long as there is a doctor's clearance and Natalie doesn't have an injury that's in the acute stage where the pain is too intense to tolerate massage, massage is indicated.

What muscles would the therapist want to work on to treat the condition?
Working muscles that would be short and tight with the condition are ideal. Plantarflexors and everters of the ankle include the gastrocnemius, soleus, peroneus longus and brevis, extensor digitorum longus, tibialis posterior, flexor digitorum longus and flexor hallucis longus. All muscles of the lower leg should be assessed. However, the therapist should pay special attention to address these muscles along their full length.

Is there anything the therapist needs to be cautious of?
The amount of pressure being used during treatment.

What is a typical cause of this condition?
Over-use.

What self-care recommendations should the therapist recommend Natalie to do at home?
Try to rest as much as possible to try to give the tissues time to heal.
Elevate the heel and apply ice to the area to reduce inflammation(can even use a frozen water bottle rolled along the bottom of the foot).
Be diligent to stretch the plantar flexors before activity.
Wear shoes with a good arch support.

16. What muscles are responsible for putting the hand and forearm into position to shake hands?
The biceps brachii begins the process of supination, which puts the hand into neutral position. Brachioradialis flexes the elbow with the hand in neutral position, when it is neither supinated nor pronated.

What action are Shawn's digits performing when he holds the guitar and places his fingers on the frets?
The digits are performing flexion in order to hold the neck of the guitar, or to hold the guitar pick.

What is the structure responsible for helping Shawn produce the sound that lets him sing?
Sound is produced in the larynx.

What bony landmark is Shawn sitting on while performing, and what muscle group originates on this landmark?
Shawn is sitting on the ischial tuberosity. The muscle group that originates on the ischial tuberosity is the hamstrings.

@ShawnJamesMusic

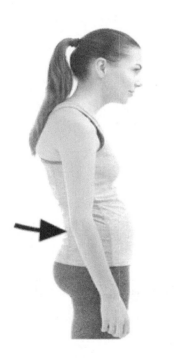

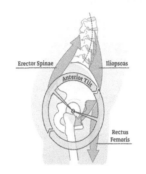

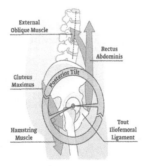

17. What condition could Dave be experiencing?
Lordosis.

What muscles may be short and tight?
Psoas major, iliacus, rectus femoris, latissimus dorsi, and quadratus lumborum. Psoas major will pull the lumbar vertebrae anteriorly, increasing the lordotic curve. Iliacus and rectus femoris will pull the pelvis into an anterior tilt, further exaggerating the lordotic curvature. On the back, latissimus dorsi and quadratus lumborum will also contribute towards pulling the pelvis into an anterior tilt.

What muscles may be stretched and weakened?
Rectus abdominis and the hamstrings. When rectus abdominis is weakened and stretched out, it is unable to properly pull the pelvis from the pubis, and other muscles such as iliacus are then able to force the pelvis into an anterior tilt. The hamstrings work similarly, pulling the pelvis into a posterior tilt at the ischial tuberosity, where they originate. If the hamstrings are weak, other muscles will pull the pelvis into an anterior tilt, and the hamstrings will become stretched.

Is massage indicated or contraindicated?
Massage therapy is indicated.

What special considerations may the therapist need to make?
Positioning and bolstering the client for comfort is important. When supine, the therapist may need to place a larger bolster than normal under the knees to keep the hip flexors, such as iliacus and rectus femoris, from fully lengthening. This can help reduce pressure felt in the lumbar spine. When prone, a bolster under the anterior superior iliac spines may help reduce the anterior pelvic tilt, and placing a bolster under the ankles may reduce any stress or pressure felt in the lower back by placing the hips into slight flexion.

What self-care recommendations should the therapist suggest to Dave?
Self-care should be performed throughout the day. Dave should take regular breaks, and should be instructed on proper standing, sitting, and body mechanics. Stretches may be demonstrated for Dave to perform to loosen tight contributing muscles, and exercises to strengthen weak muscles such as the rectus abdominis and hamstrings may be recommended. These suggestions should be documented under the Plan section of SOAP notes.

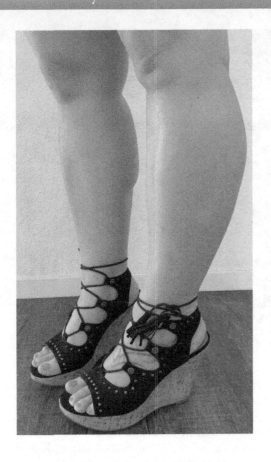

18. What position is Amanda's ankle in when she is standing in her high heel shoes?
Amanda is performing plantarflexion while she is wearing her high heel shoes.

What muscles are contracted that allow this action to be performed?
Gastrocnemius, soleus, and peroneus longus are all contracted, as they all perform plantarflexion.

What muscle is being stretched while Amanda is wearing her high heel shoes?
Tibialis anterior is being stretched, as it performs dorsiflexion.

Amanda's husband is wearing a neck tie. The tie is placed around which region of the vertebral column?
Cervical vertebrae.

The tie is tied at the origin of which muscle? This muscle is responsible for turning the head to the opposite side, and flexion of the head.
Sternocleidomastoid.

19. What condition is Doug likely experiencing?
Osteoarthritis.

What joint is most likely involved?
The carpometacarpal joint of the thumb, also called the saddle joint.

Is massage indicated for this condition?
In the acute stage, massage is a local contraindication. In the post-acute stage, it may be beneficial to increase blood flow to the area, and stimulate synovial fluid production.

What are some things Doug should do to help manage the condition?
Doug should visit a doctor for diagnosis and treatment. Doug should stop using his thumb to perform massage, and wear a brace for his thumb that helps stabilize the saddle joint.

20. What muscles are responsible for helping Robert chew his food?
Masseter is responsible for elevating the mandible, which compresses the food between the teeth. Buccinator compresses the cheeks, moving the food in towards the teeth, allowing the food to be properly masticated.

When Robert swallows the food, what structure stops food from entering the larynx, preventing choking?
The epiglottis rests atop the larynx when food or drink is swallowed, preventing choking.

Smooth muscle in the digestive tract helps to move food through the body. This process is known as what?
Peristalsis.

Steak is made of muscle. What is the contractile unit of a muscle known as?
The contractile unit of a muscle is known as a sarcomere.

21. What medical condition has Ellie likely contracted, and what type of infection is it?
Ellie has likely contracted athlete's foot, which is a fungal infection.

What kind of medication is used to combat this infection?
Antifungal medication, typically in a topical ointment.

If the infection spreads to the nails, what is it called?
Onychomycosis. "Onych/o" means "nail", "myc/o" means "fungus", "-osis" means "condition".

Running increases heart rate. What is an irregular heart rhythm?
Arrhythmia.

Heat, such as hot water from a shower, has what affect on blood vessels?
Heat causes blood vessels to dilate.

22. What medical condition may Nick have experienced?
Nick has likely experienced a herniated disc in the lumbar region.

How can this medical condition affect the spinal nerves emerging from the spinal cord?
A herniated disc may place pressure on nerves emerging from the spinal cord.

Pain radiating down the posterior thigh and leg may be an indication of what condition?
Most commonly sciatica, but may also be caused by piriformis syndrome.

What region of the vertebral column has experienced trauma?
Lumbar.

Nick enjoys snacking on cookies and a whole milk during his breaks at work. What hormone stimulates the production of milk?
Milk production is stimulated by prolactin, which is secreted by the pituitary gland.

If Nick were to stay in the cold too long, his body temperature may drop to unsafe levels. What is this condition known as?
Hypothermia.

23. Helmets are used to protect the head and brain from injury. What injury can occur when there is a blow to the head that may result in loss of consciousness?
A blow to the head with potential loss of consciousness is known as a concussion.

What bones in the skull produce a natural helmet for the body, providing protection for the brain?
The bones of the cranium: the frontal, temporal, parietal, and occipital bones.

The quarterback has to tell the other players what the play will be. What structure in the throat is responsible for producing sound used for speech?
The larynx, also known as the voice box.

After being blocked by Ross, the linebacker finds himself lying flat on his back. What body position is the linebacker in?
The linebacker is in the supine position.

The running back sprints down the field as he approaches the end zone. What actions are the running back's ankles performing as he runs?
Plantarflexion and dorsiflexion.

When celebrating, Ross sits on other players' shoulders. What is the scientific name of the shoulder joint, and what kind of synovial joint is it?
The shoulder joint is also known as the glenohumeral joint(where the glenoid fossa joins with the humerus), and it is a ball-and-socket joint.

24. Which cranial nerve is responsible for sight?
The optic nerve.

Which bones in the fingers are used on the keys when typing?
The distal phalanges.

What curvature does the cervical vertebrae have, and what can happen to this curvature if Brianna does not correct this posture?
The cervical vertebrae has a lordotic curvature. If the posture is not corrected, the cervical curvature can straighten, which stretches the posterior neck muscles.

Rounding of the shoulders may result in which condition?
Kyphosis.

Which hormone regulates the body's circadian rhythm, also known as the wake/sleep cycle, and which gland produces it?
Melatonin, which is produced by the pineal gland.

25. If Owen's face were exposed to the cold for an extended period of time, what may form in the soft tissues of his face, and what is that condition known as?
Ice crystals may form, which can damage tissue if present over an extended period. This is known as frostbite.

Pain is detected by which sensory receptor?
Nociceptors.

What path does the hot chocolate take on its way through Owen's digestive tract, ending at the stomach?
Hot chocolate enters into the oral cavity. When it is swallowed, it enters the pharynx. From the pharynx, it moves into the esophagus, and then empties from the esophagus into the stomach.

Snowboarding is typically performed at higher altitudes. What does the body consume less of at higher altitudes, and what condition is this similar to in regards to systemic function?
The body is not able to consume as much oxygen at higher altitudes due to less oxygen being present in the atmosphere. When the body isn't able to consume adequate oxygen, it is similar to anemia.

26. Assessing a person's walking pattern is known as what?
Gait analysis.

What muscle is responsible for inhalation?
The diaphragm.

Hip flexion plays an important role in walking. What are four muscles that perform flexion of the hip?
Hip flexion is performed by rectus femoris, sartorius, iliacus, and psoas major.

How many phalangeal bones are in each foot?
There are 14 phalangeal bones in each foot.

What type of protein produces hair?
Hair is produced by keratin.

27. What injury did Carl likely sustain?
Carl likely experienced whiplash.

Is this injury a contraindication for massage, and if so, what kind of contraindication?
In the acute stage, whiplash is a local contraindication for massage.

Traffic collisions and sports are the most common ways people tear the strongest ligament in the knee responsible for holding the tibia and femur together. What is this ligament?
While there are several ligaments that hold the tibia and femur together, the anterior cruciate ligament is the strongest of these, and is more prone to tearing due to sports or traffic collisions.

A seatbelt is buckled near the hip joint. What is the scientific name of the hip joint, and what kind of synovial joint is it?
The hip joint, where the femur and pelvis come together, is known as the acetabulofemoral or coxal joint. This joint is a ball-and-socket joint.

In a traffic collision, contusions may occur. What is a contusion, is a contusion contraindicated, and if so, what kind kind of contraindication is it?
A contusion is a form of internal bleeding caused by damage to blood vessels, which most commonly presents in the skin. A contusion is also known as a bruise. A contusion is a local contraindication due to the possible presence of blood clots in the area.

28. When the body is placed under stress, which division of the autonomic nervous system is activated?
The sympathetic response is activated when the body is under stress. This response is also known as "fight-or-flight".

What hormones specifically are released in a stress response, and what are effects of these hormones on the body?
The primary hormones released when in a stress response are epinephrine and norepinephrine. These hormones help to elevate heart rate, blood pressure, and blood sugar.

What condition might Colin have that results in a lack of sleep?
Colin may be experiencing insomnia.

Is this condition contraindicated for massage, and if so, what kind of contraindication is it? If not, what techniques and other elements should be utilized to help Colin?
Insomnia is not contraindicated for massage. A person who suffers from insomnia should receive a lighter, more relaxing massage to help calm the body and help it rest. Massage may also reduce stress hormones in the body, which can allow Colin to potentially have restful sleep. Essential oils may also be helpful, specifically oils that have a calming effect such as lavender.

Increased consumption of carbohydrates and caffeine may lead to which health complications?
Diabetes may result with excessive consumption of carbohydrates. Excessive caffeine may lead to the development of hypertension.

29. Blood consists of what four basic components?
Blood is made of erythrocytes, leukocytes, thrombocytes, and plasma.

Which component makes up the majority of blood, and what is its main function?
The majority of blood, roughly 56%, is plasma. Plasma is the fluid portion of blood, and is responsible for transporting blood cells, hormones, nutrients, and waste products throughout the body.

Coagulation of blood is performed by which blood cell?
Thrombocytes, or platelets.

What protein does oxygen and carbon dioxide attach to, allowing these molecules to be transported throughout the body?
Oxygen and carbon dioxide attach to hemoglobin, a protein made of iron found in the cytoplasm of erythrocytes.

If Alucard's father obtains too much "Bloody Mary mix" from another person, what condition may the person experience due to blood loss?
The person may experience anemia due to blood loss.

30. What insect is likely attached to Pierre?
There is likely a deer tick feasting on Pierre's blood.

What type of infection, and subsequent medical condition, can the insect spread to Pierre?
Ticks may cause a person to contract a bacterial infection. This infection can result in the development of Lyme disease.

What kind of rash may a person experience around the bite location?
The rash is known as a bullseye rash, because it is in a circular manner with a lighter area around the site of the bite and a darker area in the more peripheral area of infection.

Certain people may be allergic to tall grass. What may the body produce in response to allergens, which cause blood vessels to dilate?
Histamines are responsible for dilating blood vessels, allowing more blood and interstitial fluid to enter in to an area.

Sunlight exposure causes the skin to produce what nutrient?
Vitamin D.

31. What are the primary actions performed by the hip when a person is riding a bicycle?
While riding a bicycle, the hip mainly performs flexion and extension.

What are the primary actions performed by the knee when a person is riding a bicycle?
While riding a bicycle, the knee mainly performs flexion and extension.

Riding a bicycle, along with many other exercises, can increase the production of what substance, used to decrease body temperature?
Sweat is produced by sudoriferous glands. Sweat evaporates off the skin, which helps cool the body and lower body temperature.

Exercise can temporarily increase blood pressure. In a blood pressure reading of 130/85, what does the higher number represent, and what is specifically being measured that determines the number given?
The higher number presented in a blood pressure reading is the systolic pressure. This number represents the pressure felt in the walls of arteries as blood passes through them, or when the heart beats.

What number does water measure as on a pH scale?
Water is considered neutral, neither acidic nor alkaline, and therefore is 7 on a pH scale. If a substance is higher than 7, it is considered alkaline, such as blood(7.4). If a substance is lower than 7 on a pH scale, it is acidic, such as coffee(5).

32. What medical condition is Ashley likely experiencing?
Ashley is likely experiencing a migraine headache.

What are triggers that may contribute to this condition occurring?
Triggers vary from person to person, but common triggers include smoke, stress, nitrates, or in this case, tyramine. Tyramine is a substance that can be found in wine, aged cheese, and cured meats.

What structures in the body are specifically causing Ashley to experience pain?
Extracranial blood vessels are dilating and placing pressure on the meninges, which is causing the intense pain.

Wine contains alcohol, which increases the production of what substance in the body?
Alcohol is a form of diuretic, which causes the body to produce more urine.

When a person is seated in a chair, what position are the hips in?
The hips are in flexion when a person is seated in a chair.

33. The ocean contains a high concentration of which substance, an extremely important electrolyte in the body?
Sodium chloride, or salt.

Excessive exposure to sunlight over a short period may result in what?
The most common form of first degree burn, a sunburn.

Excessive exposure to sunlight over a long period of time, in some cases years, may result in the development of what?
Excessive sun exposure may result in the development of cancers such as basal cell carcinoma, squamous cell carcinoma, and malignant melanoma.

Medications that are designed to lower body temperature in cases such as fever are known as?
Antipyretics.

What are the three stages of "injury" a person may experience if their body temperature is too high for too long?
Heat cramps, heat exhaustion, and heat stroke.

34. Julius uses a hammer. What muscle is primarily responsible for performing the action of hammering?
Brachioradialis, which flexes the elbow with the hand in neutral position.

What muscles perform extension of the hip, the primary action used when pushing an object?
Semimembranosus, semitendinosus, biceps femoris, and gluteus maximus all perform extension of the hip.

What muscle is known as the "swimmer's muscle" due to its actions, which are performed when a person swims?
Latissimus dorsi.

What specific actions do the "swimmer's muscle" perform?
Latissimus dorsi performs extension, medial rotation, and adduction of the shoulder.

35. Holding a phone with the shoulder and ear produces what type of muscle contraction to be performed?
The sustained holding of the phone with the ear and shoulder produces an isometric contraction of the muscles involved in performing this action.

What muscle, which is part of the anterior triangle of the neck, may be strained from performing this action excessively?
Sternocleidomastoid, which rotates the head to the opposite side and laterally flexes the head/neck.

Becky asking Jenny to rotate and laterally flex her head/neck is part of what aspect of the massage session?
Assessment. Becky is asking Jenny to perform range-of-motion to help determine what restrictions in movement Jenny may be experiencing, which can help Becky form an effective treatment.

Jenny lies under the top sheet on the massage table. This is known as what, and what is the primary reason for this?
This is known as draping, which is used to establish boundaries between the therapist and the client.

Jenny deferring to Becky on preferred areas to be massaged due to Becky's perceived expertise, and apologizing for coughing may be a sign of what occurring?
This may be a sign of transference, in which a client views the massage therapist similarly to a person in their personal or early life. In this case, Jenny views Becky as an authority figure, and is looking for approval and guidance from Becky in regards to her massage treatment. This can happen when there is a power differential between the client and therapist.

Individual Subject Practice Test Answer Keys

Massage Therapy	Assessment	Business	Ethics
01. A	01. B	01. B	01. D
02. B	02. C	02. D	02. A
03. C	03. D	03. B	03. B
04. B	04. A	04. C	04. D
05. D	05. C	05. A	05. C
06. A	06. D	06. A	06. D
07. C	07. C	07. D	07. C
08. A	08. B	08. B	08. D
09. B	09. D	09. C	09. B
10. C	10. C	10. C	10. A
11. D	11. A	11. D	11. C
12. B	12. B	12. D	12. A
13. D	13. A	13. A	13. A
14. A	14. C	14. C	14. B
15. A	15. A	15. A	15. D
16. C	16. D	16. C	16. B
17. D	17. A	17. B	17. B
18. C	18. D	18. D	18. C
19. D	19. B	19. A	19. A
20. B	20. A	20. C	20. C
21. A	21. B	21. D	21. C
22. A	22. C	22. C	22. A
23. C	23. C	23. B	23. B
24. D	24. D	24. A	24. D
25. B	25. C	25. D	25. C

Medical Terminology	Anatomy and Physiology	Pathology	Kinesiology
01. A	01. C	01. A	01. C
02. D	02. D	02. D	02. D
03. A	03. A	03. B	03. A
04. C	04. D	04. B	04. C
05. D	05. A	05. D	05. A
06. C	06. A	06. C	06. D
07. A	07. B	07. D	07. B
08. C	08. D	08. A	08. C
09. C	09. B	09. A	09. D
10. D	10. C	10. C	10. C
11. A	11. A	11. D	11. B
12. B	12. C	12. C	12. A
13. B	13. B	13. A	13. B
14. C	14. D	14. D	14. D
15. D	15. C	15. C	15. C
16. A	16. C	16. A	16. A
17. D	17. A	17. C	17. D
18. B	18. D	18. B	18. A
19. C	19. C	19. D	19. B
20. B	20. B	20. B	20. C
21. D	21. A	21. A	21. D
22. A	22. D	22. C	22. A
23. B	23. C	23. A	23. D
24. C	24. A	24. B	24. B
25. D	25. B	25. D	25. C

Full Length Practice Tests

Welcome to the full length practice test section of the book! This is one of the most important parts of the study guide. This is where you get to finally put your knowledge to use and see what you know, what you don't know, what you need to study more of, and most importantly, using your test-taking techniques!

Just be aware: THESE ARE NOT THE EXACT SAME QUESTIONS YOU WILL SEE ON THE MBLEx. I DO NOT WORK FOR, NOR HAVE ANY ASSOCIATION WITH THE FSMTB OR HAVE ANY INSIGHT INTO THE QUESTIONS ASKED ON THE EXAM. These questions were created by me, and only me!

These questions test you on the material you MAY see on the exam! There are even questions in these practice tests covering information not seen in this study guide. Just like the MBLEx, you will have questions on things you've never seen or learned before. This is where your test-taking techniques come in! Practice answering questions on things you've never learned before and it can help you do the exact same thing on the MBLEx! If you're tested on information you've never seen before, look it up! Learn about that information, and if that information comes up on the MBLEx, you'll be even more prepared!

These practice tests have the equivalent content that you will see on the MBLEx. Each test has 11 Anatomy and Physiology questions, 12 Kinesiology questions, 14 Pathology questions, 15 Benefits of Massage questions, 17 Assessment questions, 16 Ethics questions, and 15 Guidelines for Professional Practice questions. Some of these questions cross between subjects, for example, you may have a question that can be both pathology and assessment related. I've created the tests this way to help prepare you for the varied content you will see on the MBLEx.

On the MBLEx, you may have questions giving you scenarios involving clients, therapists, coworkers, etc, and it expects you to deconstruct the situation and give the appropriate answer. Some of these questions may involve legal scenarios where a person may be potentially breaking the law. The easiest way to approach these ethical and legal question is simple. Just ask yourself, "If I wanted to keep my job or license, what would I do?" It can't get much easier than that! Some questions will of course ask the most appropriate response to specific clients who display defense mechanisms, how to communicate with clients, and other ethical situations. A good strategy for these questions is to ask yourself "How would I want to be treated?" or "What would I do if I were in the client's shoes?" Remember, clients are trusting us as massage therapists to treat them with kindness, respect, and with care. In turn, we as massage therapists expect the same from the clients, to be treated with kindness, respect, and care. How do we foster and build these relationships with our clients? How do we maintain these relationships with our clients? Think of these when answering ethics-based questions.

What I always recommend my students do while taking their exams is, if they have access to a piece of paper, write down as many test-taking techniques as they can remember before trying to answer any questions. This way, while they're taking the MBLEx, they can look at their test-taking techniques and remind themselves to do them. Write things down like: Take your time, don't change answers, identify key words, eliminate answers, stay relaxed, and read the entire question. On the page to your right, you will see an example page that I have created for you to use. Make photocopies of this page and utilize it while taking the full-length practice tests. See if you can take notes on things you may need help remembering later on in the test. See if you can successfully draw structures in the body for reference. Write down any acronyms like "SITS"(supraspinatus, infraspinatus, teres minor, subscapularis) or mnemonic devices such as "Some Lovers Try Positions That They Can't Handle"(scaphoid, lunate, triquetrum, pisiform, trapezium, trapezoid, capitate, hamate). Spend a small amount of time preparing this document, and it will give you a chance to calm down, relax, and be even more prepared for the exam than before. Use all the tools at your disposal! You don't want to leave the test thinking "would I have passed if I had used that piece of paper?"

A common theme I see with students is a fear of taking the test. The test cannot hurt you. I do understand a fear of not succeeding, however, there are much better ways to view the test. This is the test you attended school to pass. This is the test that will help grant you licensure. This is a test you should be excited for! Here's how I've always approached important tests: when it comes time to test, I know what I know, I have become exceptionally adept at taking tests due to my use of test-taking techniques, and if I pass, awesome! If I don't pass, of course I'm not satisfied, but I know I can take the test again, and I immediately look at the test I just took as the best practice test I can ever take. I now have experience with the test, I know how the questions are worded, I know the kind of information the test is looking for, I still have my notes and I can go back and highlight every piece of information from the test that I recognize to ensure I study it more thoroughly just in case I get those questions on my test again, and I will be even more prepared the next time I take the test. Just because you don't pass the test doesn't mean you have failed. If you don't pass, do not get discouraged, get motivated to conquer it the next time! Preparing for the test isn't just going over information, it's also about your mindset, and your willingness to overcome the obstacle in front of you. Vince Lombardi, former professional football head coach, once said "I firmly believe that any man's finest hour, the greatest fulfillment of all that he holds dear, is that moment when he has worked his heart out in a good cause and lies exhausted on the field of battle, victorious." It's worth the time, it's worth the effort, it's worth the struggle to come out of the test victorious. I believe in you. Believe in yourself, and you can accomplish your goals.

For a reminder of your test-taking techniques, refer to page 4.

Make a photocopy of this page for use with every practice test you take! When you take the MBLEx, replicate this page on your own scratch paper provided by the testing center and put it to use!

Test-Taking Tips:
Read the entire question
Read all the answers
Identify key words
Eliminate answers
Take your time
Don't change answers
Breathe and stay relaxed

Important Information Found For Reference

_____
_____
_____
_____
_____
_____
_____

_____
_____
_____
_____
_____
_____
_____
_____
_____
_____
_____
_____

Additional Notes

Illustrations

Practice Test 1

1. Which best describes the function of the epiglottis
A. Allows food and liquid to move from the pharynx into the esophagus
B. Prevents food and liquid from moving into the larynx upon swallowing
C. Allows food and liquid to move from the mouth into the pharynx
D. Prevents food and liquid from moving from the pharynx into the nasal sinus

2. A client states they are under the care of a physician who has referred them to a physical therapist to rehabilitate a soft tissue injury. The massage therapist suggests to the client that SOAP notes could be shared between the massage therapist, physical therapist, and physician to provide the client with a clearer path to recovery. What would the client need to sign for the massage therapist to share the SOAP notes with the client's healthcare team
A. Authorization form
B. Standards of conduct form
C. Informed consent form
D. Health history form

3. Medical procedure used to remove waste products and toxic substances from the blood when the kidneys are unable to function properly
A. Dialysis
B. Electrolysis
C. Paracentesis
D. Transfusion

4. Muscle primarily responsible for supination of the forearm
A. Triceps brachii
B. Brachioradialis
C. Brachialis
D. Biceps brachii

5. Which of the following is an example of an asset of a massage business
A. Accounting fees
B. A music subscription
C. Money dedicated to digital advertising
D. A hydraulic massage table

6. During a massage, the massage therapist performs tapotement to aid in loosening phlegm in the respiratory tract. If loosening of phlegm is accomplished, what has occurred
A. A psychological effect of massage has occurred
B. A mechanical effect of massage has occurred
C. A reflexive effect of massage has occurred
D. A physiological effect of massage has occurred

7. Pain experienced at the glenohumeral joint upon extension may be the result of an injury to which of the following muscles
A. Supraspinatus
B. Triceps brachii
C. Biceps brachii
D. Coracobrachialis

8. Licensing regulations detail the activities a massage therapist may engage in for their practice. These are known as
A. Business standards
B. Regulations
C. Scope of practice
D. Liabilities

9. Which of the following massage strokes is best in releasing metabolic waste from tissues
A. Petrissage
B. Effleurage
C. Vibration
D. Tapotement

10. Reddening and increased heat of the skin as the result of a massage
A. Varicose veins
B. Anemia
C. Hyperemia
D. Phlebitis

11. Carpal tunnel syndrome affects which nerve of the brachial plexus
A. Radial
B. Femoral
C. Median
D. Axillary

12. Anatomical law which states soft tissue will change length and strengthen under specific amounts of load or tension
A. Davis's Law
B. Hilton's Law
C. Wolff's Law
D. Campbell's Law

13. If a client experiences lower back pain due to a hypertonic psoas major while in the prone position, a bolster should be placed
A. Under the knees
B. Under the hips
C. Under the ankles
D. Under the shoulders

14. Which of the following massage strokes is best in increasing venous circulation
A. Vibration
B. Effleurage
C. Tapotement
D. Petrissage

15. Light touch massage used to increase the flow of cerebrospinal fluid from the base of the vertebral column to the skull, which aids in treatment of many medical conditions
A. Osteosymmetry
B. Orthobionomy
C. Cryotherapy
D. Craniosacral Therapy

16. Sports massage is primarily used to increase
A. Circulation
B. Inhalation
C. Excretion
D. Respiration

17. A client is referred to a massage therapist by a physical therapist to help with increasing range-of-motion and structural stability in the back. The client presents with a hunched appearance. After ten sessions, the massage therapist assesses the client's range-of-motion in the back compared to their first appointment. There seems to be no change. The client seems displeased with a lack of progress. Which of the following is not an appropriate response to the lack of progress by the massage therapist
A. Research stretches that haven't been performed on the client before
B. Refer the client to another massage therapist who may specialize in more structural work
C. Refer the client to a therapist who specializes in energy modalities
D. Communicate with the client's physical therapist to determine future treatment modifications

18. A massage therapist is working on a client when they reach the client's thigh. The client begins breathing more rapidly and shaking. The therapist asks the client if everything is okay, and the client doesn't respond, but visual cues on the client's face indicate that they are not okay. What is the client experiencing
A. An emotional release
B. Transference
C. A dual relationship
D. A physical boundary

19. Massage stroke designed to stimulate muscle spindle activity, especially useful in pre-event sports massage
A. Effleurage
B. Petrissage
C. Friction
D. Tapotement

20. Determining potential customer volume, money spent in specific locations and on specific products, and information on competitors is detailed in which aspect of business planning
A. Market analysis
B. Mission statement
C. Financial planning
D. Accounts payable

21. Essential oil commonly used to aid in relaxation of smooth muscles in the respiratory tract
A. Lavender
B. Eucalyptus
C. Grapefruit
D. Peppermint

22. A statement given under oath and outside of court, used to determine what the person specifically knows about the case, and to document testimony for trial
A. Mediation
B. Subpoena
C. Deposition
D. Arbitration

23. Gross income minus expenses deducted results in
A. Net worth
B. State income
C. Net income
D. Federal income

24. Wheezing accompanied by progressive loss of function due to alveolar degeneration in the lungs may be a sign of
A. Asthma
B. Acute bronchitis
C. Pleurisy
D. Emphysema

25. Money owed to another company, such as credit card debt
A. Accounts payable
B. Financial planning
C. Accounts receivable
D. Corporate taxes

26. Measurable information is detailed in which section of SOAP notes
A. Subjective
B. Objective
C. Assessment
D. Plan

27. Mononucleosis, warts, and cold sores are all caused by
A. Virus
B. Fungus
C. Bacteria
D. Parasite

28. While performing posture analysis, the massage therapist notices the client's left ear is tilted slightly lower than the right ear. The therapists asks the client to perform lateral flexion of the head on the left side, and then the right side. The client is able to place their left ear to their left shoulder, but unable to place their right ear to the right shoulder. What can the massage therapist assume based on this information
A. The client may have hypertonicity in the scalenes on the right side
B. The client may have weakness in the sternocleidomastoid on the left side
C. The client may have hypertonicity in the splenius capitis on the left side
D. The client may have weakness in the scalenes on the left side

29. Which of the following is not a mechanical effect of massage therapy
A. Loosening of fascia
B. Removal of waste such as lactic acid from tissue
C. Temporary localized ischemia during compression
D. Production and release of melatonin

30. A massage therapist has been working for a local spa for two years, developing a decently sized clientele. The therapist thinks they should be making more money and increasing their clientele size, so they opt to put in an application at another spa a mile from their current employer, hoping to work at both locations. If the massage therapist were to be hired, what might this be considered
A. Nepotism
B. Boundaries violation
C. Dual relationship
D. Conflict of interest

31. Upon dilation of blood vessels in the inflammatory response, the following type of cell moves into the location to destroy bacteria and debris
A. Leukocytes
B. Thrombocytes
C. Erythrocytes
D. Osteoclasts

32. Proprioceptive neuromuscular facilitation utilizes what specific kind of contraction before the secondary stretch
A. Concentric
B. Isometric
C. Eccentric
D. Isotonic

33. The widest muscle in the body is
A. Latissimus dorsi
B. Pectoralis major
C. Trapezius
D. Rectus abdominis

34. Which of the following is not a characteristic of muscle tissue
A. Extensibility
B. Excitability
C. Contractability
D. Protectability

35. A client complains of numbness in the fingers and hands. After doing visual assessment, the therapist notices pallor in the fingers, but nowhere else on the limb. What would be an appropriate treatment modification for this client
A. Increase room temperature
B. Perform PNF on the shoulder
C. Avoid the affected area
D. Apply trigger point therapy to the deltoid

36. Attack of the epithelial cells of the skin by the body's immune system results in
A. Rosacea
B. Acne
C. Psoriasis
D. Systemic lupus

37. An independent contractor receives which tax form from the contracting party for income over $600
A. Schedule K1
B. 1099
C. W-2
D. Schedule C

38. A client and massage therapist are conversing during a massage treatment. The client begins detailing their thoughts on religion. The massage therapist responds in kind, explaining how they view religion and the differences between various faiths. What is this an example of
A. Semi-permeable boundary
B. Permeable boundary
C. Impermeable boundary
D. Permeable-impermeable boundary

39. An injury to the gracilis would partially inhibit which actions
A. Hip flexion, knee extension
B. Hip abduction, knee flexion
C. Hip adduction, knee flexion
D. Hip extension, knee extension

40. Massage produces what effect on blood vessels
A. Decreases the size of blood vessel lumen
B. Develops new blood vessels
C. Increases the size of blood vessel lumen
D. Breaks down blood vessel walls

41. A massage therapist gives a diabetic client a massage. After the massage, the client tells the massage therapist that they feel light headed and dizzy, and feel extremely tired. In this instance, what should a massage therapist do
A. Ask the client to lie down on the massage table and take a nap
B. Ask the client where they keep their insulin, and inject them with insulin to lower blood sugar
C. Lie the client on the floor and immediately call for an ambulance to administer aid
D. Ask the client to sit and provide the client with something to consume with sugar such as fruit juice

42. Shortening of the tibialis anterior can be achieved with the following actions
A. Dorsiflexion and eversion
B. Plantarflexion and inversion
C. Dorsiflexion and inversion
D. Plantarflexion and eversion

43. During an assessment, the massage therapist requests to view the soles of the client's shoes. Upon viewing the soles, the therapist observes obvious wear on the medial side of the shoe's sole. This may be indicative of hypertonicity in which of the following muscles
A. Tibialis anterior
B. Peroneus longus
C. Popliteus
D. Gastrocnemius

44. Cranial nerve with three branches, inserting into the eye socket, the nose and upper teeth, and mandible
A. Zygomatic
B. Facial
C. Trigeminal
D. Hypoglossal

45. Pain experienced at the acetabulofemoral joint upon extension may be the result of an injury to which of the following muscles
A. Iliopsoas
B. Adductor longus
C. Sartorius
D. Semitendinosus

46. All of the following are proper forms of time boundaries except
A. Working on a client for the time the client is paying for
B. Having specific days put aside for non-work
C. Not beginning or ending the massage session at the scheduled time
D. Charging the client if they no-show an appointment

47. A protrusion of the nucleus pulposus from its normal location through the annulus fibrosis
A. Hiatal hernia
B. Herniated disc
C. Subluxation
D. Spondylitis

48. A massage therapist's client is suing their doctor for negligence. The client states to the court that the doctor recommended massage therapy for the client's condition, despite the condition being contraindicated for massage therapy. The massage therapist is issued a subpoena duces tecum by the court. What is required of the massage therapist after receiving this writ
A. The massage therapist must appear in court and testify in front of a judge
B. The massage therapist must give a statement outside of court for use in court proceedings
C. The massage therapist must appear in court and submit documentation as evidence
D. The massage therapist must allow inspectors to view the massage therapist's office

49. A client arrives for a massage, stating they have had a persistent cough for four weeks that they can't seem to get rid of. The massage therapist asks the client if they are experiencing any other symptoms. The client says they have also experienced fever, chills, and had bloody coughs that they contribute to the amount of coughing they are doing damaging the airways. Which of the following is a medical condition the therapist should suspect, and what would be the prime cause of the condition
A. Tuberculosis, caused by bacterial infection
B. Influenza, caused by viral infection
C. Laryngitis, caused by viral infection
D. Emphysema, caused by destruction of alveoli

50. Tearing of a muscle is considered a
A. Sprain
B. Strain
C. Contracture
D. Subluxation

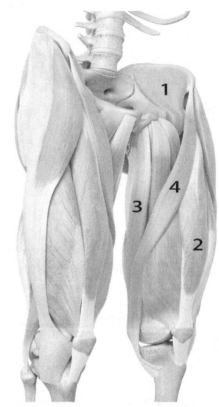

51. Which numbered muscle inserts onto the lesser trochanter
A. 2
B. 4
C. 3
D. 1

52. Streptococcal infection which enters the body through wounds, resulting in infection of the skin and surrounding tissues
A. Rosacea
B. Cellulitis
C. Cold sore
D. Boil

53. What format should a TIN be written when submitting documentation to a court or the IRS
A. 123-45-6789
B. XXX-XX-XXXX
C. XXX-12-3456
D. 123-45-XXXX

54. Three of the four rotator cuff muscles insert onto the greater tubercle of the humerus. The only one that does not is
A. Subscapularis
B. Supraspinatus
C. Infraspinatus
D. Teres minor

55. Massage stroke consisting of kneading strokes, used to break up adhesions between tissues and increase local circulation
A. Friction
B. Petrissage
C. Effleurage
D. Tapotement

56. All of the following muscles attach to either the medial or lateral lip of the bicipital groove except
A. Pectoralis major
B. Infraspinatus
C. Teres major
D. Latissimus dorsi

57. Unspoken communication, including posture, eye contact, and crossing the arms
A. Active listening
B. Body language
C. Self disclosure
D. Empathy

58. An ideal massage lubricant should be
A. Petroleum-based
B. Hypoallergenic
C. Mineral-based
D. Perfume scented

59. Goals are
A. A generalized statement about the purpose of a business
B. The theme of a business
C. Measurable or attainable accomplishments
D. Business plans detailing projected income

60. Pain in the lower back presenting with fever, nausea and vomiting may be a sign of
A. Gastritis
B. Hepatitis
C. Encephalitis
D. Pyelonephritis

61. Over the course of several months, a massage therapist sees a client on a regular basis, almost weekly. The therapist has begun developing a sexual attraction to the client. What should the massage therapist do in regards to the situation
A. Do not tell the client but keep booking with them
B. Admit the feelings to the client
C. Act on the urges
D. Refer the client to another therapist

62. Which of the following is likely irrelevant information to be listed on a client's medical history
A. Medical conditions the client has been diagnosed with
B. Conditions that may have periods of remission in which the client is not currently experiencing symptoms
C. Future surgeries or medical treatments the client is scheduled to receive
D. Medications the client is currently taking

63. Muscle inserting on the pes anserinus, responsible for flexing and externally rotating the hip, and flexing the knee
A. Gracilis
B. Semitendinosus
C. Biceps femoris
D. Sartorius

64. A self employed business owner reports gross income, net income, and deductions using which of the following tax forms
A. 1099
B. Schedule K1
C. W-2
D. Schedule C

65. The groin is also known as which body region
A. Inguinal
B. Antecubital
C. Thorax
D. Popliteal

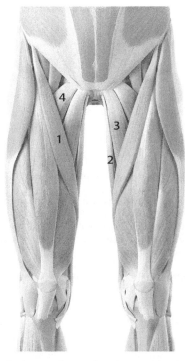

66. What action do the muscles numbered 2, 3, and 4 share
A. Hip extension
B. Hip adduction
C. Hip flexion
D. Hip lateral rotation

67. During a massage, the client states they are looking to buy a house. The massage therapist tells the client that they are selling their house, and invites them to come see the house later that day. Describe what could occur as a result of this interaction
A. Implied consent
B. Ethical dilemma
C. Dual relationship
D. Power differential

68. Stomach acid flowing from the stomach into the esophagus is a result of the following structure not functioning properly
A. Ileocecal sphincter
B. Esophageal sphincter
C. Pyloric sphincter
D. Cardiac sphincter

69. A client states they have recently participated in a double-blind study. Which best describes a double-blind study
A. A study in which neither the researcher or subjects know if the treatment is a placebo or not
B. A study in which the researchers and subjects are blindfolded and given a placebo
C. A study in which the subject unknowingly receives a placebo but the researcher is aware of the placebo being given
D. A study in which the subject is able to pick between an actual treatment and a placebo without the knowledge of the researcher

70. Mister Greene suffers from ankylosing spondylitis, which affects his intervertebral discs. If he were to schedule a massage appointment, the massage therapist would
A. Reschedule the massage until the condition has subsided
B. Perform the massage while avoiding the affected area
C. Perform the massage and do joint compression on the intervertebral discs
D. Perform the massage if the massage does not result in pain

71. The coronal suture connects the following bones of the cranium
A. Parietal and parietal
B. Parietal and frontal
C. Occipital and parietal
D. Temporal and parietal

72. The trapezium joins with the metacarpal of the thumb to create which synovial joint
A. Saddle
B. Pivot
C. Hinge
D. Condyloid

73. Action of spinalis on the vertebrae
A. Flexion and support
B. Rotation and flexion
C. Flexion and extension
D. Support and extension

74. All of the following may be appropriate reasons to ask a client to breathe during a client assessment except
A. To determine if the client is experiencing acute stages of asthma
B. To determine if the client is currently experiencing dyspnea
C. To determine if the client has recently received a massage treatment
D. To determine if the client may currently be in the sympathetic response and have increased respiration

75. The right hypochondriac region contains all of the following organs except
A. Gallbladder
B. Esophagus
C. Right kidney
D. Liver

76. Self-disclosure
A. The client sharing feelings and emotions during a massage session
B. The massage therapist sharing their feelings and emotions during a massage session
C. A massage therapist disclosing their scope of practice
D. A client viewing a massage therapist as they would a significant person in their early life

77. In a business setting, a massage therapist's credentials must be
A. Kept in a secure location away from sight
B. Posted in visibility of all clients
C. Posted beneath the massage table
D. Kept in the massage room, in a drawer

78. The coronoid process wrapping around the trochlea produces what joint
A. Elbow
B. Hip
C. Knee
D. Shoulder

79. In a pre-massage assessment, a client states that they have been experiencing pain in the ankle while walking for unknown reasons. They state the pain started a week prior, and don't recall a specific traumatic event that may have caused the pain to occur. Which of the following should the massage therapist do to properly assess the client's pain
A. Ask the client to perform range-of-motion on the opposite ankle
B. Ask the client to stretch the joint and watch for body language
C. Determine if the client is taking pain killers to deal with the pain
D. Ask the client to rate their pain from 1-10 on a pain scale

80. What personal information is usually listed on a W-2
A. The independent contractor's full name and address
B. The name of the business owner and their home address
C. The employee's full name, address, and complete social security number
D. The amount the business made and royalties paid out to the contracted associate

81. Which of the following accurately describes malignant melanoma
A. Most common, least serious, slowest growing form of skin cancer
B. Most common, most serious, fastest growing form of skin cancer
C. Least common, most serious, fastest growing form of skin cancer
D. Least common, least serious, slowest growing form of skin cancer

82. Professional liability insurance protects the massage therapist in lawsuits arising in instances such as
A. Malpractice
B. Overbooking
C. Accidental falls by the client
D. Repetitive strain injuries

83. A client calls a massage therapist to schedule a massage for later in the day. During the conversation, they indicate to the therapist that they are currently experiencing a low grade fever and chills due an infection of influenza. They ensure the therapist that they feel fine, and insist on coming in that day. What is an appropriate response on behalf of the massage therapist
A. The therapist should explain to the client that influenza is an absolute contraindication for massage, and they will need to schedule the massage for later in the future to ensure the condition has passed
B. The therapist should book the client for an appointment later that day and perform tapotement to help loosen phlegm built up in the chest
C. The therapist should book the client for an appointment the next day, and utilize cold packs to help lower the client's body temperature
D. The therapist should book the client for an appointment the next day, and tell the client they need to take a dose of an antipyretic before coming in to the massage to lower their fever

84. Blood flowing backwards in the heart between chambers due to decrease in function of valves
A. Bradycardia
B. Arrhythmia
C. Heart murmur
D. Ventricular septal defect

85. Areas of the body in which caution is advised during massage of a pregnant client include all of the following except
A. Abdomen
B. Face
C. Ankle
D. Lumbar

86. HIPAA was enacted in order to
A. Inform the client of all relevant information about the service or treatment being given
B. Ensure a good samaritan can administer aid to a person in need without fear of litigation
C. Protect the client from having medical information and confidentiality breached
D. Give healthcare providers the ability to perform treatments on persons without their express consent

87. Sympathy is best described as
A. A person feeling compassion or pity for the other person and the situation they are in
B. A person puts themselves in the shoes of another, viewing a situation from the other person's point of view
C. A person actively listening to another person, asking questions and giving feedback when warranted
D. A person passively listening to another person, not responding but taking in information and possibly documenting the information

88. A step backwards psychologically when faced with stress is known as
A. Regression
B. Displacement
C. Denial
D. Repression

89. A client who suffers from pitting edema would most likely be referred to which specialist after consulting a physician
A. Dermatologist
B. Nephrologist
C. Gastroenterologist
D. Cardiologist

90. Abduction of the shoulder can be accomplished by a concentric contraction of which muscle
A. Coracobrachialis
B. Supraspinatus
C. Infraspinatus
D. Pectoralis major

91. Glucagon, produced by the pancreas, is an enzyme responsible for
A. Increasing glucose levels in the blood
B. Increasing potassium levels in the blood
C. Decreasing potassium levels in the blood
D. Decreasing glucose levels in the blood

92. A client seeks a massage appointment after visiting their primary physician, who has indicated the client has pre-hypertension and a blood pressure reading of 133/87. If during the course of massage and after the massage the client's blood pressure lowers, what occurs
A. A psychological effect occurs
B. A mechanical effect occurs
C. A reflexive effect occurs
D. A sympathetic effect occurs

93. A client states on an intake form that they are currently prescribed a thrombolytic. What are thrombolytics used for
A. Preventing the formation of blood clots
B. Increase the production of fibrin to assist in blood clot formation
C. Increased production of blood clots
D. Destroying blood clots

94. Describe in order the positions of the right ankle, left knee, right hip, left shoulder, and right elbow
A. Plantarflexed, extended, flexed, flexed, flexed
B. Dorsiflexed, flexed, flexed, extended, extended
C. Dorsiflexed, extended, flexed, flexed, extended
D. Plantarflexed, extended, extended, flexed, extended

95. In medicolegal terms, "pro bono" refers to
A. An employer being legally responsible for the actions of an employee
B. Work performed without compensation
C. A statement given under oath outside of court
D. A plaintiff sets out to prove harm has occurred that would not have without negligence

96. A client notifies a massage therapist that they have a small area of skin affected by cellulitis. The appropriate response by the massage therapist would be
A. Reschedule the massage until the cellulitis has completely cleared up
B. Avoid the affected area but continue massaging the rest of the body
C. Work on the affected area to help break up fat deposits under the skin
D. Apply heat to the affected area to allow increased circulation to enter the area

97. Wearing a clean uniform, brushing teeth daily, keeping fingernails trimmed and clean, and not smoking during a massage shift are all important aspects of
A. Professional care
B. Licensing requirements
C. Scope of practice
D. Personal hygiene

98. If a client suffers from menopause, an ideal essential oil to use during treatment is
A. Lavender
B. Peppermint
C. Ginger
D. Lemongrass

99. All of the following are the result of bacterial infection except
A. Emphysema
B. Tuberculosis
C. Strep throat
D. Pneumonia

100. During the course of a massage, a massage therapist discovers a client's right scapula is slightly elevated in relation to the left scapula. This information would be documented under which section of SOAP notes
A. Assessment
B. Plan
C. Objective
D. Subjective

Answer Key on Page 346

Practice Test 2

1. Before a massage session, a client notifies the massage therapist that they feel tightness in their hamstrings and it's causing pain in their thigh and leg. During the massage, the massage therapist moves the client's hip into flexion and their knee into extension, testing for range-of-motion, instructing the client to relax during the movements. Which of the following has occurred
A. The massage therapist has performed a passive joint movement on the client
B. The client and massage therapist have performed an active assistive joint movement
C. The client has performed an active joint movement
D. The client and massage therapist have performed resistive joint movements

2. The stomach is located in which abdominal quadrant
A. Lower right
B. Upper right
C. Upper left
D. Lower left

3. Which of the following types of gloves should a massage therapist avoid using in a session due to potential allergies to the material the therapist or client may have
A. Rubber
B. Vinyl
C. Nitrile
D. Latex

4. A client complains of numbness and tingling sensations in the arm. The limb is extremely difficult to use and very weak. It feels colder to the touch than other areas, and even exhibits a slight bluish tint. The most likely condition causing these symptoms is
A. Myocardial infarction
B. Thoracic outlet syndrome
C. Bell's palsy
D. Myasthenia gravis

5. Cartilage found surrounding the glenoid fossa which aids in structural support of the shoulder joint
A. Bicipital tendon
B. Labrum
C. Coracoid process
D. Acetabulum

6. A client sees a massage therapist twice monthly for a year. The client enjoys interacting with the therapist, and in the client's opinion, the conversation often becomes flirtatious. The client begins developing feelings for the massage therapist. During the next session, the client nervously proclaims their feelings for the massage therapist. What is the best response on behalf of the massage therapist
A. The massage therapist should refer the client to another massage therapist
B. The massage therapist should ask the client out to dinner
C. The massage therapist should explain that the client's behavior is inappropriate and will not be tolerated
D. The massage therapist should tell the client they feel the same way to keep the client booking appointments with them

7. The greater trochanter is the distal attachment site of the following muscle, responsible for abduction and lateral rotation of the hip
A. Pectineus
B. Sartorius
C. Piriformis
D. Gluteus maximus

8. The lambdoid suture is located between which cranial bones
A. Occipital and parietal
B. Parietal and frontal
C. Parietal and parietal
D. Temporal and parietal

9. Muscle responsible for stabilizing the glenohumeral joint and abduction of the shoulder
A. Subscapularis
B. Infraspinatus
C. Teres minor
D. Supraspinatus

10. Production of egg cells and sperm is maintained by the following hormone, produced by the pituitary gland
A. Follicle-stimulating hormone
B. Prolactin
C. Epinephrine
D. Lactogenic hormone

11. During a massage, a client becomes more relaxed and tired due to the pineal gland producing and secreting melatonin. What is happening as a result of the massage
A. A psychological effect is occurring
B. A mechanical effect is occurring
C. A reflexive effect is occurring
D. A sympathetic effect is occurring

12. A client who suffers from psoriasis schedules a massage. An appropriate treatment modification would be
A. Reschedule the massage as psoriasis is contagious
B. Working on the dry patches if pain or sores are not present
C. Avoiding the affected patches to not worsen them
D. Performing vigorous friction on the patches to exfoliate dead skin

13. A massage therapist greets their client for an upcoming appointment. The client enters the massage room with a slight limp. The massage therapist asks how everything is going, and the client replies "Fine." The client places more pressure on the right foot than the left while standing, and seem to be supporting themselves by placing a hand on the massage table. The client briefly grimaces when adjusting weight on the left foot. Which of the following is the client exhibiting
A. Self disclosure
B. Body language
C. Transference
D. Counter-transference

14. A client calls to make an appointment for a few weeks later. They communicate the date and time they'd like to the massage therapist, and the therapist checks their schedule and happily books the appointment. The date of the appointment arrives, and the client comes in for their massage. The massage therapist looks confused, checks their schedule, and does not see the appointment. After looking through the schedule some more, the therapist finds the client's appointment booked for the following month. The client shows their phone and the appointment in their calendar, scheduled for the correct date and time. What would be an appropriate response from the massage therapist
A. Ask the client to leave the massage establishment to avoid causing a scene
B. Call the next scheduled client and rebook that client to make room for the current client's appointment
C. Apologize for the mix-up, offer to schedule the client for the next available appointment and offer a slight discount for the inconvenience
D. Explain to the client that they were mistaken, and that the massage therapist booked the appointment on the correct date requested

15. The pattern or design of a massage treatment is known as
A. Contact
B. Process
C. Deliberation
D. Sequence

16. The esophagus, aorta, thoracic duct, and inferior vena cava all pass through
A. The pericardium
B. The diaphragm
C. The peritoneal membrane
D. The pleural cavity

17. Before a massage session, a massage therapist scrapes their hand on a sharp door edge, resulting in an abrasion with slight bleeding. What should the massage therapist do as a result of the injury
A. Properly clean the injury and the door, and wear a glove on the injured hand during the massage
B. Cleanse the wound with hydrogen peroxide and place a bandage on the wound, proceeding with the massage as normal
C. Reschedule the upcoming massage until the injury has completely healed
D. Ignore the injury and proceed as normal

18. A cancer spreading from one location in the body to another makes it
A. Asymmetrical
B. Asymptomatic
C. Malignant
D. Benign

19. Which of the following massage strokes is best in aiding lung decongestion
A. Vibration
B. Tapotement
C. Effleurage
D. Friction

20. A client arrives 15 minutes late for their scheduled 60 massage appointment, apologizing to the therapist, stating that traffic was bad and they got stuck behind an accident. All of the following are appropriate responses to the situation on the part of the massage therapist except
A. Offer to reschedule the client for another time
B. Give the client a 45 minute massage and charge the full amount
C. Offer to rebook the appointment as a 30 minute massage and only charge for 30 minutes
D. Reschedule the next client to make time for the late client

21. Generalized myalgia, localized muscle pain, and trouble sleeping could be the result of
A. Carpal tunnel syndrome
B. Fibromyalgia
C. Muscular dystrophy
D. Tendonitis

22. Rolfing aligns major body segments, known as
A. Structural realignment
B. Mentastics
C. Somatic holding pattern
D. Balance of body and mind

23. When dealing with a client who is experiencing some form of pain, which of the following is not a question the massage therapist should think of asking
A. Is the pain acute and localized in a specific area
B. How long has the pain been present or persisted
C. Is the pain widespread and experienced in multiple areas of the body
D. How many different types of opioids has the client taken for the pain

24. Lateral rotation of the shoulder is performed by which two rotator cuff muscles
A. Teres minor, infraspinatus
B. Supraspinatus, infraspinatus
C. Infraspinatus, teres major
D. Supraspinatus, subscapularis

25. A client experiences a decrease in the ability of the abdominal skin to move as freely after surgery months prior. The client does not experience pain, but slight discomfort due to the skin feeling "stuck in place". What is the appropriate response from the massage therapist
A. Perform the massage but avoid the abdomen, as there may be an underlying hernia that needs to be observed by a physician
B. Reschedule the massage and recommend the client seek out physical therapy to increase mobility in the abdomen and trunk
C. Perform the massage and specifically target the erector spinae muscles due to potential tightness causing a decrease in abdominal muscle function
D. Perform the massage and do cross-fiber and circular friction on the area of scarring to help loosen adhesions under the skin

26. Protein found inside of red blood cells, responsible for transporting oxygen and carbon dioxide throughout the body
A. Hemophilia
B. Mitochondria
C. Leukocyte
D. Hemoglobin

27. Which of the following arteries is responsible for providing the upper limb with oxygenated blood
A. Brachial
B. Femoral
C. Coronary
D. Subclavian

28. An injury to the adductor magnus muscle would make which movements more difficult to perform
A. Hip flexion, abduction, and extension
B. Hip flexion, adduction, and extension
C. Hip extension, abduction, and medial rotation
D. Hip flexion, abduction, and medial rotation

29. A spa manager receives several applications for an open massage therapist position. In the middle of the interview process, the manager receives a call from their cousin, who is a massage therapist, asking if they are looking for employees. The manager says yes, and immediately begins hiring paperwork for their cousin, opting to forego the rest of the scheduled interviews. What is this an example of
A. Good hiring practices
B. Conflict of interest
C. Counter-transference
D. Nepotism

30. Stretch technique in which a muscle is stretched to resistance, followed by an isometric contraction by the client, then the muscle stretched further after the contraction
A. Active static stretch
B. Proprioceptive neuromuscular facilitation
C. Strain counter-strain
D. Myofascial release

31. A massage therapist asks a client to perform a gait analysis. During the gait analysis, the massage therapist notices the client's right foot is in a slightly inverted position. To further check the therapist's observation, the therapist asks to view the client's shoe. What would be viewed on the shoe if the therapist's observations are correct
A. There would be more wear on the heel of the shoe
B. There would be more wear on the inner edge of the shoe
C. There would be more wear on the toe of the shoe
D. There would be more wear on the outer edge of the shoe

32. Primary synergist to latissimus dorsi, performing extension, adduction, and medial rotation of the shoulder
A. Teres minor
B. Trapezius
C. Teres major
D. Infraspinatus

33. Tennis elbow
A. Affects the flexors of the wrist, resulting in pain at the medial epicondyle of the humerus
B. Affects the adductors of the thigh, resulting in pain at the inguinal region
C. Affects the flexors of the shoulder, resulting in pain at the acromion process
D. Affects the extensors of the wrist, resulting in pain at the lateral epicondyle of the humerus

34. Superficial friction results in the following effect in the skin
A. Hyperemia
B. Regeneration
C. Atrophy
D. Hypoemia

35. Personalizing the therapeutic relationship between the client and the massage therapist on behalf of the client is known as
A. Counter-transference
B. Transference
C. Dual relationships
D. Boundaries

36. A client comes in for a massage, complaining of pain in the upper right trapezius and neck. The first thing a massage therapist should do in this situation is
A. Determine any causes of the pain
B. Ask the client if they are taking any medications for the pain
C. Ask the client to perform range-of-motion on the affected area
D. Palpate the area to locate any adhesions present

37. Degeneration of brain tissue, resulting in loss of memory and often dementia
A. Stroke
B. Cerebral palsy
C. Alzheimer's disease
D. Parkinson's disease

38. Form of friction in which the therapist utilizes small movements that go in a circular pattern through the tissue in order to loosen adhesions
A. Compression
B. Superficial friction
C. Cross-fiber friction
D. Circular friction

39. Massage technique targeting reflex points on the hands, feet, and ears to stimulate organs and tissue throughout the body
A. Trager method
B. Reflexology
C. Reiki
D. Mentastics

40. The external iliac artery
A. Brings blood to the inferior vena cava from the lower limbs
B. Supplies blood to the internal reproductive organs
C. Supplies blood to the thigh and leg
D. Emerges from the femoral artery

41. During a conversation while on the table, the client explains that their mother has recently passed, and they are feeling extremely overwhelmed by the situation. The therapist's own mother has passed within the past two years, so the therapist lets the client know that they too have experienced the same loss, and they understand what the client is going through. What is this an example of
A. Empathy
B. Passive listening
C. Sympathy
D. Self disclosure

42. Muscle inserting onto the base of the first metatarsal, responsible for eversion and plantarflexion of the foot
A. Tibialis posterior
B. Peroneus longus
C. Peroneus brevis
D. Tibialis anterior

43. During a verbal intake, a client states they experience pain while abducting the shoulder. The massage therapist asks the client to perform range-of-motion to test which muscle
A. Pectoralis major
B. Deltoid
C. Rhomboid major
D. Infraspinatus

44. Massage is generally helpful in reduction of all of the following except
A. Adhesions
B. Stress
C. Cortisol
D. Pain

45. Multiple sclerosis affects the
A. Brain and spinal cord
B. Cranial nerves
C. Median nerve
D. Lumbosacral plexus

46. Shaking or trembling movements used to sedate or stimulate a body part
A. Nerve stroke
B. Effleurage
C. Tapotement
D. Vibration

47. A bolster is placed between the legs and arms and under the head in which position
A. Side-lying
B. Supine
C. Prone
D. Semi-reclined

48. On an intake form, a therapist should notify the client of all office policies and procedures, and explain the process of the massage session. What section of an intake form should this information be presented under
A. Medical history
B. Informed consent
C. HIPAA
D. Insurance policy

49. A massage session ends, and the massage therapist instructs the client that they will step out of the room, and the client can take their time getting up and redressing. The therapist leaves the room, and the client immediately sits up. The client swings their legs off the side of the table, then tries standing, but ends up falling off the table because their feet are caught in the sheets. The client lands on their shoulder, feeling an intense pain in the joint. Which of the following help protect a massage therapist in their business practice in this incidence
A. General liability insurance
B. Professional liability insurance
C. Massage licensure and certification
D. Malpractice insurance

50. Goblet cells spread throughout cilia secrete which substance
A. Sebum
B. Ear wax
C. Sweat
D. Mucous

51. Abrupt stoppage of range-of-motion due to structures such as bone
A. Soft end feel
B. Empty end feel
C. Hard end feel
D. Nervous end feel

52. Statins are used to aid in combatting
A. Allergies
B. Trauma
C. Arrhythmia
D. Hypertension

53. Which of the following, with the client's permission, allows the client's health information to be shared between healthcare professionals so assessments and diagnoses do not need to be performed multiple times
A. HIPAA
B. Informed consent
C. Omnibus Reconciliation Act
D. TRICARE

54. If a massage therapist suspects a coworker of theft, what is the best response
A. Confront the coworker
B. Notify the police
C. Ignore the situation
D. Notify management

55. Actions of the pectoralis major include flexion of the shoulder, horizontal adduction of the shoulder, extension of the shoulder, and
A. Lateral rotation of the shoulder
B. Abduction of the shoulder
C. Medial rotation of the shoulder
D. Flexion of the elbow

56. Form of friction in which the massage therapist presses tissue down against deeper tissue to broaden or flatten the tissue
A. Circular friction
B. Compression
C. Superficial friction
D. Cross-fiber friction

57. Water, telephone, and linen service are all
A. Business arrangements
B. Business assets
C. Business property
D. Business expenses

58. Lymphatic drainage massage stimulates increased lymph circulation directed
A. Proximally
B. Distally
C. Laterally
D. Medially

59. If a client makes a sexual advance towards a therapist, or a therapist is placed in a similar type of harmful situation, which boundary is recommended
A. Compounded
B. Impermeable
C. Semi-permeable
D. Permeable

60. A wart is caused by
A. Fungus
B. Virus
C. Bacteria
D. Parasite

61. Emulsification of lipids in the duodenum is performed by which substance
A. Insulin
B. Glucagon
C. Bile
D. Amylase

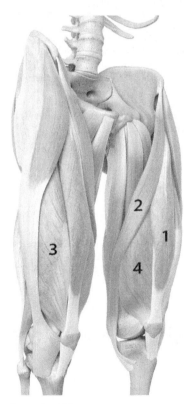

62. Identify the muscle numbered 3
A. Vastus lateralis
B. Sartorius
C. Gracilis
D. Vastus intermedius

63. In a client with lordosis, the following muscle might be weakened, resulting in an exaggerated anterior tilt of the pelvis
A. Rectus abdominis
B. Quadratus lumborum
C. Latissimus dorsi
D. Psoas major

64. Using the same linen between two separate clients is known as
A. Common sheet
B. Same linen
C. Same towel
D. Common towel

65. A set of guiding moral principles is known as
A. Scope of practice
B. Reputation
C. Ethics
D. Regulations

66. When performing visual assessments of a client, all of the following may be assessed by the massage therapist just by looking at the client except
A. Asking the client to detail the extent of pain utilizing a pain scale
B. Asking the client to walk slowly from one side of the room to the other
C. Evaluating the skin for any inflammation or contagious infections
D. Determining relative height of the client's acromion processes

67. Limitations set by the massage therapist or the client, which can be established verbally or non-verbally
A. Liabilities
B. Confidentiality
C. Scope of practice
D. Boundaries

68. Which of the following describes primary intention healing
A. A person suffers a wound in which the sides are closed together by blood clots, which turn into a scab and allow new tissue to form underneath
B. A person suffers a wound from an animal bite, and the wound is intentionally left open for some time to ensure there is no infection before closing
C. A person suffers a large wound in which the sides cannot be approximated, and granulated tissue and scar tissue fill in the area of missing tissue
D. A person suffers a wound and the area is cleaned with saline solution, and the sides are cauterized to stop any potential bleeding and infection

69. A massage table which is controlled by motors to adjust the height is called
A. Hydraulic
B. Adjustable
C. Portable
D. Pressurized

70. Pressing of tsubo points to increase the flow of Ki
A. Tshanpau
B. Ayurveda
C. Shiatsu
D. Amma

71. Stance used to perform long, gliding strokes
A. Warrior
B. Horse
C. Swimmer
D. Archer

72. Movement of a joint through the entire extent of its action
A. Traction
B. Stretching
C. Range-of-motion
D. Active movement

73. A disease that is present at birth is known as
A. Acquired
B. Hereditary
C. Autoimmune
D. Congenital

74. In a pre-massage assessment, a client states they are experiencing a painful sensation in their shoulder, only during certain movements. The massage therapist asks the client to demonstrate the actions that are causing pain, and the actions that are not. The client performs lateral rotation and extension of the shoulder to demonstrate actions that are causing pain, and medially rotates and flexes the shoulder to demonstrate actions that do not cause pain. Which of the following has occurred
A. The client and massage therapist have performed an active assistive joint movement
B. The client has performed an active joint movement
C. The massage therapist has performed a passive joint movement
D. The client and massage therapist have performed a resistive joint movement

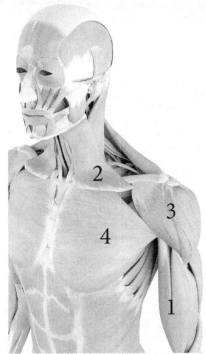

75. Order the muscles from deep to superficial
A. 2 > 1 > 4 > 3
B. 3 > 2 > 4 > 1
C. 4 > 2 > 1 > 3
D. 1 > 4 > 3 > 2

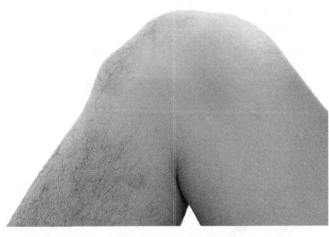

76. A 30 year old client is positioned supine on a massage table. The massage therapist undrapes the lower limb, and they see the condition pictured. What would be an appropriate treatment modification on behalf of the therapist
A. Ask the client if the area is experiencing pain, adjust pressure accordingly, and massage and stretch the quadriceps
B. Ask the client if they are suffering from an infection of bone, reschedule the massage if they are
C. Ask the client if they have broken a bone, massage proximal to the injury if so
D. Ask the client if they have visited a dermatologist, suggest they do so if they have not

77. If a client is unable to withstand any amount of pressure during a massage, a treatment the therapist might recommend would be
A. Reiki
B. Rolfing
C. Myofascial release
D. Lymphatic drainage

78. Reciprocal inhibition should be utilized if a client suffers from
A. Headaches
B. Cramping
C. Seizures
D. Sciatica

79. A client calls to book a massage appointment. During the phone call, the massage therapist suggests hot stone massage as a treatment the client may receive. After detailing the treatment and everything involved, the client agrees to receive a hot stone massage. What is this an example of
A. Express consent
B. Standards of conduct
C. Quality of care
D. Implied consent

80. Client records, consultations, and transactions occur in the
A. Changing room
B. Massage room
C. Bathroom
D. Business area

81. While at work, Chris falls and lands on his back, injuring it. The next day, he calls to make a massage appointment, hoping the massage will help with his pain. The appropriate response would be
A. Perform the massage and do compression onto the back
B. Perform the massage and apply heat to the affected area
C. Reschedule the massage and refer the client to a physician
D. Perform the massage and do passive joint mobilization on the vertebrae

82. All of the following should be utilized if client records are kept electronically on a website except
A. Access to administrative panel by client
B. Backup of information kept on password protected cloud storage
C. Two-step authentication
D. Strong passwords

83. An increased amount of interstitial fluid in an area results in
A. Inflammation
B. Thrombus
C. Aneurysm
D. Edema

84. Suggestions for future treatments by the massage therapist would be documented under which section of SOAP notes
A. Subjective
B. Plan
C. Assessment
D. Objective

85. Bone strength and density increasing under significant load is described by which anatomical law
A. Wolff's Law
B. Davis's Law
C. Harrah's Law
D. Hilton's Law

86. A massage therapist places an order for a crate of hypoallergenic massage oil. The company receives the purchase order, processes the order, and ships out the crate of oil. Included in the crate is an invoice. The amount of money detailed on the invoice would be considered
A. General liability
B. Accounts receivable
C. Accounts payable
D. Financial planning

87. Essential oil commonly used to aid in treatment of insomnia and chronic fatigue syndrome
A. Rose
B. Ginger
C. Peppermint
D. Lavender

88. Johnny is a new business owner, having opened a massage establishment the previous year. He is preparing his taxes, calculating gross income, expenses, and deductions. After finishing his taxes, he submits the paperwork to the IRS. What tax form is Johnny responsible for submitting as a self employed business owner
A. 1099
B. Schedule K1
C. Schedule C
D. W-2

89. Stretching the rhomboids can be accomplished by moving the body in which way
A. Adduct scapula
B. Elevate scapula
C. Depress scapula
D. Abduct scapula

90. A massage therapist moving a joint through its range-of-motion with the client completely relaxed is an example of which joint movement
A. Active
B. Passive
C. Assistive
D. Resistive

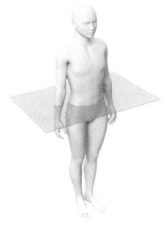

91. Which of the following is a movement that takes place along the pictured body plane
A. Abduction
B. Rotation
C. Flexion
D. Elevation

92. Tinnitus is best described as
A. Ringing in the ears
B. Contraction of cervical vertebrae laterally
C. Dizziness and nausea
D. Formation of cataracts in the eyes

93. Hormone produced by the thyroid which helps regulate the concentration of a specific nutrient in the blood
A. Norepinephrine
B. Calcitonin
C. Melatonin
D. Hemoglobin

94. A common area used to assess a client with jaundice is
A. Eyes
B. Hair
C. Tongue
D. Teeth

95. Slightly bent knees, straight back, and limp wrists are all examples of
A. Proper massage techniques
B. Improper body mechanics
C. Proper body mechanics
D. Improper massage modalities

96. On an intake form, a client indicates they are currently suffering from hypertension, have previously experienced influenza, and have intermittent eczema. What section of an intake form is this information listed under
A. Informed consent
B. HIPAA
C. Medical history
D. SOAP

97. A massage therapist contracts work with a professional sports team. The therapist agrees to see as many of the team's players as they want in exchange for a monthly fee of $2000. When performing accounting, what would the therapist's $2000 monthly fee be considered before the therapist receives the payment from the team
A. Assets
B. Accounts payabale
C. General liabilities
D. Accounts receivable

98. A massage therapist has decided they'd like to incorporate lomi lomi into their private practice. What are the appropriate means of adding this treatment to services the massage therapist offers
A. The massage therapist should research lomi lomi techniques online and practice on clients
B. The massage therapist should attend courses and become certified in lomi lomi
C. The massage therapist should interview therapists who perform lomi lomi to determine how to perform it
D. The massage therapist should add lomi lomi to their service menu immediately

99. A massage therapist uses citrus based essential oils in their massage lubricant. Which of the following may occur if the client were to spend time in the sun immediately after receiving a massage with this lubricant without bathing
A. The client may experience heat exhaustion
B. The client may experience lentigo
C. The client may experience sunburn
D. The client may experience muscle cramping

100. Describe which of the following occurs if a massage therapist gives a client psychological advice during a massage session
A. The massage therapist is working outside of their scope of practice
B. The massage therapist is giving the client a more personal session
C. The massage therapist is up-selling the massage and may charge more
D. The massage therapist is giving the client advice they should follow

Answer Key on Page 346

Practice Test 3

1. While performing gait analysis, the massage therapist notices the client's body drops lower to the right side when taking a step with the right foot. The therapist asks the client to stand straight, and the therapist examines the pelvis, noticing the left side of the pelvis is elevated compared to the right side. What might this indicate to the massage therapist in relation to the client
A. The client may have weakness in latissimus dorsi on the left side
B. The client may have hypertonicity in piriformis on the right side
C. The client may have hypertonicity in rectus femoris on the left side
D. The client may have weakness in quadratus lumborum on the right side

2. Which of the following best describes EIN
A. Encapsulated Internal Neuralgia, pain around a joint capsule caused by compression to a nerve that innervates the joint
B. Excite Isometric Neuroglia, form of stretch requiring the use of isometric contractions followed by compression of the muscle nearest to its origin
C. Employer Identification Number, number used to identify employers, self employed, and partnerships to the IRS
D. Extra-intravenous Needle, form of needle used to deliver intravenous medications into major blood vessels to administer medication more quickly than oral or topical medication

3. The descending order of the small intestine is
A. Jejunum, duodenum, ileum
B. Ileum, jejunum, duodenum
C. Duodenum, jejunum, ileum
D. Duodenum, ileum, jejunum

4. A client arrives for a massage. During the verbal intake, the client states they have not felt well for a few weeks, with a persistent cough, fever, chills, night sweats, and they have lost several pounds due to a reduced appetite. What is an appropriate response to these symptoms being present on behalf of the massage therapist
A. The massage therapist should perform lymphatic drainage to increase the flow of leukocytes through the body to fight the infection
B. The massage therapist should administer aromatherapy to stimulate the client's limbic system
C. The massage therapist should perform percussion to loosen phlegm that may be contributing to the cough
D. The massage therapist should reschedule the massage and refer the client to a physician

5. A doctor whom a massage therapist is friendly with approaches the massage therapist, proposing an agreement wherein for every patient the massage therapist refers to the doctor, the doctor will pay the massage therapist a small fee. What would be the most appropriate response on behalf of the massage therapist to this proposal
A. The massage therapist should accept the proposal and begin referring clients to the doctor to supplement income
B. The massage therapist should negotiate pay with the doctor before agreeing to any proposal to ensure the massage therapist is receiving adequate compensation
C. The massage therapist should decline the proposal to avoid any potential ethical dilemmas that may arise
D. The massage therapist should notify the local medical board that the doctor is not operating under the Hippocratic oath and may be causing harm to potential patients

6. A wage and tax statement detailing income and withheld taxes from the previous year for an employee
A. 1099
B. Schedule C
C. Schedule K1
D. W-2

7. Josh is a professional football kicker. His team has just scored a touchdown, and he has to kick an extra point. Josh lines up, the ball is snapped and placed by the holder, and Josh kicks the ball with the medial surface of his right foot. What muscle is primarily responsible for helping Josh kick the extra point
A. Gracilis
B. Sartorius
C. Iliopsoas
D. Semimembranosus

8. During an assessment, the massage therapist requests to view the soles of the client's shoes. Upon viewing the soles, the therapist observes obvious wear on the lateral side of the shoe's sole. This may be indicative of hypertonicity in which of the following muscles
A. Gastrocnemius
B. Peroneus longus
C. Tibialis anterior
D. Popliteus

9. Of the following, which is not a smaller cavity located in the ventral body cavity
A. Pleural cavity
B. Cranial cavity
C. Pelvic cavity
D. Pericardial cavity

10. Capillaries located in the kidneys, allowing waste products to be filtered from the blood for elimination
A. Nephron
B. Glomeruli
C. Renal arteries
D. Adrenal

11. Stance used to perform massage strokes such as petrissage, friction, and tapotement
A. Warrior
B. Bow
C. Swimmer
D. Archer

12. A client sees a massage therapist twice monthly for a year. The client enjoys interacting with the therapist, and in the client's opinion, the conversation often becomes flirtatious. The client begins developing feelings for the massage therapist. Which of the following describes the situation
A. The client is exhibiting self-disclosure
B. The client is exhibiting counter-transference
C. The client is exhibiting power differential
D. The client is exhibiting transference

13. Which of the following is a tax form that is not filed by a person who owns a business
A. Schedule K1
B. W-2
C. Schedule C
D. 1099

14. Muscle inserting onto the medial border of the scapula, responsible for protraction and depression of the scapula
A. Rhomboid major
B. Rhomboid minor
C. Serratus anterior
D. Pectoralis minor

15. A client enters a massage establishment walking with crutches and their left leg in a cast. The therapist sees the client, and asks what happened. The client states they were in a car crash, and ended up breaking both the tibia and fibula. The therapist states they've never experienced that, but they can imagine it would be awful to deal with, and they're sorry the client has to live with it for the time being. What is this an example of
A. Passive listening
B. Sympathy
C. Self disclosure
D. Empathy

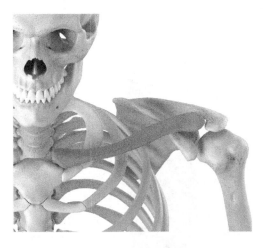

16. All of the following muscles attach to the pictured bone except
A. Pectoralis major
B. Sternocleidomastoid
C. Pectoralis minor
D. Anterior deltoid

17. A massage therapist's client is suing their doctor for negligence. The client states to the court that the doctor recommended massage therapy for the client's condition, despite the condition being contraindicated for massage therapy. The massage therapist is issued a subpoena duces testificandum by the court. What is required of the massage therapist after receiving this writ
A. The massage therapist must allow inspectors to view the therapist's office
B. The massage therapist must appear in court and testify in front of a judge
C. The massage therapist must give a statement under oath outside of court for use in the case
D. The massage therapist must appear in court and provide documentation

18. A client seeks a massage appointment to prepare for an upcoming ranked tennis match they are playing in. The client states their blood pressure is at 107/62 when at rest. If the blood pressure is increased to 115/66 after the massage, what has occurred
A. A mechanical effect has occurred
B. A psychological effect has occurred
C. A sympathetic effect has occurred
D. A reflexive effect has occurred

19. Paralysis of one half of the face, caused by stimulation of the herpes simplex virus, which affects the facial nerve
A. Trigeminal neuralgia
B. Cerebral palsy
C. Bell's palsy
D. Graves' disease

20. A client attempts to make an appointment with a massage therapist, but the therapist tells the client they cannot accept any new clients because their schedule is completely full. The client asks the therapist to stay after their scheduled shift to fit the client in, but the therapist declines, stating they cannot stay past the scheduled shift. Which of the following is the therapist establishing
A. The therapist is establishing a time boundary
B. The therapist is establishing a permeable boundary
C. The therapist is establishing a negotiation with the client
D. The therapist is establishing a violation of the Civil Rights Act of 1964

21. A massage therapist has been employed by a spa for the past six months. During the therapist's employment, the therapist and the spa manager have been flirtatious, had personal conversations with one another, and developed an emotional attachment. If the massage therapist and the spa manager were to start a romantic relationship, what would this be categorized as
A. Breach of contract
B. Conflict of interest
C. Transference
D. Nepotism

22. A client states they suffer from spells of vertigo. Which of the following is the best course of action for the massage therapist to take after receiving this information
A. The massage therapist should offer to give the client fruit juice before the treatment begins to raise blood sugar
B. The massage therapist should decline to work on the client and reschedule
C. The massage therapist should offer to assist the client off the table after the massage has ended to avoid potential falls and injuries
D. The massage therapist should treat the condition as a local contraindication

23. A massage therapist opens an office to perform massage out of. The next year, when it is time to report taxes, the therapist begins filling out tax documents to submit to the IRS. The tax form has a section where the massage therapist may detail deductions. Of the following, which is not a deduction the massage therapist can claim on their taxes
A. Time spent performing market analysis and financial planning
B. Money spent on a hydraulic massage table
C. Advertising expenses, including pay-per-click advertising
D. Any funds spent on a desk for the business area

24. Treatment utilizing light gliding strokes directed towards the heart to increase circulation of a certain substance to decrease edema
A. Rolfing
B. Craniosacral therapy
C. Lymphatic drainage
D. Myofascial release

25. Muscle originating on the sternum and clavicle, responsible for neck flexion and unilateral head rotation to the opposite side
A. Pectoralis major
B. Sternocleidomastoid
C. Scalenes
D. Levator scapulae

26. Palpating, rejoining, opposing, kneading, pressing, lifting, holding, and pushing are the eight basic techniques of which modality
A. Rolfing
B. Thai massage
C. Reiki
D. Tuina

27. A massage therapist gives a diabetic client a massage. After the massage, the client tells the massage therapist that they feel light headed and dizzy, and feel extremely tired. In this instance, what should a massage therapist do
A. Ask the client where they keep their insulin, and inject them with insulin to lower blood sugar
B. Ask the client to lie down on the massage table and take a nap
C. Lie the client on the floor and immediately call for an ambulance to administer aid
D. Ask the client to sit and provide the client with something to consume with sugar such as fruit juice

28. In a conversation with a client during a session, the client expresses concern over the massage therapist's credentials, stating they don't believe they are actually licensed and certified to perform massage. What is the best way for massage therapists to avoid this kind of thought from clients
A. Schedule massage sessions only with family and friends
B. Assure the client beforehand that they are licensed verbally
C. Ignore the client concerns as they are being a Grade-A jerk
D. Have massage credentials posted in plain view of all clients

29. Excessive force placed against the big toe, pushing it against the first metatarsal, causing the toe to subluxate laterally and the first metatarsal medially
A. Turf toe
B. Bunion
C. Dislocation
D. Gout

30. A massage therapist moves a client's shoulder and elbow both into extension. Which muscle is stretched, and which is shortened
A. Coracobrachialis is stretched, brachioradialis is shortened
B. Supinator is stretched, anconeus is shortened
C. Triceps brachii is stretched, brachialis is shortened
D. Biceps brachii is stretched, triceps brachii is shortened

31. Full-body steam bath used to increase activity of sudoriferous glands
A. Swiss bath
B. Russian bath
C. Vichy shower
D. Swedish shower

32. A massage therapist engages in conversation with their client, and during the course of conversation discovers that their client cleans houses for a living. The massage therapist and client negotiate a deal to allow the client to receive one massage per month in exchange for cleaning the massage therapist's house once per month. When reporting this trade to the IRS, what percentage of the massage service's normal cost is the massage therapist required to report
A. 100%
B. 30%
C. 50%
D. 25%

33. A sudoriferous gland is a type of exocrine gland that produces what substance
A. Milk
B. Testosterone
C. Oil
D. Sweat

34. A person suffers from a fever of 103 degrees Fahrenheit. What type of medication would be given to help return the internal body temperature to a normal range
A. Expectorant
B. Antihistamine
C. Antipyretic
D. Antibiotic

35. A concentric contraction of the rectus femoris would result in which actions taking place
A. Hip flexion and knee extension
B. Hip adduction and knee flexion
C. Hip abduction and knee flexion
D. Hip extension and knee extension

36. A client details on an intake form that their occupation requires them to use a computer for several hours a day and answer phones. After consulting with the massage therapist, it is determined that the client holds the phone between their ear and shoulder the majority of the time while typing on a keyboard and inputing data. The client states they experience pain in the right shoulder and neck. What is a recommendation the massage therapist can give to assist the client in alleviating pain
A. Recommend the client use a standing desk
B. Recommend the client get a headset that connects to the telephone
C. Recommend the client quit their job
D. Recommend the client use dictation software for inputting data

37. During a massage session, the client and massage therapist begin talking. The client seems to be asking some personal, probing questions of the therapist, which is making the therapist slightly uncomfortable. Finally, towards the end of the massage, the client asks where the therapist lives. Which of the following is an appropriate response on behalf of the massage therapist
A. The massage therapist should utilize impermeable boundaries
B. The massage therapist should utilize semi-permeable boundaries
C. The massage therapist should utilize permeable-impermeable boundaries
D. The massage therapist should utilize permeable boundaries

38. A pre-event sports massage requires the following kinds of strokes to be performed to activate muscle spindles
A. Invigorating
B. Relaxing
C. Slow
D. Light

39. Which of the following describes net income
A. Money loaned to another company to be paid for services rendered
B. Money owed to a company as debt
C. Income before taxes
D. Income after taxes and expenses have been paid

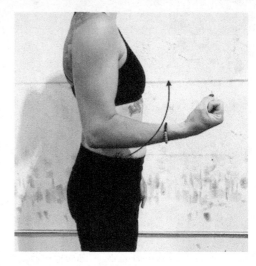

40. The pictured action moves in which plane
A. Sagittal
B. Coronal
C. Horizontal
D. Midsagittal

41. When is it appropriate for a massage therapist to release a client's records
A. When issued a written request by a client's employer
B. When issued a written request from the client's doctor
C. When issued a verbal and written request by a client's spouse
D. When issued a subpoena by a court

42. Contrast baths should always end with immersion in
A. Cold water to reduce inflammation
B. Hot water to increase circulation to areas experiencing damage
C. Warm water to dilate blood vessels and drain lymph
D. Lukewarm water to increase blood pressure

43. A trigger point that results in pain only when being palpated
A. Acute
B. Active
C. Latent
D. Passive

44. Of the following, which describes the function of hyaline cartilage
A. Surrounds organs in the abdomen to prevent friction
B. Found on articular surfaces of bones to prevent friction
C. Holds bones to bones to provide structural support
D. Connects muscles to bones to allow movement

45. A massage therapist schedules their friend for a massage appointment. Because the therapist and client are friends outside of the massage setting, what is this known as
A. Dual relationship
B. Partnership
C. Sexual misconduct
D. Transference

46. If a person were to fall forward, landing on their outstretched arms, the shoulder joint would most likely become dislocated in which direction
A. Laterally
B. Anteriorly
C. Posteriorly
D. Distally

47. A client books a Swedish massage, stating to the therapist that they receive massage all the time and just need help relaxing a bit. The client arrives for the appointment, quickly signing all paperwork on the intake form. Without going into details of everything involved with the treatment, the therapist and client begin the session. What has the client given the massage therapist in regards to the massage session
A. The ability to determine the length of the massage session
B. Authorization to share the client's intake form with the client's physician
C. Implied consent for all standard Swedish techniques to be performed
D. The chance for the massage therapist to be sued for malpractice

48. Increase of calcium in the blood stream is achieved by secretion of the following hormone
A. Epinephrine
B. Oxytocin
C. Prolactin
D. Parathyroid hormone

49. The massage therapist revealing too much information about themselves to a client may potentially lead to which of the following
A. Trust issues
B. Transference
C. Respect
D. Power differential

50. Blood returns to the heart from the trunk and lower limbs via the
A. Superior vena cava
B. Pulmonary vein
C. Inferior vena cava
D. Aorta

51. The overall objectives and values of a business are detailed in
A. Market analysis
B. Mission statement
C. Project management
D. Financial planning

52. On an intake form, a client lists "pyelonephritis" as a current condition. What is an appropriate response from the massage therapist
A. Reschedule the massage and refer the client to a physician
B. Perform the massage and stretch hip flexors such as iliopsoas
C. Perform the massage, working over the abdomen in clockwise movements
D. Perform the massage and apply positional release on the neck

53. Rhythmic contractions occurring in the esophagus, stomach, small intestine, and large intestine, helping to move food through the alimentary canal
A. Tetanus
B. Peristalsis
C. Concentric
D. Isotonic

54. Gift taxes reported per client per year may not exceed
A. $40
B. $100
C. $25
D. $75

55. Brian is a soccer player, playing in a match. He sprints down the pitch, when he suddenly feels and hears a popping sound come from his ankle. He falls to the grass and clutches his ankle, feeling intense pain. He's helped off the pitch, and taken to a hospital for evaluation. The following day, his ankle is severely bruised and inflamed, and he cannot move the joint without pain. What type of injury has Brian likely sustained
A. Grade 1 sprain
B. Grade 3 strain
C. Grade 1 strain
D. Grade 2 sprain

56. A person carrying a heavy bucket with one hand for an extended period of time may result in soreness in the following muscle, the result of an isometric contraction
A. Levator scapulae
B. Rectus abdominis
C. Scalenes
D. Sternocleidomastoid

57. Contraindications for hydrotherapy generally include all of the following except
A. Contagious conditions
B. Acne
C. Hypertension
D. Skin rash

58. A client notifies the massage therapist on the intake form that they suffer from intermittent trigeminal neuralgia that is currently in the acute stage. After consulting with the client on the condition, which of the following should the massage therapist do to best serve the client
A. Perform lymphatic drainage on the limbs to decrease the accumulation of fluid and swelling
B. Recommend the client perform exercises that strengthen the rectus abdominis and loosen iliopsoas to ease pressure on the lumbar vertebrae
C. Perform the massage but remove the face cradle so the client's face is not being compressed with the client prone
D. Refer the client to a chiropractor to increase mobility in the intervertebral joints and ease pressure on the brachial plexus

59. Which is the only organ in the body that contains both endocrine and exocrine glands
A. Pancreas
B. Liver
C. Stomach
D. Lungs

60. During the course of a massage, the client requests that the massage therapist pop their wrist joint. If the massage therapist were to comply with the request, it would be a violation of
A. Certification
B. Malpractice
C. Licensing
D. Scope of practice

61. Massage stroke best utilized to sedate an area
A. Nerve stroke
B. Tapotement
C. Vibration
D. Friction

62. An independent contractor does not receive
A. Gratuity
B. Pay
C. Compensation
D. Benefits

63. Form of friction in which the therapist moves the stroke perpendicular to the direction of muscle fibers
A. Compression
B. Circular friction
C. Cross-fiber friction
D. Superficial friction

64. The bone that comprises the upper jaw is also called
A. Vomer
B. Zygomatic
C. Mandible
D. Maxilla

65. A client comes in for a massage, complaining of pain in the posterior thigh and buttocks. Which is the least important piece of information the therapist should try to determine about this client's situation
A. If the pain the client is experiencing acute or chronic
B. If the client remembers any specific instances that caused the pain
C. If the client is experiencing pain elsewhere related to this issue
D. If the client has received massage in the past six months

66. A massage therapist is summoned to a court proceeding to deliver testimony or documentation for use in a case. Which of the following is the writ issued by the court to compel the massage therapist to attend the proceedings and testify
A. Subpoena
B. Res ipsa loquitur
C. Respondeat superior
D. Deposition

67. Cinnamon essential oil should be avoided in clients who are
A. Bulimic
B. Elderly
C. Allergic to nuts
D. Pregnant

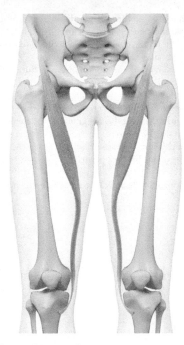

68. Identify the muscle pictured
A. Vastus lateralis
B. Sartorius
C. Gracilis
D. Biceps femoris

69. In an effort to tarnish a competitor's business and gain more clientele, a rival business owner creates several online accounts and creates numerous negative reviews on the competitor's online business page. The reviews contain information the business owner knows is false, but the owner posts the reviews regardless. The competitor notices the reviews, observes the false statements, and reaches out to their lawyer. Which of the following describes the situation
A. The business owner has committed libel
B. The competitor is accusing the business owner of engaging in antitrust practices
C. The competitor is practicing their right of disengagement
D. The business owner has committed slander

70. The umbilical region holds which of the following organs
A. Liver
B. Small intestine
C. Spleen
D. Stomach

71. Charging the client full or partial fees for failing to make a scheduled appointment is a way for the massage therapist to establish
A. Scope of practice
B. Dual relationships
C. Time boundaries
D. Ethical dilemmas

72. Massage stroke directed toward the heart used to increase circulation, transition between strokes, and apply massage lubricant
A. Friction
B. Effleurage
C. Petrissage
D. Tapotement

73. A patient is admitted to a hospital after suffering a large third degree burn on their leg. As the injury begins to heal, physicians determine the sides of the wound created by the burn cannot be approximated, and the wound will need to be filled in via granulated tissue and a skin graft will be required to close the wound and allow it to heal and form scar tissue in the damaged area. Which of the following is the proper name given for the form of healing described
A. Secondary intention healing
B. Primary intention healing
C. Quadrilateral intention healing
D. Tertiary intention healing

74. Dopamine is a neurotransmitter which helps to stabilize the body in specific movements. A reduction of dopamine in the body would result in
A. Parkinson's disease
B. Anemia
C. Alzheimer's disease
D. Sleep apnea

75. Book-keeping and taxes for a massage business may be handled by a massage therapist or
A. Client
B. Insurer
C. Accountant
D. Practitioner

76. An injury to the hamstrings might inhibit which actions
A. Hip extension and knee flexion
B. Hip extension and knee extension
C. Hip flexion and knee extension
D. Hip flexion and knee flexion

77. During a massage, a client begins cramping in their gastrocnemius. The cramp is very painful. What is the proper technique for helping to eliminate this specific cramp
A. The therapist should stretch the gastrocnemius with the client completely relaxed, performing proprioceptive neuromuscular facilitation
B. The therapist should massage the gastrocnemius to help the muscle relax
C. The therapist should have the client contract the tibialis anterior to force gastrocnemius to relax, known as reciprocal inhibition
D. The therapist should apply a cold pack to the gastrocnemius to numb the muscle

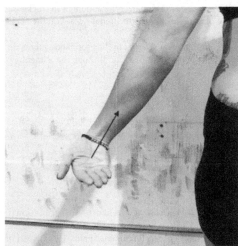

78. Origin of the muscle group responsible for performing the pictured action
A. Lateral epicondyle of humerus
B. Lateral supracondylar ridge of humerus
C. Anterior distal shaft of humerus
D. Medial epicondyle of humerus

79. If the massage therapist were to intentionally ignore a client's request to lighten pressure, they may be suspected of
A. Power differential
B. Physical abuse
C. Scope of practice violation
D. Dual relationship

80. A therapist is seeing a new client. During the massage, the client tells the therapist that they usually visit another massage establishment on the other side of town, but they were booked. In an effort to convince the client to rebook, the therapist tells the client that they used to work at the other establishment, and they engage in illegal drug trade. The therapist knows this is not true, but is hoping to trick the client. What has just occurred
A. The therapist has slandered the other business
B. The therapist has established a power differential
C. The therapist is unknowingly engaged in a kickback
D. The therapist is engaging in malpractice

81. While calculating taxes, a massage therapist calculates their gross income, along with money spent on items necessary to run the business during the year such as massage lubricant, linen service, music subscriptions, and telephone service. This information is submitted with the massage therapist's tax return in which of the following tax forms
A. Form 1098-T
B. 1099-MISC
C. Profit and loss statement
D. Form 1040 EZ

82. During the course of a massage, the massage therapist notices a pre-existing contusion on the client's leg. The massage therapist should
A. Work over the contusion to help break up potential blood clots that may have formed during the course of healing
B. Apply a cold compress to the affected contusion to reduce blood flow to the contusion
C. Avoid the contusion, notify the client where the contusion is located, and document the contusion in SOAP notes
D. Reschedule the massage until the contusion has resolved, as contusions are absolute contraindications

83. The largest lymph vessel in the body, responsible for draining lymph into the left subclavian vein
A. Brachiocephalic vessel
B. Thoracic duct
C. Spleen
D. Aorta

84. Multiple sclerosis is what type of disorder
A. Ulcerative
B. Viral
C. Bacterial
D. Autoimmune

85. Of the following, all are useful in assessing inflammation a client may be experiencing except
A. Asking the client to perform breathing techniques to help return body temperature to normal levels
B. Palpation of the suspected area to detect a warmer area than other areas of skin
C. Asking the client to perform range-of-motion if the suspected area is around a joint
D. Asking the client to detail whether or not they are experiencing pain and inflammation in the suspected area

86. A client calls a large chain massage establishment and requests an appointment, telling the receptionist he has been experiencing pain and discomfort in his upper back for some time and would love to have the area worked on. The receptionist apologizes and informs the client that they do not book appointments with male clients, and only allow female clients to come in for massage. Which of the following describes this situation
A. The client is being inappropriate in their topic of phone conversation
B. The massage establishment is engaging in gender discrimination
C. The client is engaging in deceptive appointment scheduling practices
D. The massage establishment is setting boundaries with their clientele

87. A massage therapist sets a policy to charge more for services rendered to wealthy clients. Which of the following best describes this policy
A. Financial abuse
B. Dual relationship
C. Power differential
D. Wise business practice

88. A massage therapist asks a client to perform a gait analysis. During the gait analysis, the massage therapist notices the client's right foot is in a slightly inverted position. This may indicate all of the following to the therapist except
A. The client may have hypertonicity in the tibialis posterior
B. The client may have weakness in the peroneus longus
C. The client may have hypertonicity in the tibialis anterior
D. The client is experiencing pain due to shin splints

89. Muscle originating on the anterior superior iliac spine
A. Sartorius
B. Gracilis
C. Rectus femoris
D. Adductor magnus

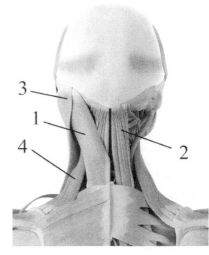

90. Order the muscles from superficial to deep
A. 4 > 1 > 2 > 3
B. 1 > 2 > 3 > 4
C. 3 > 1 > 2 > 4
D. 2 > 1 > 3 > 2

91. During a Swedish massage, the client tells the massage therapist that their pressure can be more firm. The massage therapist replies by telling the client that the pressure they are using is the most that can be used with Swedish massage, but the therapist can go deeper if they change the appointment to a deep tissue massage, which costs $10 more. The client agrees, and the appointment is changed from a Swedish massage to a deep tissue massage. Which of the following has occurred
A. The massage therapist has taken advantage of the client and tricked the client into accepting a modality they did not want
B. The massage therapist utilized a technique known as up-selling to entice the client to spend more money
C. The client has encroached on the massage therapist's boundaries by instructing the therapist to add pressure
D. The client has influenced the massage therapist to perform a modality that is outside the therapist's scope of practice, violating the scope of the therapist's license

92. Synergist to the hamstrings while flexing the knee
A. Tibialis anterior
B. Soleus
C. Gastrocnemius
D. Rectus femoris

93. Chronic degeneration of alveolar sacs, reducing the exchange of carbon dioxide and oxygen in and out of the blood
A. Pneumonia
B. Asthma
C. Bronchitis
D. Emphysema

94. A massage therapist is hired by a marathon runner to perform massage immediately before an event. During the course of the brief massage, the therapist uses vigorous massage strokes to increase circulation of blood, and performs tapotement to activate the muscle spindles to help prevent injury during the marathon. Which of the following effects is increasing circulation of blood due to strokes such as effleurage
A. A reflexive effect
B. A mechanical effect
C. A dynamic effect
D. A stretch effect

95. Common areas utilized for visual assessment include all of the following except
A. Position of the rectus abdominis
B. Position of the heads of the fibulae
C. Position of the ears
D. Position of the anterior superior iliac spines

96. Urea and ammonia are filtered from the blood by the
A. Spleen
B. Kidneys
C. Bladder
D. Large intestine

97. A client details to a massage therapist during a session that they have felt a sense of unease regarding a potential breakup with a significant other. The massage therapist is unsure how to respond, and has decided to choose their words extremely carefully when discussing the situation with the client. Which of the following best describes the situation
A. The massage therapist is utilizing a permeable boundary in regards to communicating with the client
B. The massage therapist is utilizing a permeable-impermeable boundary in regards to communicating with the client
C. The massage therapist is utilizing an impermeable boundary in regards to communicating with the client
D. The massage therapist is utilizing a semi-permeable boundary in regards to communicating with the client

98. Bilateral contraction of the pectineus muscles would have what action on two abducted lower limbs
A. Rotate them laterally
B. Move them into adduction
C. Take them further apart
D. Bring them into an extended position

99. A client receives a massage, unaware that they have a contagious skin disorder known as dermatophytosis. During the massage, the massage therapist notices the area of infection, and notes that it closely resembles a dermatophytosis infection. The massage therapist avoids the area and treats it as a local contraindication, continuing with the massage as normal in every other area. After the client's massage has finished and the client has left, what is the proper course of action the massage therapist should take regarding the linens used during the session
A. The massage therapist should contact infectious disease control to remove the sheets so they can be properly incinerated and destroyed
B. The massage therapist should mix the sheets with all other linens, washing the sheets as normal with regular laundry detergent
C. The massage therapist should immediately throw the sheets into the garbage to ensure the sheets are never used again
D. The massage therapist should store the linens in a biohazard bag, then treat the linens with a dilution of ten parts water to one part bleach, washed in hot water

100. A client explains to a massage therapist that they lift weights as a hobby, and have been performing more squats than usual in an effort to break their personal record of 315 pounds. The client states they cannot go down as far as they need to, and then demonstrates their squat technique for the therapist. When demonstrating the squat technique, what actions are performed
A. The hips are flexed and the knees are extended, then the hips are extended and the knees are flexed when returning to the starting point
B. The hips and knees are both flexed, then both are extended when returning to the starting point
C. The hips are extended and the knees are flexed, then the hips are flexed and the knees are flexed when returning to the starting point
D. The hips and knees are both extended, then both are flexed when returning to the starting point

Answer Key on Page 346

Congratulations! You've made it to the end of the study guide! How do you feel? How prepared are you? What do you still need to work on?

A common mistake a lot of people make is thinking they need to know EVERYTHING to pass the MBLEx. That's not the case at all. This line of thinking can make studying extremely stressful for some people.

Think about the amount of content you're actually studying when you crack open a book. It's a ton of information! It's extremely unlikely you're going to learn every bit of information. The key is to learn enough information where you can utilize test techniques like eliminating answers! You won't know everything on the test, but you can know enough where you'll likely recognize at least some piece of information in almost every test question. Even if you only see a term, identify that you've seen it, and that the term doesn't match with the information in the test question, that's still extremely helpful!

Keep your head up, learn as much as you can, but don't get discouraged because you feel like you're not learning everything in my study guide. You'll be shocked at the amount of information you've learned, even when you feel like you haven't learned anything!

While grading the test, try to identify what strategies you incorporated that were successful, which strategies didn't work, information you may have been confused by or mixed up with other information, and do research on the questions you did not answer correctly. The way we learn is by challenging ourselves, breaking out of our comfort zones, and approaching each chance to engage with information as an opportunity to take one step closer towards passing the MBLEx.

Go forth with the determination necessary to conquer the MBLEx. You have the capability to do great things for yourself. Keep pushing, keep driving, keep enduring, and you will break through the wall ahead of you and vanquish the MBLEx.

I believe in you. Believe in yourself.

You can do this.

Full Length Practice Test Answer Keys

Practice Test 1		Practice Test 2		Practice Test 3	
01. B	51. D	01. A	51. C	01. D	51. B
02. A	52. B	02. C	52. D	02. C	52. A
03. A	53. A	03. D	53. A	03. C	53. B
04. D	54. A	04. B	54. D	04. D	54. C
05. D	55. B	05. B	55. C	05. C	55. D
06. B	56. B	06. A	56. B	06. D	56. A
07. B	57. B	07. C	57. D	07. B	57. B
08. C	58. B	08. A	58. A	08. C	58. C
09. A	59. C	09. D	59. B	09. B	59. A
10. C	60. D	10. A	60. B	10. B	60. D
11. C	61. D	11. C	61. C	11. A	61. C
12. A	62. C	12. B	62. A	12. D	62. D
13. C	63. D	13. B	63. A	13. B	63. C
14. B	64. D	14. C	64. D	14. C	64. D
15. D	65. A	15. D	65. C	15. B	65. D
16. A	66. B	16. B	66. A	16. C	66. A
17. C	67. B	17. A	67. D	17. B	67. D
18. A	68. D	18. C	68. A	18. D	68. B
19. D	69. A	19. B	69. A	19. C	69. A
20. A	70. D	20. D	70. C	20. A	70. B
21. B	71. B	21. B	71. D	21. B	71. C
22. C	72. A	22. A	72. C	22. C	72. B
23. C	73. D	23. D	73. D	23. A	73. A
24. D	74. C	24. A	74. B	24. C	74. A
25. A	75. B	25. D	75. D	25. B	75. C
26. B	76. A	26. D	76. A	26. D	76. A
27. A	77. B	27. A	77. A	27. D	77. C
28. C	78. A	28. B	78. B	28. D	78. D
29. D	79. D	29. D	79. A	29. B	79. B
30. D	80. C	30. B	80. D	30. D	80. A
31. A	81. C	31. D	81. C	31. B	81. C
32. B	82. A	32. C	82. A	32. A	82. C
33. A	83. A	33. D	83. D	33. D	83. B
34. D	84. C	34. A	84. B	34. C	84. D
35. A	85. B	35. B	85. A	35. A	85. A
36. C	86. C	36. A	86. C	36. B	86. B
37. B	87. A	37. C	87. D	37. A	87. A
38. B	88. A	38. D	88. C	38. A	88. D
39. C	89. B	39. B	89. D	39. D	89. A
40. C	90. B	40. C	90. B	40. A	90. C
41. D	91. A	41. A	91. B	41. D	91. B
42. C	92. C	42. B	92. A	42. A	92. C
43. B	93. D	43. B	93. B	43. C	93. D
44. C	94. C	44. C	94. A	44. B	94. B
45. D	95. B	45. A	95. C	45. A	95. A
46. C	96. B	46. D	96. C	46. B	96. B
47. B	97. D	47. A	97. D	47. C	97. D
48. C	98. A	48. B	98. B	48. D	98. B
49. A	99. A	49. A	99. C	49. B	99. D
50. B	100. C	50. D	100. A	50. C	100. B

References

This study guide was created with assistance from the following resources:

Tappan's Handbook of Massage Therapy: Blending Art with Science(6th Edition), 2015 – Patricia J. Benjamin, PhD
ISBN: 0-13-408269-9
30 Second Anatomy: The 50 Most Important Structures and Systems in the Human Body, Each Explained in Half a Minute, 2013 – Gabrielle M. Finn, Judith Barbaro-Brown
ISBN: 978-1-4351-4065-3
Anatomica: The Complete Home Medical Reference, 2010 – Ken Ashwell
ISBN: 978-1-74048-046-8
Mosby's Pathology for Massage Therapists(3rd Edition), 2013 – Susan Salvo
ISBN: 9780323084727
The Four Hour Chef: The Simple Path to Cooking Like a Pro, Learn Anything, and Living the Good Life, 2013 – Timothy Ferriss
ISBN: 0-547-88459-1
Gray's Anatomy – Henry Gray
ISBN: 9781435145467
Essentials of Anatomy and Physiology(4th Edition), 2002 – Rod Seeley, Trent Stephens, Philip Tate
ISBN: 0-07-027260-3
Introducing Medical Terminology Specialties: A Medical Specialties Approach with Patient Records, 2003 – Regina Masters, Barbara Gylys
ISBN: 0-8036-0907-8
Exploring Medical Language: A Student-Directed Approach(5th Edition), 2002 – Myrna LaFleur Brooks
ISBN: 0-323-01218-3
Basic Clinical Massage Therapy: Integrating Anatomy and Treatment, 2003 – James H. Clay, David M. Pounds
ISBN: 0-683-30653-7
Milady's Theory and Practice of Therapeutic Massage, 1999 – Mark F. Beck
ISBN: 1-56253-536-6
The Ethics of Touch: The Hands-on Practitioner's Guide To Creating a Professional, Safe, and Enduring Practice, 2003 - Ben E. Benjamin, Ph.D., Cherie Sohnen-Moe
ISBN: 1-882908-40-6

Recommended Reading

The Obstacle is the Way: The Timeless Art of Turning Trials into Triumph, 2014 – Ryan Holiday
ISBN: 1591846358
Ego is the Enemy, 2016 – Ryan Holiday
ISBN: 1591847818
Outliers: The Story of Success, 2008 – Malcolm Gladwell
ISBN: 0316017930
Tools of Titans, 2016 – Timothy Ferriss
ISBN: 1328683788

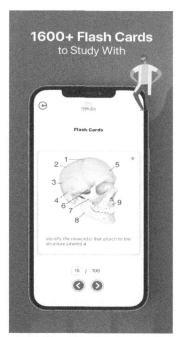

Apple iPhone

Android

Presenting the brand new **MBLEx Test Prep app**! Available for iPhone and Android devices, the MBLEx Test Prep app features a full content review, 2200 practice test questions, a leaderboard so you can see how you stack up against other students taking practice tests, 1600 flash cards, and the full MBLEx Test Prep Podcast archives! Come learn on-the-go with the best MBLEx preparation app ever created! Free content includes 100+ practice test questions, and an updated Question of the Day every single day!

On iPhone, search for **"Merlino's MBLEx Test Prep"** in the App Store, on Android search for **"MBLEx Test Prep"** in the Google Play Store, or just scan the QR Code using your smart phone's camera above for your specific device!

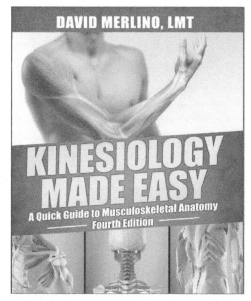

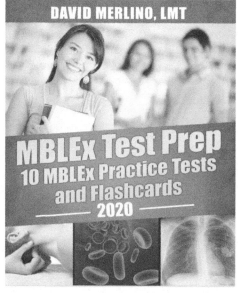

Kinesiology Made Easy - A Quick Guide to Musculoskeletal Anatomy gives everyone looking to learn about the structures of the body all the important information needed! From origins and insertions, to actions and innervations, bony landmarks, nerves, and reviews of the Skeletal, Nervous, and Muscular systems, Kinesiology Made Easy makes learning Kinesiology, well, easy!

Looking for practice tests? Prepare to pass your MBLEx with this book, containing 10 practice tests, 1000 test questions, study skills, test-taking techniques, and tips on how to reduce test anxiety!

Other MBLEx practice exam books only contain two or three exams. *MBLEx Test Prep - 10 MBLEx Practice Tests and Flash Cards*, as the name says, contains 10! This book gives the most value for the price, and is sure to help refine your test-taking ability, drastically increasing your chances of passing the MBLEx!

Included in the book are pre-made flash cards that you only need to cut out! Grab the scissors and put these flash cards to use while saving time and money in the process!

Made in the USA
Las Vegas, NV
30 October 2023

79982113R00195